The Light of Christmas

THE LIGHT OF

NEW YORK E. P. DUTTON & CO., INC. 1964

CHRISTMAS

Edited by FRANCES BRENTANO

First Edition

Published simultaneously in Canada by Clarke, Irwin
& Company Limited, Toronto and Vancouver

Library of Congress Catalog Card Number: 64-19546

Copyright Acknowledgments

LISTED BY AUTHORS

The editor wishes to thank the many authors, agents, and publishers
whose interest, cooperation, and permission to reprint and use material have
made possible *The Light of Christmas*.

"Christmas on the Prairie" from *A Lantern in Her Hand* by Bess Streeter
Aldrich. Reprinted by permission of Appleton-Century. Copyright, 1928,
by D. Appleton and Company.

"When the Wise Man Appeared" by William Ashley Anderson. Reprinted
by permission. Copyright, 1942, by The Philadelphia Evening and Sunday
Bulletin.

"The Song of the Heavenly Chorus" from *Raphael, The Herald Angel* by
David Appel and Merle Hudson. Reprinted by permission of Channel
Press, Publishers. Copyright, ©, 1957, by Channel Press.

"Mrs. Barber's Christmas" from *The Bazaar and Other Stories* by Martin
Armstrong. Published by Jonathan Cape, 1924. Reprinted by permission
of A. D. Peters, literary agent, on behalf of Mr. Armstrong. Copyright by
Martin Armstrong.

"Christmas"* by Faith Baldwin published as "Christmas Eve" in *Christian
Herald*, December, 1949. Reprinted by permission of Faith Baldwin Cuthrell.
Copyright, 1949, by Christian Herald Association.

* An asterisk denotes titles selected by the editor from the text.

"The Chanukah Bush"* by Gertrude Berg from *Christmas with Ed Sullivan*. Reprinted by permission of Gertrude Berg and McGraw-Hill Book Co., Inc. Copyright, ©, 1959, by Ed Sullivan.

"The Stable" from *When Jesus Came* by Handel H. Brown. Reprinted by permission of Wm. B. Eerdmanns Publishing Co. Copyright, ©, 1963, by Handel H. Brown.

"Christmas Day in the Morning" by Pearl S. Buck published in *Collier's*. Reprinted by permission of Harold Ober Associates Incorporated. Copyright, ©, 1955, by Pearl S. Buck.

"One Small Child" by Esther S. Buckwalter published in *Christian Herald*. Reprinted by permission of Esther S. Buckwalter. Copyright, ©, 1960, by Christian Herald Association.

"A Feast Day in Kuwait" from *My Arabian Days and Nights* by Eleanor Taylor Calverley. Thomas Y. Crowell Company, New York, publishers. Copyright, ©, 1958, by the author, Eleanor Taylor Calverley.

"Rather Late for Christmas" by Mary Ellen Chase published in *Vogue*. Reprinted by permission of Mary Ellen Chase. Copyright, ©, 1942 by The Condé Nast Publications Inc.

"The House of Christmas" by G. K. Chesterton from *The Collected Poems of G. K. Chesterton*. Reprinted by permission of Dodd, Mead & Company. Copyright, 1932, by Dodd, Mead & Company, Inc. Reprinted outside the United States by permission of Miss D. E. Collins, the owner of Mr. G. K. Chesterton's copyrights, and of Burns & Oates, Ltd. the publishers of the book *The House of Christmas and Other Poems*. By courtesy of A. P. Watt & Son.

Journey to Christmas by B. J. Chute. Reprinted in its entirety by permission of E. P. Dutton & Co., Inc. Text, Copyright, ©, 1955, by B. J. Chute. This story first appeared in *Good Housekeeping Magazine* under the title "The Year There Was no Christmas."

"The Kingdom" by Thomas Curtis Clark. From *Christ in Poetry* compiled and edited by Thomas Curtis Clark and Hazel Davis Clark. Reprinted by permission of Association Press. Copyright, ©, 1952, by National Board of Young Men's Christian Associations.

"Christmas in Maine" from *Christmas in Maine* by Robert P. Tristram Coffin. Published by Doubleday & Company, Inc. Copyright, 1941, by Robert P. Tristram Coffin. Reprinted by permission of the Estate of Robert P. Tristram Coffin, through Mrs. Peggy Coffin Helvosa.

"Nazareth" from *The Light of the World* by Greville Cooke. Published by Hodder & Stoughton, Ltd. and reprinted by their permission. Copyright 1950, by Greville Vaughan Turner Cooke.

"So Long as There Are Homes" from *Light of the Years* by Grace Noll Crowell. Reprinted by permission of Harper & Row, Publishers, Incorporated. Copyright, 1936, by Harper & Brothers.

"There is a Balm in Gilead" from *The Little Professor of Piney Woods* by Beth Day. Reprinted by permission of the author and Julian Messner, Inc. Copyright, ©, 1955, by Beth Day.

"The Waits" by Margaret Deland from *Christmas* edited by Robert Haven Schauffler. Published, 1907, by Moffat, Yard & Company.

"Mama's Nice Little Man" from *A Time to Remember* by Lloyd Cassell Douglas. Reprinted by permission of Houghton Mifflin Company. Copyright, ©, 1951, by J. Welldon Wilson, Executor of the Estate.

"But Once a Year" from *Life Was Simpler Then* by Loula Grace Erdman. Reprinted by permission of Dodd, Mead & Company. Copyright, ©, 1963, by Loula Grace Erdman.

"Christmas at Peace-Pipe"° from *And Now Tomorrow* by Rachel Field. Reprinted by permission of The Macmillan Company. Copyright, 1942, by The Macmillan Company.

"This Must We Keep" from *This Must We Keep* by Dorothy Canfield Fisher. Published by Christian Herald Association. Reprinted by permission of Sarah Fisher Scott. Copyright, 1940, by Dorothy Canfield Fisher.

"A Letter from Santa Claus" by Mark Twain from *My Father, Mark Twain* by Clara Clemens Gabrilowitsch. Reprinted by permission of Harper & Row, Publishers, Incorporated. Copyright, 1931, 1959, by Clara Clemens Gabrilowitsch.

"Cherished and Shared of Old" from *A Christmas Booklet* by Susan Glaspell. Published by Julian Messner, 1940. Reprinted by permission of the author's estate. Copyright, ©, 1941, by Susan Glaspell.

"But the Greatest of These Is Charity"° from *A City of Bells* by Elizabeth Goudge. Copyright, 1936, by Coward-McCann, Inc. Reprinted by permission. Reprinted in Canada by permission of Gerald Duckworth & Co., Ltd.

"Christmas on the Farm" from *Farmer Takes a Wife* by John Gould. Reprinted by permission of William Morrow and Company, Inc. Copyright, 1942, 1943, 1944, 1945, by John Gould.

"Mary Speaks" from *No One Ever Told Me* by Lucile Graham. Reprinted by the author's permission. Copyright, 1947, by Lucile Graham.

"A Day of Pleasant Bread" from *Adventures in Friendship* by David Grayson (Ray Stannard Baker). Reprinted by permission of Doubleday & Company, Inc. Copyright, 1909, by Phillips Publishing Company.

"Holy Night" from *A Mountain Township* by Walter Hard. Published by Stephen Daye Press; new revised edition 1963. Copyright, 1933, by Walter Hard.

"Let Nothing You Dismay" by Ruth Harnden. Published in *Collier's Magazine*. Reprinted by permission of the author. Copyright 1950, by Ruth Harnden.

"Christmas Closes a Gulf"° from *Act I* by Moss Hart. Reprinted by permission of Random House, Inc. © Copyright, 1959, by Catharine Carlisle Hart and Joseph M. Hyman, Trustees.

"And the Word Was Made Flesh"° from "Brother Sun" in *Little Plays of St. Francis* by Laurence Housman. Reprinted by permission of the Executors of the Laurence Housman Estate and of Jonathan Cape Limited.

"A Different Christmas" from *How Dear to My Heart* by Emily Kimbrough. Reprinted by permission of Dodd, Mead & Company. Copyright, 1944, by Dodd, Mead & Company, Inc.

"Christmas Bells" from *The Works of Henry Wadsworth Longfellow*.

"A Partridge in a Pear Tree" from *Like a Mighty Army*, Selected Letters of Simeon Stylites, by Halford E. Luccock. Reprinted by permission from The Christian Century. Copyright, 1951, by Christian Century Foundation.

"How Can the World Be Redeemed by a Child?" from *The Lost Gospel* by Robert E. Luccock. Reprinted by permission of Harper & Row, Publishers, Incorporated. Copyright, 1948, by Harper & Brothers.

"Christmas Eve"* from *For Our Vines Have Tender Grapes* by George V. Martin. Reprinted by permission of Harold Matson Company, Inc. Copyright, 1940, by Wilfred Funk, Inc.

"Who Gives a Child"* from *The Everlasting Mercy* by John Masefield. Reprinted by permission of The Macmillan Company, The Society of Authors, and Dr. John Masefield, O.M. Copyright, 1911, by John Masefield. Copyright, 1912, by The Macmillan Company.

From *Ode on the Morning of Christ's Nativity* by John Milton.

"A Gift for Molly" from *Wide Meadows* by Jean Bell Mosley. The Caxton Printers Ltd., Caldwell, Idaho. Reprinted by permission of the author and publishers. Copyright, ©, 1960, by Jean Bell Mosley.

"Christmas Problems with Rascal" abridged from the book *Rascal* by Sterling North. Reprinted by permission of E. P. Dutton & Co., Inc. Copyright, ©, 1963, by Sterling North.

"The First Meeting" from *Crossroads*, by John Oxenham (William Arthur Dunkerley). Copyright, 1931, by Longmans, Green & Co., Ltd.

"Incarnate Love" by Christina Rossetti.

"Down Pens" from *The Short Stories of Saki* by H. H. Munro. Reprinted by permission of The Viking Press, Inc. and The Bodley Head, Ltd. All rights reserved. Copyright, 1930, by the Viking Press, Inc. and The Bodley Head, Ltd.

"Anniversary" by Margaret E. Sangster published in *Good Housekeeping* Magazine, December, 1936. Reprinted by permission of Margaret E. Sangster and *Good Housekeeping* Magazine. Copyright, ©, 1936, by the Hearst Corporation.

"Gifts for the First Christmas"* from the chapter "Seeking the Way" from *This Way to Christmas* by Ruth Sawyer. Reprinted by permission of Harper & Row, Publishers, Incorporated. Copyright, 1916, by Harper & Brothers.

"Herod's Way"* from *The Man Born to be King* (a radio presentation) by Dorothy L. Sayers. Reprinted by permission of A. Watkins, Inc. Copyright, ©, 1943 by Dorothy L. Sayers.

"Christmas Cookies"* from *The Chinese Ginger Jars* by Myra Scovel. Reprinted by permission of Harper & Row, Publishers, Incorporated. Copyright, ©, 1962, by Myra Scovel.

From *Hamlet* by William Shakespeare.

"The First Gift" from *The Crown and The Cross* by Frank G. Slaughter. Reprinted by permission of The World Publishing Company. Copyright, ©, 1959, by Frank G. Slaughter.

"A Large Christmas"* from *Memory of a Large Christmas* by Lillian Smith. Reprinted by permission of W. W. Norton & Company, Inc. Copyright, ©, 1961, 1962 by Lilliam Smith.

"The Sequel to Bethlehem"° from *The Salty Tang* by Frederick B. Speakman. Reprinted by permission of Fleming H. Revell Company. Copyright MCMLIV by Fleming H. Revell Company.

"Yuletide Festival at Fort Dodge"° from *Get Thee Behind Me* by Hartzell Spence. Reprinted by permission of McGraw-Hill Book Company, Inc. Copyright, ©, 1942, by Hartzell Spence.

Once on Christmas by Dorothy Thompson. Copyright, 1938, by Henry Z. Walck, Inc. Reprinted by permission.

"Seeking the Light"° from *The Other Wise Man* by Henry van Dyke.

"The Star Which They Saw in the East" from *Stories from Holy Writ* by Helen Waddell. Reprinted by permission of The Macmillan Company. Copyright, 1949, by Helen Waddell.

"The Old Ladies"° abridged from "Christmas Eve—Polchester Winter Piece," Chapter V of *The Old Ladies* by Hugh Walpole. Reprinted by permission of Rupert Hart-Davis, Limited, Publishers. Copyright, 1924, by George H. Doran, now Doubleday & Company, Inc.

"The Greatest Christmas Story Ever Told" by Jerome Weidman. Reprinted by permission of Brandt & Brandt. Copyright, ©, 1953, by The Curtis Publishing Company.

"The Inn That Missed Its Chance" by Amos Russel Wells. Reprinted from *The Christian Endeavor World* and used by permission.

"The Spirit of Giving"° originally "The Glad Evangel" by Kate Douglas Wiggin from *Christmas*, edited by Robert Haven Schauffler. Published, 1907, by Moffat, Yard & Company.

"Something New Is Born"° from *Beloved Bondage* by Elizabeth Yates. Reprinted by permission of Coward-McCann, Inc. Copyright, ©, 1948, by Elizabeth Yates McGreal.

All illustrations in this volume courtesy

THE BETTMANN ARCHIVE

CONTENTS

III: THE HEARTS OF CHILDREN

IV: THE BOSOM OF THE FAMILY

V: THE SPIRIT OF CHRISTMAS

VI: CHRISTMAS MEMORIES

A Note of Thanks

In addition to the authors, publishers, and agents named in the copyright acknowledgments, the compiler wishes to express her gratitude to all the friends and associates who have helped in preparing *The Light of Christmas*.

Many, especially rights and permissions editors, have given freely of their time and counsel to this collection of spiritual prose and poetry. Only a few co-workers are mentioned here with cordial appreciation:

Miss Ruth M. Elmquist, devoted editor of *Christian Herald's Family Bookshelf*. Her friendship, enthusiasm, judgment, and suggestions helped to frame and complete the book.

Miss Kathy Hutton, assistant to Miss Elmquist, for her interest and kind secretarial aid.

Miss Ella J. Klein, associate editor of *Christian Herald*, for access to back Christmas numbers and aid in locating authors.

Miss Ruth M. Stollar, an executive secretary and friend, for abundant support in collating and proofreading.

Mr. Philip Wittenberg, an authority on law and literature, for guidance in matters of contract and copyright.

The entire staff of the Mercantile Library Association, now under the direction of Miss Audrey Eve. Over many years they have rendered constant and invaluable aid in research, as well as the use of a vast and varied collection of volumes.

In the beginning was the Word, and the Word was with God, and the Word was God.

The same was in the beginning with God.

All things were made by him; and without him was not any thing made that was made.

In him was life; and the life was the light of men.

And the light shineth in darkness; and the darkness comprehended it not. . . .

That was the true Light, which lighteth every man that cometh into the world.

(John 1:1-5; 9)

I   Out of Bethlehem

And thou Bethlehem, in the land of Juda, art not the least among the princes of Juda: for out of thee shall come a Governor, that shall rule my people Israel. (Matthew 2:6)

Nothing could be more wonderful, moving, and enlightening than the Christmas story itself. It happened to a people who suffered beyond endurance under the Roman rule, with a mad Asmodean king tormented by prophecies of his own destruction. The yearning for a Messiah, a leader to freedom and a better way of life, filled all their thoughts and prayers. Then out of Bethlehem came the Nativity, prophetic, mysterious, and unearthly: choirs of angels singing from the skies; a strange radiance on the dark hills; shepherds stunned and speechless as they watched their flocks in the lonely night; Wise Men from afar following an unknown star to pay homage to a Baby born in a manger with a gleaming aureole about his head. All testified to the deep significance of "the things that are and cannot be." Until almost two thousand years ago, the greeting at midwinter was, "I give you light for the year." About a century after the first Christmas, John, author of the Fourth Gospel, wrote of Advent in terms of spiritual Light shining through the world's darkness. And the greeting gradually became, "I give you Christ, the Light of the World."

❄ ❄ ❄

From ODE ON THE MORNING
OF CHRIST'S NATIVITY

BY JOHN MILTON

This is the month, and this the happy morn,
Wherein the Son of Heaven's eternal King,
Of wedded maid and virgin mother born,
Our great redemption from above did bring;
For so the holy sages once did sing,
    That he our deadly forfeit should release;
And with his Father work us a perpetual peace. . . .

CHRISTMAS

BY FAITH BALDWIN

The snow is full of silver light
Spilled from the heavens' tilted cup
And, on this holy, tranquil night,
The eyes of men are lifted up
To see the promise written fair,
The hope of peace for all on earth,
And hear the singing bells declare
The marvel of the dear Christ's birth.
The way from year to year is long
And though the road be dark so far,
Bright is the manger, sweet the song,
The steeple rises to the Star.

THEIR FIRST MEETING

from *Crossroads*

BY JOHN OXENHAM

Eternal verities pervade the ageless, eloquent prose and poetry of John Oxenham. He uses Crossroads *to highlight four meetings between Dysmas and Jesus in the years spanning the Master's lifetime. Here we have the first meeting, at the birth of Jesus, in which is given the prophecy of the Glory-to-come.*

It was a cold night up there in the hills, and the men were all gathered close about the fire they had lighted near the entrance to the sheep-fold.

It was little Dysmas's business to keep the fire properly fed. So every now and again he would creep away and come back with another branch and place it carefully on top of the half-burned ones, and he was well repaid for his trouble by hearing it spit and hiss and burst into yellow flame as the withered leaves caught and the sap ran out. But in doing this he missed some of the talk that was going on round the fire.

He was ten years old, this was his first year out with the shepherds, and he was bent on doing his very best to deserve well of them.

Some of the talk he could understand,—as when Gestas said, "They killed a wolf down Tekoa way last week."

He rather wished a wolf would come along their way. It would be rare fun to see them kill it.

But Matthat crushed his hopes with his dry, "It was nought— an ancient beast, cast out, and gone astray."

Some other bits of the gossip round the fire interested him. Stories of the iniquities of the tax-gatherers, and of the foolish rising over there in Iturea, which Rome had trampled out with a heavy heel, as she always did.

"Great foolishness!" commented Old Jeconiah on that. "Why can't they wait? . . . as we others have done all these years. It will be soon now."

"You've preached that these forty years, old one," said Jona.

"The Deliverer is always coming but he never comes. Our fathers hoped for him just as we do, and they are dead."

"He is coming, I tell you. It will not be long now, and when he comes Rome will go, and Israel will be a nation once more and will lead the world."

"We have heard it so often—all our lives. One grows tired of hearing it."

"All the same you may live to see it. . . . You young ones are so impatient."

Some of them were men of forty and fifty, but to him they were still young ones, for he had known their fathers and mothers before they were born.

"If Israel loses heart and hope, maybe he will never come. He will not come to a nation without heart and hope."

They had heard him on that subject so often before that they had come not to pay any great heed to him. In fact he rather wearied them.

He was very old. No one knew quite how old he was—far past the ordinary span of life and long past work. But he had been a shepherd all his days, he knew more about sheep and their ways than any of them, and he was more at home in the company of sheep and shepherds than of ordinary men.

And he was something of a seer. During all his lifelong lonely vigils on the hills he had dreamed dreams—chiefly of the coming of the promised Deliverer; and seen visions—mostly of what would happen when he came. And, in the more ordinary affairs of life among his neighbours, he had a reputation for foreseeing and foretelling things—mostly fortunes—which at times actually came to pass, as misfortunes have a way of doing.

So, though he wearied them with his unwearying positiveness about the Coming of the Deliverer—which did not come to pass— he was still held in some esteem by reason of the smaller things that did.

With his tall figure and bent shoulders, his long grey hair and flowing beard, and his eyes still bright—especially when he discoursed on his favourite theme—he looked very like what they imagined the prophets of old must have been—Moses or Elijah or Isaiah. There had indeed been no such prophets in their time, but they had their ideas of what they must have looked like, and that was like Old Jeconiah.

It was a cold, still night, the sky illimitably black above them, and the stars shining very near and large and bright. The sheep in the fold were snuggled close for warmth. The dogs squeezed in between the men to get their noses as near to the fire as possible, and little Dysmas fed it with broken branches whenever it began to get low, and found a dog in his place each time he came back.

"Ay!" said Old Jeconiah musingly, as though he was just thinking aloud, "don't give up hoping. For if one loses hope there is nothing left . . . and one never knows when . . ."

And then it came—that of which they never ceased to tell for the rest of their lives.

As though one of the great bright stars had fallen right upon them, they were suddenly enveloped in dazzling light—light so purely white and wondrous that no man had ever seen the like, and they fell on their faces in fear.

All except Old Jeconiah. He sat bowed, but gazing with eyes that shone responsive and triumphant and without fear.

The sheep in the fold woke up and cried out to one another in wonder. The dogs sat up all abristle and whimpered, for dogs at times see more than men.

And in the brightness Old Jeconiah saw a being in white—one the like of whom he had never seen before, and who shone even in the wonder and splendour of that most wonderful light; and he was not afraid.

And the Shining One spoke, in a full sweet voice: "Have no fear! It is good news I am bringing you, news of a great joy that is meant for all the people. To-day you have a saviour born in the town of David—the Lord Messiah. And here is proof—you will find a baby there wrapped up and lying in a stall for cattle. That is he!"

And then—wonder on wonder!—the Shining One was suddenly surrounded by a host of others, and they broke into wondrous song:

"Glory to God in high heaven,
And peace on earth for men whom he favours!"

Joyously and triumphantly they sang, till the whole sky seemed filled with the sound of it.

Then, as suddenly as they came, they were gone, and the earth was dark as before. But up in the black sky the silvery voices grew fainter and fainter till they died away, and the stars twinkled and sparkled as though they knew all about it and were still singing joyously.

Old Jeconiah rose up, tall and straight as if the years had never bowed his broad shoulders; and his face, if they could have seen it, had in it the eagerness of youth and the overpowering joy of his at-last-fulfilled hope.

"Let us go!" he said simply.

"What of the sheep?" asked Matthat.

"The sheep will take no harm this night."

"I will stop with the sheep," said Gestas. He was a heavy, stolid fellow of two-and-twenty. "I would not walk a mile to see any baby that ever was born. I've got one at home that cries night and day."

Old Jeconiah turned to him, but thought better of it and said nothing. It was never any use arguing with Gestas. It was like arguing with a sheep.

"The boy could stop with him," said one.

"Nay," cried little Dysmas, half crying, "I go too!" for he was young and eager, and wanted to see all that was doing.

"Let him come," said Jeconiah. "No man may forbid him." And they set off down the hill in the darkness, Old Jeconiah keeping pace with the best of them; and when they got to the foot of the hill they found that the dogs had come too.

So they came at last to the little town of Bethlehem and found it crowded with many strangers.

Jeconiah went straight to the Khan to pick up what news he could, and found it overflowing. In time he found the harassed master, and held on to his robe till he answered.

"A baby—just born? . . . Look in the stable there. . . . A man came in a while ago saying his wife was taken with child, and that was the only place. It was hard on her, but we're crowded out, you see, with the folks come up for the Census," and he hurried away after his duties.

They went round to the stable, and there, by the dim light of a lantern which hung among the cobwebs from a beam, they found the child with his mother and father, as the angel had said.

When the strangers came in the mother lifted him from the feeding-trough, where he had been lying in the hay, and held him close to her breast.

"May we see the little one who is to save the people?" said Jeconiah very reverently.

And he told her how an angel had come to them, far away in the hills, and bidden them seek the babe in a manger in Bethlehem.

And he told her all that the angel had said, and what the host of angels had sung. And her sweet girlish face was full of wonder and of joy as she heard it all.

She held the little one in the bend of her arm so that they should see him properly, since they had come so far for that purpose.

And Old Jeconiah went close and knelt by him, and looked upon him long and earnestly—gazed deep into his baby eyes, which could not surely have seen much. But yet he seemed to look back at Jeconiah with understanding. And what Jeconiah saw in the baby's eyes he never told, but he probably saw there more than any other would have done.

Little Dysmas had no little brothers or sisters, nor even a father or mother, and he did not care much for babies, unless they were lambs. But the baby's mother he thought was the most beautiful girl he had ever seen, and he stood gazing at her with wide eyes and open mouth, and a strange new feeling inside him, as though he had suddenly found someone to whom he belonged, say a father and a mother and a little brother.

The dogs went sniffing among the cattle, and the cattle swayed about with wide eyes, and snorted and blew at them till the air was full of the sweet wholesome smell of them.

Old Jeconiah bent lower and kissed the soft downy head of the child very gently and reverently, saying, "One day his head will wear a crown."

And he kissed the hand that clasped the child, and said, "Surely you are the most blessed among women, for you have given a new hope to the world," and then, with one last look at them, he turned to go and the rest with him.

And as Matthat went he said, "When he is big enough we will bring him a clean little white lamb to play with," at which the little mother smiled and thanked him, knowing that in a few days they would be far away in their own home.

Outside were many waiting to hear why they had come and what they had heard. And Old Jeconiah told them; and he looked so exactly like one of the prophets of old, with his long hair and flowing beard, that they believed him, not knowing how often before he had been mistaken in the things he foretold.

On the way back he went heavily, as though he had left something behind him. When they came to the foot-hills he sat down by the side of the path, panting and bowed on his staff, and said, "Go on, you others. . . . Get back to the sheep. . . . For me, I would rest awhile,"—and then, as though speaking to himself— "My heart has seen its desires and is satisfied. . . . The Wonder of the World! . . . God be thanked! . . . I have seen the beginning. . . . Who shall see the end?"

So, since they could not get him to go on and their sheep claimed them, for Gestas would certainly have fallen asleep, they left him sitting there, and went on their way.

But little Dysmas lingered behind the others and kept looking back. And suddenly he saw the old man's hands slip down his staff and he fell forward with his face on the ground.

Dysmas gave a loud cry and ran back down the hills, and the others came running after him.

But Old Jeconiah was dead, and his face was full of joy and peace. He had seen of the desire of his soul and was satisfied.

So they wrapped him up in his robe and bore him up into the hills to his own place.

THE STABLE

from *When Jesus Came*

by Handel H. Brown

English born and educated, Handel H. Brown is an authority on Scripture, its origins, history, and contemporaneous importance. His writing and preaching show the manifold application of religion in every-day living and his own keen personal enjoyment of faith and works. "The Stable," part of a chapter in his book When Jesus Came,

*radiates incisive knowledge and moral courage, as Dr. Brown depicts
the lowly scene where "Mary brought forth her first born son."*

Many of us imagine that when Jesus was born, conditions were
about idyllic. Perhaps this impression is due in part to the
pastoral emphasis. To a larger degree, however, it is due to our
failure to read the New Testament intelligently.

Politically, Palestine was seething with unrest. Economically,
the great masses of the poor were getting poorer and the few
rich were getting richer. Socially, there was a great gulf fixed
between the highly educated Scribes, Pharisees, Sadducees, and
Herodians on the one hand, and "the people of the land," as
they contemptuously called them, on the other. The only thing
which united the Jews was their common hatred of Rome.° At
this particular time, their grumbling was against the "decree of
Caesar Augustus that all the world should be enrolled" (Luke
2:1).

In obedience to the mandate of Caesar, Mary and Joseph went
south. But Caesar was simply the executor of a Higher Will, the
Will that moves silently but surely back of all thrones and
principalities and powers.

They came to Bethlehem. It was a one-horse town. Its solitary
street was cobbled with round black stones. They were hard on
the feet. They harbored refuse. They caused many a stranger to
stumble with a stubbed toe.

Inns, or *Khans*, were usually quite crude affairs. They consisted
of a series of thatched rooms built round a central courtyard.
Often they were no more than covered porches. The travellers
brought their own food for man and beast. They brought the pot
in which to cook it on an open fire in the yard. They brought their
bedding, and often their firewood. They looked to the innkeeper
for water and shelter.

The lone inn of Bethlehem was a shabby sort of place. It
blended with its surroundings. Both had seen better days. The
inn was extremely old. It may have been the one built by
Chimham, who was one of David's favorites (2 Samuel 19:37ff.).

° It is by no means certain that the Herodians can be included in this
generalization. Many of them were "collaborators."

If so, Jeremiah tells us it was the place where the murderers of Gedaliah rested on their flight into Egypt (Jeremiah 41:17).

For many centuries there was an inn built on land which belonged to the family of David. It was widely known as "The Inn of Chimham." Legend said it occupied the exact site of the house where David was born. If that old story is true, it throws new light on the events we are considering, and gives added significance to some of them.

When Mary and Joseph reached Bethlehem, no one took any notice of them. They were lost in a milling crowd of nameless ones. None of them had wanted to come. Some of them decided to make the best of their compulsory vacation. They had not tasted the good rich wine of Bethlehem for a long time and there was plenty on hand. They were too busy with their conviviality to pay any attention to stragglers and strangers.

Like most of the men, Joseph wore crude sandals which were made of castoff rope. They were the badge of the poor. Mary was barefooted. It is usually assumed that she rode on a donkey. There is no evidence for this, but I hope it is correct. While it is true that under normal conditions even a pregnant Eastern woman would have to walk while her lord and master rode, we may be sure that Joseph was anxious to protect "that holy thing" (Luke 1:35) carried by his wife.

The innkeeper took one look at them, and when he said, "No room," he meant it.

Joseph had to lead the weary donkey to a common stable. Those who have seen an Eastern byre, retch at the thought. There was no trace of the sapphire mist, or the scent of sandal-wood, of which sentiment is so fond. It was full of insects with shrill voices. The loathsome blueflies gorged themselves on offal. Neither door nor curtain covered the opening of the cave.

The grotto that is now shown as the Lord's birthplace is in the southeast section of the town. The tradition that connects this particular cave with His birth is very ancient. It reaches back at least to the middle of the second century. Justin Martyr (A.D. 150) mentions it, and so does Origen, who lived a hundred years later.

The Scriptures, Josephus, and many authorities speak of the numerous caves which are found throughout Palestine, and of the different uses to which they were put in Bible times . . .

A new interest in old caves has been created by the discovery of the Dead Sea Scrolls. Near a valley called "Wadi Qumran," at the northwest corner of the Dead Sea, more than ten caves have yielded Hebrew and Aramaic manuscripts of great antiquity. Some of them are portions of the Old Testament, a thousand years older than anything scholars have hitherto known.

✤   ✤   ✤

In religion, anything mechanical is false. God did not "wave a wand" and magically provide marvelous lodgings for the needy travellers. He who "measured the waters in the hollow of his hand, and meted out the heavens with a span" (Isaiah 40:12),

> . . . laid His glory by,
> He wrapped Him in our clay;
> Unmarked by human eye,
> The latent Godhead lay;
> Infant of days He here became,
> And bore the mild Immanuel's name.
> —Charles Wesley

> O strange indifference!—low and high
> Drowsed over common joys and cares:
> The earth was still—but knew not why;
> The world was listening—unawares;
> How calm a moment may precede
> One that shall thrill the world for ever!
> To that still moment, none would heed,
> Man's doom was linked, no more to sever,
> In the solemn midnight
> Centuries ago.

> It is the calm and solemn night!
> A thousand bells ring out and throw
> Their joyous peals abroad, and smile
> The darkness, charm'd and holy now!
> The night that erst no name had worn,
> To it a happy name is given;
> For in that stable lay new-born
> The peaceful Prince of Earth and Heaven,
> In the solemn midnight
> Centuries ago.
> —Alfred Domett

He who ended in a cave, the sepulcher of Joseph of Arimathea, also began in a cave. Neither was unforeseen. Neither was "an emergency." God is big enough—even for Christmas!

When Mary "brought forth her first-born Son" in all the discomfort and inconvenience of a stable, she "wrapped him in swaddling clothes" (Luke 2:7).

A Jewish baby was often sprinked with salt at birth, after his initial washing (Ezekiel 16:4). Then the arms were laid at his side, and he was wrapped snugly in bandages. This was supposed to strengthen him. Such were the "swaddling clothes" in which the newborn Jesus was wrapped.

Then Mary laid Him in "a manger." This was a feeding trough used by animals. It was probably a hollowed-out stone. It was heavy enough so that the cattle could not push it around or upset it. To turn the manger into a crib was a simple matter for Mary. Nothing more was needed than a supply of clean hay and, we may suppose, some sort of cloth with which to cover it.

> Hay! hay did you say?
> Surely it was not hay
> On which the Christ-Child lay?
> Humble indeed the shed,
> Awkward the manger bed,
> Was there no linen spread?
> Come, was it hay you said?
>
> Yes, it was common hay,
> Cut on a summer's day . . .
> As the sweet crop they drest—
> Dividing good from best—
> They knew not some would rest
> This world's most holy Guest.
> —Anonymous

There is a lovely old folk tale which says that on the day when the Lord Jesus was born, there was a little brown creature awake in the hay. He saw the Shepherds come with their simple offerings of bread and milk. He watched the resplendent Wise Men bring their costly gifts. He wanted with all his heart to do something for the newborn Saviour. But what could he do?

At last he thought of something within his power. Clutching hold of a specially fragrant piece of hay, he pushed, carried, and dragged it, with a tremendous struggle, to the manger. There he added it to the hay on which the Baby Jesus lay.

Just as he did so, the Baby smiled, stretched out His hand, and touched him. Immediately the little brown thing began to glow with light. Ever since, the glow-worms, whose far away ancestor wanted so much to serve Jesus, and finally found a way, have shone in the darkness.

The coming of Jesus has made a greater difference to the history of mankind, than any other event that has ever happened. Yet when He came, not only was there no one to welcome Him, there were few even to recognize Him.

> They had no room for Him,
> No handkerchief to fold under His head,
> No old coat to throw over His bed.
> The candle flickered and grew dim,
> Her shadow leapt and dwindled over Him;
> And in her shadow's dance
> The secret hosts advance.
> Angels are there, philosophers and kings,
> Herdsmen, artificers of humble things,
> Hidden behind His mother, on the floor
> Of mud and clay they drop down to adore.
> —George Every

It is interesting that in the New Testament Bethlehem is never mentioned as having been visited by our Lord. It is in no way mentioned with His ministry. Its sole claim to fame is that it was the place of His birth. Yet on every hand Bethlehem reveals the touch of Christ.

> Cradled in a manger, meanly
> Laid the Son of Man His head;
> Sleeping His first earthly slumber
> Where the oxen has been fed.
> —George Stringer Rowe

> Were earth a thousand times as fair,
> Beset with gold and jewels rare,
> She yet were far too poor to be
> A narrow cradle, Lord, for Thee.
> —Martin Luther

THE STAR WHICH THEY SAW IN THE EAST

from *Stories from Holy Writ*

BY HELEN WADDELL

Dr. Helen Waddell, the distinguished medievalist and scholar, has animated historic lives, events, and periods with her colorful interpretation. Stories from Holy Writ were told to children and then written for a missionary magazine some decades ago. The demand for them in book form has never ceased, and they still appear with the rich detail and poetic thought which make all her writing memorable. "The Star Which They Saw in the East" is a beautiful vignette.

Up in the deep blue fields of air the great stars wheeled and burned. Jupiter and Saturn stood together in the House of the Fish for the first time in eight hundred years, and the glory of them lightened all that part of heaven. Twice eight hundred years after Christ was born, a man stood by his telescope in Prague, brooding over the lines and circles on the sheets before him. Night after night he watched, while Mars, the star of the war-god, burned his slow way through heaven to join his great brethren. And some time on a winter night in 1603, the three stars came together, and the patient watcher saw a thing that made his heart burn. For even as Mars came nearer, a new strange star, shining and changing like a precious stone, flamed for a while between Jupiter and Saturn, and slowly went out. To this man, watching, it was as though he clasped hands across a great gulf of years with those men, wise like himself in the counsels of the stars, who had stood on the flat roof of a house in an Eastern town and watched the planets wheel and the strange star burn, and knew it for the coming of a King. Once in every eight hundred years Jupiter and Saturn come together in the House of the Fish, with Mars to follow them. That they had so come, Kepler knew, but that the strange new passing star had flamed to their eyes, even as now, he could not surely know. But he wrote of what he had seen, the wonder and the mystery of it, in a book called *De Stella Nova*; and yet another wise man laid his gift at the cradle of the King.

Now that the stars of the three gods, Jupiter, Saturn and Mars, stood together, about the time our Lord was born, the records of the stars can show. But of the strange star there is no record, except that on the tables of the Chinese—for they, too, are in the counsels of the stars—there is mention of some such vanishing radiance as this, and at such a time; a record that is almost 2,000 years old.

There is no surety. Nor do we know the names of the Wise Men, though the Middle Ages made a rich legend of them. We do not know if they were kings or princes, nor whence they came. They come out of darkness into starlight, and go from starlight again into darkness. But in the starlight they are noble figures, the first of the great caravan of those who go in pilgrimage to find the King. The Chaldeans were stargazers always; and it may be that they came from that same plain where the first Hebrew, the man from Beyond the River, saw the sun set and the stars come out, and craved for a God who would not change and pass, and went out, not knowing whether he went to find him. "Abraham rejoiced to see My Day," said Christ in the Temple; "he saw it and was glad." These three saw only the morning of it; "and when they saw the star," says St. Matthew, "they rejoiced with exceeding great joy."

> "See how from far upon the eastern road
> The star-led wizards haste with odours sweet."

Always on the road they are, with a great dark land behind them, and the night above it brooding and mournful; but these have their faces to a star, and they are greater than men in the darkness, for they stand for the Wisdom of the world. And again in the lantern-light, kneeling, their heads bowed to the earthen floor, and their hands outstretched with their offerings to the King. There are shadows about the crib, and on their bowed heads, but the lantern light gleams on the precious things they hold. For they are the gifts that the world has brought to its King; gold, for the glory and honour of the nations; incense, for worship; myrrh, for death.

THE FIRST GIFT

from *The Crown and the Cross*

BY FRANK G. SLAUGHTER

There have been many literary physicians, but few have combined medicine, fictional material, history, biography, and religion as successfully and well as Dr. Frank G. Slaughter. The Crown and the Cross is an imaginative retelling of the New Testament story from which comes "The First Gift."

Elam was up early for he was anxious to reach the bazaars of Jerusalem with his bales of cloth soon after the shops opened for business. Later in the day, when more merchandise had come in, prices would be lower, but since it was only a few miles to the Holy City, he planned to be among the first-comers and thus be sure of a good price.

Word had gone through the inn that a child had been born in the stable during the night. With a good night's rest behind him and the prospect of a handsome profit on the sale of his goods, the Pharisee was in a good humor when he stopped by the stable to give his blessing to mother and child. But as he looked at the sleeping baby, he gave a muffled exclamation of surprise. Reaching down he took a corner of the swaddling cloth between his fingers and for an instant a look of astonishment showed in his eyes, to be quickly replaced by a crafty gleam.

"This fabric is too fine to be wasted as a swaddling cloth," he said casually to Joseph. "I will give you a good price for it."

"I cannot sell the cloth." Joseph glanced quickly at Jonas, who had come in to tell the family good-by before leaving.

"Why not sell it?" Elam demanded of Joseph. "You could not bid against me for the couch last night. You must be poor."

"We have no other swaddling cloth for the baby," Joseph protested.

Elam shrugged away that objection. "The shops of the town will soon be open. With what I will pay you for the cloth, you can buy another and still have money to spare. Hurry and name a price, man. I must get to Jerusalem early."

31

Joseph shook his head. "The cloth was a gift, the first gift to the baby. It is not for sale."

"A gift?" Elam's eyes narrowed and he looked quickly around the stable. Obviously no one there could afford such a gift. "Who gave it?" he demanded.

"I—I cannot say, sir."

"You mean it was stolen, don't you?" Elam seized upon the advantage Joseph had given him. "Then it is my duty to impound the cloth and hold it for the rightful owner." Elam knew that if the carpenter did not divulge the name of the owner now, the cloth would probably never be claimed and in due time it would become his property at no cost.

"Joseph did not steal the cloth, master," Jonas said. "I gave it to the child."

"You!" Elam wheeled upon his servant. "Where would you get such a fabric as this, Jonas?"

"I wove it myself. Nights, after my work was finished."

"You stole the wool from me, then."

"It was made from scraps that had been thrown away. I carded and spun the wool into thread myself, and wove it upon a loom I made with my own hands."

"You were going to sell the cloth in Jerusalem and keep the money for yourself!" Elam accused him.

"No, master." Jonas realized fully that he was inviting harsh punishment at Elam's hands for contradicting him. "It was to be a gift to the Temple for an altar cloth."

"If it was intended for the Temple, why did you let such a valuable fabric be used for swaddling a baby?"

"The child—it was cold," Jonas stammered. "I thought it needed the cloth more than the priests."

Elam snorted indignantly. "You were a fool to soil such a fine piece of fabric. Especially as it belongs to me." He turned to Joseph. "Unwrap the child and give me the cloth. I am a generous man, so I will still pay you enough to buy another, though this one is mine by right."

Joseph shook his head. "Jonas has explained to you that he wove it after his day's work was finished, from wool that had been cast aside. The cloth was his to do with as he chose."

"The work of a servant belongs to the master," Elam insisted. "That is the Law."

"You Pharisees speak much of the Law when it is to your own

benefit," Joseph said firmly. "Let us take this question before a judge and see who is right. These men here in the stable will witness that you covet a cloth which Jonas gave the child and seek to get it for yourself."

"I will gladly be a witness for Jonas," a burly fellow bystander offered, glowering at Elam. "It will be good to see a Pharisee feel the weight of the Law on his own neck for a change."

When several others pushed forward to offer themselves as witnesses, Elam hesitated. If he took this dispute before a judge, the ruling would probably be in his favor, since it would be the word of a wealthy man against his servant. On the other hand, much of the "Oral Law" governing the conduct of the Jews was not set down in writing, and each judge could interpret it according to his own conviction. If the ruling should go against him, Elam would not only lose face—an important thing to a man of his sort—but he would have failed to reach the shops of Jerusalem early and might be forced to hold his bales until tomorrow's market.

Characteristically, the Pharisee turned his anger and frustration upon one who could not resist. "Strip to the waist," he ordered Jonas and, going to the wall, took down a leather strap hanging there. Elam had no fear that anyone would try to keep him from flogging Jonas, for the right of the master to punish a servant was undisputed.

Jonas' face was pale as he dropped the upper part of his robe, baring his back and shoulders. He flinched as the strap fell upon his unprotected skin, but he did not cry out. The Pharisee was skilled in punishing servants, laying on the leather with enough force to cause pain and raise an angry red welt which would be exquisitely tender for days, yet not enough to break the skin. Skin wounds could mean inflammation and even death, and a servant was too valuable a property to be destroyed simply to satisfy the owner's anger.

Soon Jonas' back was a crisscross pattern of red welts. The pain was excruciating but the little man bit into his lip and did not beg for mercy. Finally, though, a blow brought a slight stain of red, and then Elam, almost exhausted, tossed the leather strap aside.

"Get the animals ready while I refresh myself with wine," he ordered curtly. "We will leave for Jerusalem at once."

Jonas pulled up his robe and started for the courtyard where the animals were tied, but Joseph was there before him. "I should have felt the strap instead of you," he said humbly as he loosened the tether of Elam's pack animal for Jonas and tested the thongs lashing the bales upon its back.

Jonas managed to grin, although his back was a throbbing mass of agony. "The pain will go away. I have been flogged before."

"And will be again, if I judge that master of yours right," Joseph said grimly. "He was humbled in pride and purse, both tender spots for a man such as he."

The pain lines were gone from Mary's face when Jonas came to bid the little family farewell. Her serene beauty reminded him of the star that has shone over Bethlehem last night, and the sleeping child, too, seemed to have a radiance of its own.

"Jonas!" Elam's sharp voice sounded in the doorway. "Stop wasting time, unless you want another beating!"

The little man hurried to pick up the tether of the pack animal. To keep the rough cloth of his garment from scraping against his tender skin, he tried to walk stiffly erect. But even that little relief was denied him, for Elam at once kicked the ass he rode into a near trot, so anxious was he to get to Jerusalem by the time the shops opened, and Jonas was forced to hurry on behind him.

Busy with his own misery while he tried to urge the reluctant pack animal along, Jonas was paying little attention to the road ahead when he heard his master's voice ring out sharply.

"You there!" Elam called. "Don't block the road."

Three men, shepherds by their dress and the fact that one of them carried a crook made from the gnarled limb of a small tree, stood aside for Elam's little procession to pass. Jonas remembered seeing other such men when traveling near Jerusalem. The flocks in this area near the Holy City and its great Temple were for the most part dedicated for sacrifice upon the altar, and the shepherds who guarded them were set apart and treated with respect by all who met them.

Elam now recognized the men and pulled the ass to a stop. Jonas, plodding behind with the lead rope of the second animal, also halted.

"Are you not the shepherds of the sacred flock?" the Pharisee asked in a more pleasant tone.

"One of us is keeping the flocks today so the rest of us can come to Bethlehem," one of the men said.

Elam frowned. Some landlord and owner was being cheated if shepherds were allowed to roam the countryside or go into the town for a cup of wine while their flocks were left poorly guarded in the field. Elam knew that many rich men in Jerusalem owned land and flocks in this area. No doubt some of them would reward him well for discovering the shortcomings of his shepherds.

"Would your masters be pleased if they knew of this?" Elam demanded.

The taller shepherd who seemed to be the spokesman answered. "Last night something happened," he explained. "A thing so strange that we felt it should be reported in Bethlehem."

"What was that?"

"We were abiding in the field as is our custom when a bright light shone around us and we were sore afraid. But we heard a voice say, 'Fear not, for behold I bring you good tidings of great joy, which shall be to all people. For unto you is born this day in the City of David, A Saviour which is Christ the Lord.'"

As an educated man, Elam knew what was written concerning the coming of the Expected One, the Messiah who would rule over Israel and free her from domination by others. He doubted strongly that so momentous an event would be announced to ignorant shepherds; it would be the High Priest in Jerusalem who would be the first to know of it—if it really had occurred. If it had, though, and the Temple authorities had not heard . . . Elam was shrewd enough to realize they would pay well for information about it. . . .

If he were to be the bearer of such good tidings, he had best press on and say no more about it here. "No doubt you were dreaming," he said in a disparaging manner calculated to make the men doubt the value of what they had seen, if indeed it had any value. "Your dream has led you on a fool's errand. The Saviour of Israel would hardly be born without notice." And kicking his mount, Elam directed it once again along the road.

Jonas did not follow at once, but beckoned the shepherds to come nearer. "Did this voice say how you would know the Christ?" he asked in lowered tones.

The tall shepherd nodded. "The angel said, 'And this shall be a sign: you will find the babe wrapped in swaddling clothes, lying in a manger.'"

A great light burst in Jonas' brain, almost as bright as had been the star last night. But first, he knew, he must make sure the shepherds did not intend to harm the babe.

"Why do you seek the child?" he asked them.

"We would worship him, for when the angels finished speaking there was a multitude of the heavenly hosts praising God and saying, 'Glory to God in the highest, and on earth peace, good will toward men.'"

"Are you sure the voice said the child would be found in a manger?"

The tall shepherd looked at him keenly. "Why do you ask? What do you know of this?" he demanded.

"A child was born in Bethlehem last night, in the stable of an inn where we stayed," Jonas explained. "I myself gave it the swaddling cloth. There was no cradle, so the baby was placed in the manger."

"That is just as the angel described it!" The tall shepherd said excitedly. "You say you gave it the first gift?"

Jonas nodded proudly. "A swaddling cloth of finest wool, woven with my own hands!"

"Then you are more honored than we can ever be," the shepherd told him. "But if we hurry, we will be able to worship him too!"

"Hurry, Jonas!" Elam's querulous voice floated back along the road. "I must sell the goods early, so I can make my gift to the Temple today!"

Jonas left the shepherds and followed his master, but he no longer noticed the pain from his flayed back. Nothing Elam could do would be able to hurt him now. For by some strange miracle, which he did not even try to understand, he had been singled out for a great honor, for a privilege greater than had been given any man, that of making the first gift to the Son of God.

THE INN THAT MISSED ITS CHANCE

(The Landlord Speaks, A.D. 28)

BY Amos Russel Wells

What could be done? The house was full of folks!
His honor, Marcus Lucius, and his scribes
Who made the census: honorable men
From farthest Galilee, come hitherward
To be enrolled; high ladies and their lords;
The rich, the rabbis, such a noble throng
As Bethlehem had never seen before
And may not see again. And there they were,
Close-herded with their servants, till the inn
Was like a hive at swarming time, and I
Was fairly crazed among them.

                    Could I know
That they were so important? Just the two,
No servants, just a workman sort of man,
Leading a donkey, and his wife thereon
Drooping and pale,—I saw them not myself,
My servants must have driven them away;
But had I seen them,—how was I to know?
Were inns to welcome stragglers up and down
In all our towns from Beersheba to Dan,
Till He should come? And how were men to know?

There was a sign, they say, a heavenly light
Resplendent: but I had no time for stars,
And there were songs of angels in the air
Out on the hills; but how was I to hear
Amid the thousand clamors of an inn?

Of course, if I had known them, who they were,
And who was He that should be born that night—
For now I learn that they will make him King,
A second David, who will ransom us
From these Philistine Romans—who but He
That feeds an army with a loaf of bread,
And if a soldier falls, He touches him

37

And up he leaps, uninjured? Had I known,
I would have turned the whole inn upside down,
His honor, Marcus Lucius, and the rest,
And sent them all to stables, had I known.
So you have seen Him, stranger, and perhaps
Again may see Him? Prithee say for me,
I did not know; and if He comes again
As he will surely come, with retinue,
And banners, and an army, tell my Lord
That all my inn is His to make amends.

Alas! Alas! to miss a chance like that!
This inn might be the chief among them all,
The birthplace of Messiah, had I known!

HEROD'S WAY

from *The Man Born To Be King*

BY DOROTHY L. SAYERS

Dorothy L. Sayers characterized the Gospel story as "the Classic of classics." After profound study of the rich but fragmentary Biblical sources and many learned works, she adapted this matchless theme for radio presentation in The Man Born To Be King. *Miss Sayers' creative delineation of character and incidents imparts new dramatic power to the familiar cosmic and historic tragedy. "Herod's Way," which follows, forms a powerful unit in the series of twelve unforgettable scenes.*

(*Enter* KING HEROD THE GREAT, *with* QUEEN ELPIS, *the* HIGH PRIEST, *the* COURT PHYSICIAN, *the* CHIEF ASTRONOMER, LORDS, LADIES, *and* ATTENDANTS)

ALL: God Save King Herod!

HEROD (*in a voice ragged with pain and exhaustion*): Set me down carefully. If you shake me, your bones will pay for it.

EPHRAIM: Here, slaves, here. . . . Will it please your Majesty to lie on this couch?

HEROD: In my chair—in my chair of state. Fool and traitor, what would you make of me? I am King Herod still.

EPHRAIM: And for many a long year, please God.

HEROD: You are a hypocrite. You think and hope I am dying. You are in league with my traitor sons, who would snatch at my sceptre before my carcase is cold. Don't deny it. I have seen you, licking the hand of Archelaus, fawning at the heels of Antipater—plotting, plotting—nothing but plots and treachery. (*His voice dies away into a groan*)

EPHRAIM: Alas! Why should your Majesty think so? We are all your most devoted, loving, faithful subjects.

HEROD: So every traitor says. You had best be careful, my lord Ephraim.

EPHRAIM: I am the King's dog. May the plague light on me if ever one disloyal word or thought—

HEROD: Bah!

ELPIS: Oh, sir; when my royal husband is in this mood it is better not to cross him. His sickness makes him impatient—but it will pass.

HEROD: Doctor, give me something to ease this pain. Though I daresay you are in league with my heirs to poison me.

PHYSICIAN: Heaven forbid, sir.

HEROD: Heaven, or somebody, will know how to deal with you if you play tricks with me. . . . Now then! Who are these foreign princes, and what do they seek at the hand of Herod, King of Jewry?

CASPAR: O King, live for ever! I am Caspar, King of Chaldaea.

MELCHIOR: I am Melchior, King of Pamphlia.

BALTHAZAR: I am Balthazar, King of Ethiopia.

HEROD (*with the utmost graciousness: it is like a different man speaking*): Royal brothers, you are all most heartily welcome to my Queen and me.

CASPAR: We are Magi, humble searchers after the hidden Wisdom.

ELPIS: My lord and I are the more honoured by your visit. We love the company of good and learned men.

MELCHIOR: To you, King Herod, and to the whole realm of Judaea, we bring glad tidings from the High Lords of Heaven.

BALTHAZAR: Glory and dominion to the uttermost ends of the world, and the promise of an everlasting sceptre.

HEROD: That is good tidings indeed.

MELCHIOR: Therefore, O King, in the name of the most High God, we pray you to grant us our heart's desire.

HEROD: Ask what you will. Our royal bounty and favour are open to you.

CASPAR: Show us, we beg you, the noble child himself.

HEROD: Child? What child?

MELCHIOR: Show us him that is born King of the Jews.

BALTHAZAR: We have seen his star in the east, and have come to pay homage to him.

HEROD (*in a dangerous tone*): Sirs, I do not understand you.

CASPAR: Do not deny us; we have journeyed many miles for this.

MELCHIOR: We know that the boy is born. Nine months long the hosts of heaven were troubled. Fiery Mars glowed like gold in a furnace, and Saturn's leaden cheek grew pale. Jove himself, the imperial star, was smitten and afflicted between the sun and moon in the constellation of the Virgin.

BALTHAZAR: While yet it lay beneath the horizon, we felt the coming of the Star, and marvelled what this might be. And in our books, we read how the truth should be made known in Judaea, and in the House of the Lion, which is the House of Judah.

HEROD: Judah!

EPHRAIM (*in an agitated whisper*): You have touched him nearly. He is an Idumaean. He is not of Judah's line. I beseech you, my lords—

HEROD: What are you muttering there? Proceed, sirs, proceed.

CASPAR: Then we took horse and rode across the desert. And as we sat by night beside the waters of Araba, we saw the rising of the Star. Between the midnight and the day it stood, burning upon the cusp of the First House, lord of the ascendant.

MELCHIOR: And all the rulers of the firmament were gathered to do it honour. Never were such conjunctions seen in the horoscope of any earthly potentate.

BALTHAZAR: Then we knew that the hour had come, when he that should establish the kingdom was born a prince in Israel.

HEROD: Have a care, you little lords. Who sent you hither to mock me?

ELPIS: Indeed, sirs, you do not know what you are saying.

HEROD: I think there's treason here. Who sent you?

CASPAR: Herod, Herod—

HEROD: I say, who sent you? Answer me, or I will have your ancient and lying tongue torn out by the roots.

CASPAR: Our commission is from the gods, and from the God of gods.

HEROD: Villains and mountebanks! You shall be racked, impaled, crucified.

ELPIS: ⎫ Herod, my lord, dear husband, have patience.

EPHRAIM: ⎬ I warned you not to vex him.

PHYSICIAN: ⎭ Pray, sir, control yourself. You will be ill.

HEROD: Leave me alone, you fools. (*He struggles for breath, and resumes silkily*) Noble kings, learned Magi, I beg you to forgive me. You took me by surprise. You see what I am— an old man stricken with disease. No son has been born to my Queen Elpis and me. Sons I have, but they are all grown men, with sons of their own. Is it a grandson of mine, that shall sit upon my throne and rule an empire?

MELCHIOR: My lord, we do not know. But it is written in the heavens that he that is born shall be both priest and king.

HEROD: Priest and king? Priest? Are you sure?

BALTHAZAR: So it is written.

HEROD: This is serious. You do not know the history of this kingdom. For many years it was torn by wars and rebellions, till Augustus Caesar took it under the protection of Rome. Under his imperial mandate, I assumed the crown; for thirty years I have kept the peace, by force and policy. It has not been easy. There have been continual revolts against the Roman order—all made, do you understand, in the name of religion.

HIGH PRIEST: Pardon me, your Majesty. Not with our approval.

HEROD: As the High Priest says, not with the approval of the official priesthood, who know better. Religion has been the pretext for political ambition. It was I, Herod, that broke the power of the Hasmoneans. They were the priestly house. They claimed to sit upon this throne, and rule as priests and kings. They were traitors to Rome and to me, and I slew them. I slew my own sons for treason. I slew my queen, my first queen Mariamne, whom I loved—my queen and my sons, whom I loved. . . .

CASPAR: Sir, do not distress yourself and us—

HEROD: They were traitors. Their children are traitors to this day. Conspiring against me. Conspiring against Rome. Looking always for the warrior Messiah that shall lead them to victory, and independence. But there is no security in independence. The only safety for this country lies in playing her part within the great new order of Imperial Rome.

MELCHIOR: My lord, it is written in the stars that the man born to be king shall rule in Rome.

(*Murmurs*)

HEROD: In Rome also? What do you say to that, Captain Proclus?

PROCLUS: Nothing. I am a soldier. It is my business not to say, but to do. If Caesar will command.

HEROD: Mark that, sirs. Your prophesy, Herod reasons, but Caesar will command.

EPHRAIM (*tentatively*): My lord, if your Majesty's dog may presume to speak, may not these learned kings have made some error in their calculations? After all, we have no confirmation. Your Majesty's court magicians have issued no official prophecy in connection with this—er—alleged astral appearance.

HEROD: That is true. (*With instant suspicion*) And why not? Are they in the plot as well? Here, you, Zorastes—what are you doing there? I see you, skulking behind the skirts of the High Priest. Have you nothing to say about this? Hey? Come out, my lord Chief Astrologer, come out and speak the truth. Who has bribed you to hide things from Herod?

ZORASTES: No one, my lord.

HEROD (*with savage mockery*): No one, of course. No one. Stand up, man. Look at him now, white as a sheet, and his knees knocking together. Tell me, you dog, have you seen the star these wise men talk about?

ZORASTES: The star? Oh, yes, yes, my lord. A very bright star indeed. Quite remarkable.

HEROD: And what do you make of it?

ZORASTES: O King, live for ever! The favour of the King's face is brighter than the stars. (*Disconcerted by a snarl from* HEROD, *he goes on hurriedly*) Doubtless, my lord, a most happy conjunction of fortunate planets of ever-blessed augury for Jerusalem and for the high, mighty, and resplendent house of—

HEROD: I've heard all that before. You have read the Jewish prophecies?

ZORASTES: Yes, magnificence.

HEROD: Where do they say that the Messiah of the Jews will be born?

ZORASTES: Sir, it is said—that is, it appears most probable—the High Priest could tell you better than I.

HEROD: Out with it then, High Priest, where will the Christ be born?

HIGH PRIEST: Presumably, my lord, in Bethlehem of Judaea; for so it is written in the Book of the Prophet Micah; "Thou, Bethlehem, though thou be little among the thousands of Judah, yet out of thee shall he come forth that is to be ruler of Israel."

HEROD: Bethlehem, eh? Then, my wise princes, you will not have far to go. Though I doubt if you will find much when you get there. A very squalid little village. It is not usual for kings to be born in such a collection of mud walls and sheep-cotes. Boy, tell the groom of the stables to prepare horses for these gentlemen and set them on the road to Bethlehem.

BOY: Immediately, magnificence.

HEROD: And now, withdraw, all of you. I would speak with these royal astrologers in private. And hark'ee—keep your mouths shut.

ALL: We are the King's slaves. God save your Majesty.

BOY (*with a malicious consciousness that he can be infuriating with perfect impunity*): We are Caesar's slaves. Hail Caesar!

ALL (*dutifully*): Hail Caesar!

HEROD: Shut the doors.

(*Doors shut*)

HEROD (*Rapidly and smoothly*): Gentlemen, you see how I am placed. Men call me tyrant and autocrat, but I am not my own master. The grip of Rome is on Judaea, and I cannot openly countenance revolt. But if it please Heaven to raise up a leader in Israel, then I am ready, heart and soul, to strike a blow for Jewish independence. May I trust you?

CASPAR: It is no part of our commission to betray the counsels of kings.

HEROD: It is well. Now, tell me: when exactly did this royal star appear?

BALTHAZAR: Twelve days ago we beheld its light in the east.

HEROD: Twelve days. (*musingly*) In the House of the Lion—the Lion of Judah—the House of David. It may be so. Bethlehem is called the City of David—did you know that? And the Scriptures speak of Bethlehem. Priest and king. Have you calculated his horoscope? What sort of man will this be that is born to be King of the Jews?

MELCHIOR: Prouder than Caesar, more humble than his slave; his kingdom shall stretch from the sun's setting to the sun's rising, higher than the heavens, deeper than the grave, and narrow as the human heart.

CASPAR: He shall offer sacrifice in Jerusalem, and have his temples in Rome and in Byzantium, and he himself shall be both sacrifice and priest.

HEROD: You speak mysteries. Tell me this: will he be a warrior king?

BALTHAZAR: The greatest of warriors; yet he shall be called the Prince of Peace. He will be victor and victim in all his wars, and will make his triumph in defeat. And when wars are over, he will rule his people in love.

HEROD: You cannot rule men by love. When you find your king, tell him so. Only three things will govern a people—fear and greed and the promise of security. Do I not know it? Have I not loved? I have been a stern ruler—dreaded and hated,—yet my country is prosperous and her borders at peace. But wherever I loved, I found treachery—wife, children, brother—all of them, all of them. Love is a traitor; it has betrayed me; it betrays all kings; it will betray your Christ. Give him that message from Herod, King of Jewry.

CASPAR: Sir, when we have found the Christ—

HEROD: True; I had forgotten. When you find him, return and let me know. We must work quickly and cunningly. The patriotic party only need a leader, and a name—some name that will unite instead of divide them. They will not support *me*, because I am not of Jacob's house; but if I myself go and swear allegiance to this royal child, then they will all fall into line behind me. But first we must make certain of the boy. May I rely on you to bring me news at once?

CASPAR: These intrigues are no affair of ours. Yet to whatever end a man is born, to that end he shall come at last, no matter how dark and devious the way. We are all the instruments of destiny, and Herod himself but a tool in the hand of God.

HEROD: If it be my privilege to restore the kingdom to Israel, then blessed is the House of Herod. . . . You will do me this favour, and guide me to the young king's feet?

MELCHIOR: The high gods permitting, we will certainly do so.

HEROD: I thank you from my heart. For your visit, your good news, and the great opportunity shown me, Herod is grateful. . . . Forgive me; I find it difficult to move. Do me the favour to strike upon that gong.

(*Gong struck*)

Remember, no word of this to my people, if you value your young king's safety.

BALTHAZAR: We will be silent.

(*Enter* BOY)

BOY: Your Majesty desires?

HEROD: The Princes are leaving immediately for Bethlehem. See them to their horses. And send me my secretary. Farewell, sirs. Heaven speed your quest. I hope you may not find it a wild-goose chase.

CASPAR:
MELCHIOR: } Farewell. May Herod's name be written in the book of life.
BALTHAZAR:

(*Doors shut*)

HEROD: Fools! May their own prophecies choke them! But there is danger—very grave danger. No matter. Old as he is, Herod will ride out this storm too. Let me think. To seize the child—that's the first step. To kill him straight away—that's the simplest. But if only we can implicate all the rebels—tempt them to show their hand—then strike, and clear out the whole hornets' nest at once—Yes! that is the way. That is Herod's way. . . . But we must see that no garbled accounts reach Rome. We must write—

SECRETARY: Your Majesty needs a secretary?

HEROD: Yes. Take your pen. I will dictate: "To the Divine Emperor, Caesar Augustus, from Herod, King of Jewry, greeting . . ."

* * * * *

THE EVANGELIST: Then Herod, when he saw that he was mocked of the wise men, was exceeding wroth. . . .

PROCLUS: Your move, my Lord Ephraim.

EPHRAIM: I beg your pardon, Captain. There! . . . For Heaven's sake, boy, stop strumming. How often am I to tell you? It's not seemly, with the King at the point of death in the very next room.

BOY: It won't hurt him. He's too far gone to hear.

EPHRAIM: I don't care. It gets on my nerves.

PROCLUS: I huff you, my lord.

EPHRAIM: Tut, tut, tut. How did I come to overlook that?

PROCLUS: Your mind's not on the game tonight.

EPHRAIM: I was listening.... Will you stop making that noise? ....

(BOY *stops strumming with a final defiant twang*)

Hark! Don't you hear shouts in the distance?

(*Noise of* CROWD *running outside*)

BOY: I think something's happening up near the Temple. Everybody's running that way.

EPHRAIM: Oh, dear! Oh, dear! We live in troubled times. Captain Proclus, if there's going to be a disturbance—

PROCLUS: Somebody at the door. Yes? Who are you and what do you want?

MESSENGER: A letter, to be delivered into the hand of King Herod.

PROCLUS: He's ill. You can't see him. Better leave it with me.

MESSENGER: My orders were: into the King's own hand. But they're saying in the street King Herod's dead.

EPHRAIM (*nervously*): They've no right to say any such thing. The King is not dead. Certainly not. He's not very well, that's all. You'd better sit down and wait.

(*Uproar in the street*)

God of Abraham, what's that?

BOY (*Excitedly*): Oh, I say! It's a riot or something . . . there's a big crowd up by the Temple . . . they've got torches . . . they're coming this way . . . the street's simply swarming . . .

(*Hubbub increases*)

PROCLUS: What are they shouting?

BOY: I can't hear. . . . Now the High Priest has come out of his house. . . . He took one look and went in again, double quick. . . . Here they come . . . I can see them now. . . .

EPHRAIM: You'll be out of the window in a moment.

BOY: They're carrying something . . . they're holding it up . . . something big and shining . . . Oh! oh! oh! . . . they've torn down the Eagle!

PROCLUS: They've done what?

BOY: The Eagle! the gold Eagle from over the Temple gate . . . they've pulled it down!

PROCLUS: Pulled down the Roman Eagle? . . . Get out . . . let me look. . . .

EPHRAIM (*whimpering*): That disastrous Eagle . . . it ought never to have been put there . . . it offends pious people. . . . All these fierce young men . . .

CROWD (*surging nearer*): Down with the Eagles! . . . Jewry for the Jews! The King's dead—long live Archelaus! Long live Antipater! . . . Up the true Religion! . . . Down with tyranny! . . . Down with Rome . . . Fire the palace, etc.

SLAVES (*rushing in*): Help! help! the city's in arms.

PROCLUS: Slaves! What are you doing here? Have you left the King alone!

SLAVE: The King's unconscious. . . . I think he's dead. . . .

EPHRAIM: Oh, heavens, we shall all be murdered!

CROWD (*under the window, cries of*): Freedom! . . . Independence! . . . A free Jewry! . . . Down with the graven images . . . Tear down the false gods. . . . Blasphemy . . . Sacrilege . . . Down with Caesar! . . . Throw off the yoke of the Empire! . . . Jewry for ever . . . A Messiah! a Messiah! . . . Stones, stones, stones! . . . etc. (*Mingled with counter-cries of*): Hail Caesar! . . . Down with the rebels! . . . Down with the Priests! . . . Treason . . . Stone the traitors! . . . etc.

(*Noise of fighting*)

EPHRAIM: O, Captain Proclus—can't you do something?

PROCLUS: Hey, there, you Jewish dogs—

(*Several sharp crashes. Cries from the* SLAVES)

EPHRAIM: Come away! They're throwing stones!

(*Another crash, followed by a sound of breaking crockery*)

Ow! The Etruscan vases!

(*And another*)

There goes the lamp! Ow!

PROCLUS: In the name of the King—

CROWD: The King's dead!

(*Cheers and laughter*)

PROCLUS: In the name of the Emperor—

CROWD (*rather less confidently*): Down with the Emperor!

VOICE: Run back to Rome, little soldier!

(*Laughter*)

VOICE (*off*): Peace, there. Hear me speak!

CROWD: Matthias! Hear Matthias! Silence for the Rabbi Matthias! Shove him up on the rostrum.

MATTHIAS: People of Israel! Servants of the true religion! (*"Hear, hear!"*) You see this idolatrous image (*Groans*), this odious symbol of a pagan power (*Hisses*) impiously set up over the sacred doors of the Temple (*"Shame! Jewry for the Jews!"*), in defiance of the law which forbids graven images. Are you not ashamed to have let it stand there so long? . . . Are you Jews? . . . are you believers? . . . are you men? . . . What are you afraid of? . . .

(*Mumbling from the* CROWD; *the noise quietens down a little, so that we can hear, loudly and suddenly in the room itself, the voice of* HEROD)

HEROD: Stand back from the window!

EPHRAIM: The King! (*in an awed whisper*) Alive and walking! . . . Oh, sir! you will not show yourself . . . they'll attack you. . . .

(*Crowd noises continue*)

HEROD: Silence, fool! Fetch candles! . . . Proclus!

PROCLUS: Sir?

HEROD: Run to the fortress. Turn out the guard.

(PROCLUS *clatters out*)

Here, boy!

BOY: Yes, sir!

HEROD: Candles, you slaves, candles! Hold them up to my face!

MATTHIAS: Take courage, Israel! We will endure this oppression no longer! (*Cheers*) Lift up your hearts. (*Cheers*) The tyrant Herod is dead!

(*Tremendous cheers and cries as before*)

HEROD (*in a fearful voice, dominating the uproar*): How now, rebels! Do you know me? Do you know Herod?

(*Deathly silence, in which you could hear a pin drop*)

(*Icily, and with alarming irony*) I see you do. I am obliged to you for the funeral oration. To be sure, it is a little premature, but Herod will not forget. (*With a sudden roar*) Stop where you are, fellow! (*quietly*) If anybody tries to leave while I am speaking, I will have him broken on the wheel. I observe that somebody has been carried away by his enthusiasm for the Imperial emblem. That Eagle is not intended for private use as a garden ornament. However, Caesar shall be informed of your devotion. No doubt he will be delighted. Next time you wish to hold these public demonstrations of loyalty, will you kindly do so at a more convenient hour; you have disturbed my rest and roused all these worthy citizens from their beds.

(*Sound of quick marching*)

There, you see! the Guard is coming to see what all the noise is about.

(CROWD *utters murmurs of alarm: "Look out! The soldiers! Run! run!" etc.*)

HEROD (*Cont'd*): I think you had better be getting home.

(*Confused shuffling*)

Hey, there! Is that Captain Darius?

CAPTAIN: Yes, sir.

HEROD: Get hold of those four men with the Eagle—and that fellow in green—and the gentleman with the hammer—and the two rabbis who are trying to sneak down off the rostrum. Then go to the High Priest's house and put him under arrest. Let the other imbeciles go.

CAPTAIN: Very good, sir.

HEROD: And report back to me with Proclus.

CAPTAIN: Very good, sir . . . Go on, lads, you've got your orders. Move along there. Off with you!

(CROWD *is moved off, with scuffling and noise dying away*)

HEROD: Very pretty indeed. The High Priest will answer for this behaviour. Give me a chair. And some wine.

EPHRAIM (*bleating*): Yes, magnificence. At once, magnificence. Oh, my lord, we were so afraid—we thought you were—that is, we thought—are you sure you are not hurt—

HEROD: Stop gibbering, man. Here, slaves, pick up the lamp and sweep up all this mess. Who's that fellow in the corner?

EPHRAIM: That? Oh, he came with a letter. Yes. So he did. (*Giggling feebly*) I'd forgotten all about him.

HEROD: A letter, from whom?

MESSENGER: From the noble King of Chaldaea; for your Majesty's own hand.

HEROD: From Caspar of Chaldaea? Give it to me.

EPHRAIM: Shall I read it to your Majesty?

HEROD: No!

(*Pause, while he opens and reads the letter*)

Ten thousand plagues smite them! Leprosy seize their flesh! Listen to this piece of insolence:

(*Reading*)

"We have seen; we have heard; we have worshipped. But we may not return as we had promised, for the command of the Most High stands in our way. Farewell."

Is that a way for one king to write to another?

EPHRAIM (*warmly*): Abominable. I don't know what it means. But it's abominable.

HEROD (*grimly*): It means trouble. Worse trouble. Insurrection. Civil war.

(EPHRAIM *utters a protesting squeak*)

But I will defeat them yet. I will have order in Judaea. I'll spread a net that their Messiah shall not slip through. Proclus!

PROCLUS: Here, sir, with Captain Darius, to report everything quiet, sir.

HEROD: Good. Here's another order. Take a band of my Thracians. Go to Bethlehem. Search out every male child in the cradle—

PROCLUS: Children, sir?

HEROD: From twelve days old—No. I don't trust them. No. Take all the male children from two years old and under and put the lot to death. All of them. The whole brood of adders. Do you hear? Let none escape. Kill them all.

PROCLUS: Sir, I am a soldier, not a butcher.

HEROD: You will obey orders.

PROCLUS: I won't, and that's flat. I am a Roman, and Romans do not kill children. Send one of your own barbarians.

HEROD: Insolent. You are a soldier in my pay.

PROCLUS: Excuse me, sir. I am in your service, but I am still a Roman born. You have the right to dismiss me. But if you imprison or execute me, I think there will be trouble.

HEROD: Proclus, you are a fool, but an honest fool. Captain Darius!

CAPTAIN: Sir.

HEROD: You heard the order.

CAPTAIN: Yes, sir.

HEROD: Carry it out, immediately.

CAPTAIN: Very good, sir.

(*The* CAPTAIN *stamps out*)

PROCLUS: Am I to go back to Rome, if you please?

HEROD: No, you mean well. But which is worse? To kill a score or so of peasant children or to plunge a whole kingdom into war? The Jews cry out for a Messiah. Shall I tell you Messiah's name? Fire and sword. Fire and sword. I will not have it. This country shall have peace. While Herod lives, there shall be but one king in Jewry.

VOICE (*without*): Squad, 'shun! . . . right turn! . . . quick march!

(*The troops march out*)

HEROD: I am sick. Carry me in.

PROCLUS: So that is the end of the new Messiah.

THE EVANGELIST: But the angel of the Lord appeared to Joseph in a dream, saying, Arise and take the young child and his mother, and flee into Egypt; for Herod will seek the young child to destroy him.

And when he arose he took the young child and his mother by night, and departed into Egypt, and was there until the death of Herod.

SEEKING THE LIGHT

from *The Other Wise Man*

BY HENRY VAN DYKE

We all know the story of the Three Wise Men or Magi, how following the star in the east, they journeyed from distant lands to offer their gifts at the manger cradle in Bethlehem. Henry van Dyke, eminent writer, educator, diplomat, and clergyman, tells the story of The Other Wise Man, *who also saw the star and set out to join the travelers, but, until the day of the Crucifixion and his own end, was denied his heart's desire. His wanderings, during the thirty-three years of Jesus' life, and the three greatest trials of his soul were told in fragments "in the Hall of Dreams in the palace of the Heart of Man." Dr. van Dyke here records a part of Artaban's pilgrimage and the probation involved in the slaughter of the Innocents, as* The Other Wise Man *moved indirectly but steadfastly toward the Light which he sought.*

There was a silence in the Hall of Dreams, where I was listening to the story of the Other Wise Man. Through this silence I saw, but very dimly, his figure passing over the dreary undulations of the desert, high upon the back of his camel, rocking steadily onward like a ship over the waves.

The land of death spread its cruel net around him. The stony waste bore no fruit but briers and thorns. The dark ledges of rock thrust themselves above the surface here and there, like the bones of perished monsters. Arid and inhospitable mountain-ranges rose before him, furrowed with dry channels of ancient torrents, white and ghastly as scars on the face of nature. Shifting hills of treacherous sand were heaped like tombs along the horizon. By day, the fierce heat pressed its intolerable burden on the quivering air. No living creature moved on the dumb, swooning earth, but tiny jerboas scuttling through the parched bushes, or lizards vanishing in the clefts of the rock. By night the jackals prowled and barked in the distance, and the lion made the black ravines echo with his hollow roaring, while a bitter, blighting chill followed the fever of the day. Through heat and cold, the Magian moved steadily onward.

Then I saw the gardens and orchards of Damascus, watered by the streams of Abana and Pharpar, with their sloping swards inlaid with bloom, and their thickets of myrrh and roses. I saw the long, snowy ridge of Hermon, and the dark groves of cedars, and the valley of the Jordan, and the blue waters of the Lake of Galilee, and the fertile plain of Esdraelon, and the hills of Ephraim, and the highlands of Judah. Through all these I followed the figure of Artaban moving steadily onward, until he arrived at Bethlehem. And it was the third day after the three Wise Men had come to that place and had found Mary and Joseph, with the young child, Jesus, and had laid their gifts of gold and frankincense and myrrh at his feet.

Then the Other Wise Man drew near, weary, but full of hope, bearing his ruby and his pearl to offer to the King. "For now at last," he said, "I shall surely find him, though I be alone, and later than my brethren. This is the place of which the Hebrew exile told me that the prophets had spoken, and here I shall behold the rising of the great light. But I must inquire about the visit of my brethren, and to what house the star directed them, and to whom they presented their tribute."

The streets of the village seemed to be deserted, and Artaban wondered whether the men had all gone up to the hill-pastures to bring down their sheep. From the open door of a cottage he heard the sound of a woman's voice singing softly. He entered and found a young mother hushing her baby to rest. She told him of the strangers from the far East who had appeared in the village three days ago, and how they said that a star had guided them to the place where Joseph of Nazareth was lodging with his wife, and her newborn child, and how they had paid reverence to the child and given him many rich gifts.

"But the travellers disappeared again," she continued, "as suddenly as they had come. We were afraid at the strangeness of their visit. We could not understand it. The man of Nazareth took the child and his mother, and fled away that same night secretly, and it was whispered that they were going to Egypt. Ever since, there has been a spell upon the village; something evil hangs over it. They say that the Roman soldiers are coming from Jerusalem to force a new tax from us, and the men have driven the flocks and herds far back among the hills, and hidden themselves to escape it."

Artaban listened to her gentle, timid speech, and the child in her arms looked up in his face and smiled, stretching out its rosy hands to grasp at the winged circle of gold on his breast. His heart warmed to the touch. It seemed like a greeting of love and trust to one who had journeyed long in loneliness and perplexity, fighting with his own doubts, and fears, and following a light that was veiled in clouds.

"Why might not this child have been the promised Prince?" he asked within himself, as he touched its soft cheek. "Kings have been born ere now in lowlier houses than this, and the favourite of the stars may rise even from a cottage. But it has not seemed good to the God of wisdom to reward my search so soon and so easily. The one whom I seek has gone before me; and now I must follow the King to Egypt."

The young mother laid the baby in its cradle, and rose to minister to the wants of the strange guest that fate had brought into her house. She set food before him, the plain fare of peasants, but willingly offered, and therefore full of refreshment for the soul as well as for the body. Artaban accepted it gratefully; and, as he ate, the child fell into a happy slumber, and murmured sweetly in its dreams, and a great peace filled the room.

But suddenly there came the noise of a wild confusion in the streets of the village, a shrieking and wailing of women's voices, a clangour of brazen trumpets and a clashing of swords, and a desperate cry: "The soldiers! the soldiers of Herod! They are killing our children."

The young mother's face grew white with terror. She clasped her child to her bosom, and crouched motionless in the darkest corner of the room, covering him with the folds of her robe, lest he should wake and cry.

But Artaban went quickly and stood in the doorway of the house. His broad shoulders filled the portal from side to side, and the peak of his white cap all but touched the lintel.

The soldiers came hurrying down the street with bloody hands and dripping swords. At the sight of the stranger in his imposing dress they hesitated with surprise. The captain of the band approached the threshold to thrust him aside. But Artaban did not stir. His face was as calm as though he were watching the stars, and in his eyes there burned that steady radiance before which even the half-tamed hunting leopard shrinks, and the bloodhound pauses in his leap. He held the soldier silently for an instant, and then said in a low voice:

"I am all alone in this place, and I am waiting to give this jewel to the prudent captain who will leave me in peace."

He showed the ruby, glistening in the hollow of his hand like a great drop of blood.

The captain was amazed at the splendour of the gem. The pupils of his eyes expanded with desire, and the hard lines of greed wrinkled around his lips. He stretched out his hand and took the ruby.

"March on!" he cried to his men, "there is no child here. The house is empty."

The clamour and the clang of arms passed down the street as the headlong fury of the chase sweeps by the secret covert where the trembling deer is hidden. Artaban re-entered the cottage. He turned his face to the east and prayed:

"God of truth, forgive my sin! I have said the thing that is not, to save the life of a child. And two of my gifts are gone. I have spent for man that which was meant for God. Shall I ever be worthy to see the face of the King?"

But the voice of the woman, weeping for joy in the shadow behind him, said very gently:

"Because thou hast saved the life of my little one, may the Lord bless thee and keep thee; the Lord make His face to shine upon thee and be gracious unto thee; the Lord lift up His countenance upon thee and give thee peace."

THE SEQUEL TO BETHLEHEM

from *The Salty Tang*

BY FREDERICK B. SPEAKMAN

Dr. Frederick B. Speakman is a leader among the forceful preachers of today. His messages are always exciting, poignant, and full of wisdom in the light of everlasting truth. In "The Sequel to Bethlehem" he tells, in vivid retrospect, of the coming of the Child and His claim.

Yes, I'm Jesse Benhadad. Yes, Jesse of Jericho, if you wish. Forgive my smile at the name, Roman. I've been in Jericho long enough that I should feel like a fixture here, part of the local scenery, my roots as deep as its sycamores. But, as a matter of fact, I don't. After all these years I still would have answered more easily to the name, Jesse of Bethlehem.

But come in out of that drafty hall. I have a fire stirred up in my counting den here, and we can talk out of earshot of the serving girls. I'm told the foxes of Idumaea have sharp ears, can hear a twig snap a mile away. But I'll put those maids of mine up against any beasts from here to Sinai for their hearing of what's no business of theirs.

Sit there on the cushioned bench. No, closer to the fire, man! You Gentiles never learn to take a Judaean winter seriously. "It's a mild climate," you say, and forget that when the wind is from Samaria and it's raining through this valley, that chill of the air can have devils in it.

There, that's right, where I can see your face. Now that I see it, I'm sorry that I kept you waiting. But forgive me, it isn't often a Jew gets a chance to keep a Roman waiting. "Luke," you call yourself? Luke, a physician? And I'd know at a glance you were Roman. That slight but tell-tale swagger to your shoulders. That so clean tunic that you're wearing. And the painful way you speak our tongue, as if its very syllables were brine in your Western mouth.

Now, don't flush up! If we are to talk you'll have to grant me

58

the license all Jericho allows me—Jesse, the innkeeper, the blasphemous old Jew who laughs at the Synagogue and tells off the Romans to their faces, and still gets by on wits and tongue. Still thrives, that is, in my way.

But you spoke the magic word to Leah, my wife, that will keep a fairly civil tongue in my head. So you know our Benjamin. Know him in Jerusalem. How is the lad? Is he well? Will he marry soon, or ever, for that matter? How is he at his trade? We've sent so many messages hinting at a visit home. We wouldn't plead for one, you know, not much, we wouldn't. Don't ever let a son of yours know quite how proud you are of him, Roman. It gives them the upper hand.

And it was really my son who sent you to talk to me? Sent you to hear from me the story? There you are now. Think of that. Why, he had laughed at it with all the others. It was his laughter even more than the others' that made me swear by the eyes of the prophets I'd never mention it again. It simply shows you, Roman, that you should never be bothered by the laughter of youth. Cherish it like music. For it isn't the scornful affair that it seems. It's the noise of a heart that's still fluid. It's the sound of tenderness that's as yet ashamed to show itself. It's the murmur of wonder and clean delight at this mysterious life of ours before the new rubs off and we learn to take it for granted. I know, Luke—that was the name, Luke? I so well recall laughing one night long ago, laughing because I didn't know what else to do. And the laughter was at once a prayer and an affirmation.

Yes, I remember Bethlehem. Remember it too well! God knows there have been countless times when I'd have gladly forgotten! But—how long has it been since your Caesar's first census here? Well over thirty years. And that long the memory's been with me. Maturing with maturity, but still bright, sharply bright, remembering that other inn, that other night sky, canopy for a world that for an hour was another world.

We were married there at Bethlehem, Leah and I. I worked for her father, Eliab, there at his inn. No dowry came with Leah; she was dowry enough! Tall, with the grace of any tree they boast about in Lebanon. With the true Judaean's brown of eye and the low voice of the brooks from off Mount Hermon. But love is never for long an escape from the harshness of the world, Luke. That's the sob in its throat, of course, and yet the strength in its song, when those who love awaken to what the world is like and try to make its harshness yield and reflect what they feel in their hearts.

We had awakened, Leah and I, to what a world's like under Caesar, any Caesar who wants his face not just on your coins but on your soul. So that existence becomes only that. And all its simple joys must be treasured quickly and furtively under constant tears. And the work which should make us men making us drudges. Effort without reason and with only animal rewards! And night the short pause between burdens. And dread the staple of the daily fare, dread of poverty and war and disease and pain and death, those keeping your heart too busy to dread the real riddle of life. And never a foothold on the certainty that the struggle's worth it! Never a consistent assurance that He who caused it all means to stand by it and see it through. Do you stare to hear such rantings from a child of pious Israel? Then you should read some of our holy books, the ones the Pharisees never mention, those the priests can't caper to, the Book of Job for one, or a little scroll known as Ecclesiastes.

And to have all that rebellion, all that constant and unspoken protest whetting its cutting edge in my heart, and then for it to happen. For that night to take place, noticed by so few, and yet— But business was brisk that season, you see. Turning guests away, we were. Old father Eliab was almost cheerful, sacking up quite a piece of coin. And, irony of ironies, it was all Caesar's doing! His new law for a head tax in the provinces demanded that every mother's son alive return to the town of his birth to register for taxing. The inn was crowded as never before; we had bedding on the roof and even tents pitched in the alleys. And when this fellow of about my age came along that evening imploring us for lodging, he was just another like the many I'd turned away all day.

How are you ever going to know life's moments when they come, Luke? The great hours, the shining hours, the ones that, later, can mean much—they come walking up looking like any other hour. And always when you're busy. Always when you're so convinced that something else you're doing is so important. And you let them go on and never know. I think that has gnawed me the rawest—that I'd have sent that couple away. Oh, kindly enough. With that cheap, easy kindness you use when you're sure of yourself in saying no to strangers. But Leah saved me. It was she who noticed the woman. Maybe the man had told me, but we busy ones seldom listen. It was Leah who thought of the stable out back. And I laughed. That was my contribution. I laughed, a little proud of Leah, a little embarrassed at myself, a little intrigued with the thought that if this business continued we could use an annex built where that rickety stable stood out back.

She awakened me long after midnight. I awoke with that abrupt, complete alertness which always proves the rest of you has been awake long before your mind has agreed. And I awoke to a different world, Luke, I tell you, a different world! There was Leah, with a look on her face that I'd seen only hints of before. Her normal reserve all shattered, and her words a torrent, a jumble and a Psalm! All about this Babe she had helped birth in the stable, and weird, weird visions the Mother had told her! And how this was no ordinary child, but the Gift of God Himself! Such a yarn as normally would have set me raging, but this night brought me running! There in a silence you could fairly feel! You've never heard a Judaean town really silent till your ears throb with it. Not so much as the bark of a dog, or the creak of a tardy wagon's wheel. As if the whole world were asleep. As if the very sky had caught its breath. Only the sound of the stairs as we hurried out, and the crunch of the stubble in the yard beneath our feet.

And halfway across the yard, we heard it and saw it. But how will I tell you, man? Here the words always sag and fail. It was silent and yet there was music. It was dark and yet there was light. The music! It was the music of life that you know is there but never quite hear. Oh, you nearly hear it in the spring sometimes. You catch it as an overtone in the voice of some children. There are certain people who remind you of its melody. There are certain times when you feel it's about to be played. But that night, bless you, it was being strummed from every tree top and hymned from every cloud bank! And the light! There's a moment just before dawn that nearly has it. The sky still black but everything around you beginning to reflect that coming wonder. That's how we felt standing hand in hand there in the dark. As if we too were luminous, if you please, reflecting some untraceable radiance! Certain that had we stood in the distance we'd surely have seen that over Bethlehem some tremendous signal fire of glory had been lighted.

I don't know how long we stood there, letting it speak to us what can't be said. But then Leah told me of the shepherds who had come while I had slept. All abashed and uncertain, but determined in their quest. Stammering through their story of a sky punctured by voices, leaking wonders, phrasing their errand and choiring an anthem of God's intended peace. And how they all had become ill at ease but had left, heads back, their eyes flashing praise.

It was then I could wait no longer to go in. I didn't stay long. Just long enough to pretend to see that all was well. Just long enough to worship with eyes wide open, to etch that scene indelibly here behind my forehead. A peasant and her baby and her husband hovering near them. And then I went out while Leah busied herself in that way of hers which can make even a manger seem for the moment a home. I went back out under the stars.

Oh, I've doubted my senses many times since, but that night it was all so sure. And I found myself wondering why I was so willing to accept an incredible claim without even knowing what it all meant. But I knew somehow I'd always been waiting for that night, and that music and that light, and this Child and this claim, which my heart would never have dared to phrase, but which the frightened shepherd lads had stammered. For it's a remarkable thing that God has fashioned in the human heart. I surveyed it that night. I rehearsed all those promises of not quite captured beauty which those Judaean hills had whispered to my boyhood, and all the lures and urges toward what life could be which maturity and love suggested to my manhood. And somehow I'd never been able to write it all off as a web of lies. Somehow, I knew that what was best in me was linked with what was highest among those stars. My heartbeat here was at least a feeble echo of some Heart beating there. But what had come of it all? This, that the whey-faced rabbis tell me of how God once took common dirt of Eden and breathed into its dustiness a speck of Himself. But was He wise to do it? Can flesh stand it? Can humanity bear this imprint of His image? To be a part of a rotting world, yet never really at home here? To be haunted by dreams we can't create, driven by laws we can't keep, tortured by goals we can't attain? Such themes as love and justice and truth forever crooning to our souls, yet because of the muddy, vile thing we are, settling, instead, for the grasping, sordid scheme of wars, the hates, the corrosive pain, the closing of our eyes to the glory, then cursing the darkness. Was man to be the Eternal's big mistake, too flawed ever to be salvaged?

But, Luke, what if God should decide to abide by the rules of His own game? What if He should decide to get into this, not just with His breath, but Himself? To be just as limited as we, just as prone to suffering, to risk our sorrows and our death, take the full and undiluted dose of His own medicine? For then He'd know, and we'd know. He'd know what this is like here and what it will take to salvage us. We'd know what He's like there and what we can expect from Him.

And if He did that—if, I say, it surely would have happened, not in Caesar's halls, not in Herod's court, but quietly somewhere. Unannounced, as it were. Do you catch the thrust of it? God arriving incognito, till He could get His moorings? Among a people who, whatever virtues they had lost, had kept alive expectancy? Had kept looking for Him to turn up among them?

We sold the inn at Bethlehem soon after Eliab's death. We came here. And here we've stayed. And, Luke, in my way, in my wondering, ranting way, I've been faithful to that night. Oh, nothing came of it. We had a flurry a year or so ago, when a Nazarene teacher came through Jericho. It was He whom my Benjamin followed to Jerusalem. But I understand the Nazarene got in trouble there.

But you'd know about that, you might even have—Wait! Yes! You in Jerusalem. Knowing our Benjamin. Hearing of my story. Making this trip. And you've listened without amusement or scorn. You're smiling only now. You've come, not just to hear, but to tell! Let me call Leah. Leah! Leah! This man knows what came of it all. That night I mean. This man knows the sequel to Bethlehem.

ONE SMALL CHILD

BY Esther S. Buckwalter

One little child . . . no more, no less—
And could His mother Mary guess
Salvation for the human race
Depended on that night, that place?
And did she know this child would cause
All heaven to rock with glad applause?
Would cause the angels to rehearse
Their midnight song of sacred verse?
Would cause a star of strange design
To leave its orbit, and to shine
A brilliant path, from east to west?
Would cause wise men to choose the best
Of hoarded treasure, and to search
The nations from a camel perch?
Would make a king (in craven fear)
Destroy small man-children near?
To this small child the nation thrilled,
For He was prophecy fulfilled.
But could His mother, even, guess
While rocking Him with tenderness
The whole import of His advent,
This one small child—from heaven sent.

II Christmas Tales and
Traditions

Therefore, brethren, stand fast, and hold the traditions which ye have been taught, whether by word or our epistle. (II Thessalonians: 2, 15)

Over the centuries, the Light of Christmas has been interpreted and expanded through creative, enlightening tales and traditions. Not only the birth of Jesus but his entire life and influence have been a favorite theme with people everywhere: in folklore, in histories of times now remote, in legends and romances, in novels, poems, essays, and biographies. This subject matter has range, inner validity, and charm. It enhances the value of the spiritual truths we know, and sustains our hope that the glory of the Spirit, the divine spark in man, will light our world to a better day.

❋   ❋   ❋

From HAMLET

BY WILLIAM SHAKESPEARE

Some say that ever 'gainst that season comes
Wherein our Saviour's birth is celebrated,
The bird of dawning singeth all night long:
And then, they say, no spirit can walk abroad;
The nights are wholesome; then no planets strike,
No fairy takes, nor witch hath power to charm,
So hallow'd and so gracious is the time.

MARY SPEAKS

from *No One Ever Told Me*

BY LUCILE GRAHAM

*We know that Luke, the beloved physician, went on several memorable
missions to Jerusalem. While there, many people believe, he sought out
Mary, the mother of Jesus, and learned directly from her the details of
the Nativity and later Life. Lucile Graham gives poetic reality and
enlightenment to such a meeting.*

It was a day in old Capernaum;
And since those stirring and tempestuous times
When my dear Son had taught and healed and died
Long quiet years had passed. Within my mind
Sorrow had changed to joy, perplexity
To peace; the bitter had grown sweet.
I sat within the courtyard where the sun
Came slanting down through quaking leaves

And mirrored them in shadow on the ground.
The purple grapes hung fragrant on the wall.
I had a letter from that other son—
The one He gave me, one He loved, who took
Me to his home in Galilee from Calvary.
There came a step, a curtain drawn aside,
And there stood Luke, the young and slender Greek,
With arched dark brows and shining eager eyes,
Long-fingered hands, as gentle as a girl.
He sat beside me, took his stylus out,
His waxen tablets balanced on his knee.
And swift and keen his questions—reverent, too.
He wished to trace, he said, the accurate course
Of all things from the first, and then to write
Them down in order. He had the time,
While Paul was prisoner in Caesarea,
For questioning and composition, too.
And so I shared them all with him, the things
I long had kept and pondered in my heart.
Long, long ago it was—
The crowded town, the stable sweet with hay,
The shepherds with their story of the song
The angels sang against the lighted sky.
The sleeping Baby nestled in my arms,
So warm, so helpless, and so wonderful.
I told him of the temple where we went
To offer turtle doves for sacrifice;
The old man Simeon, whose blessing fell
So gently on the Child, who prophesied
The bitter anguish that would pierce my soul.
And then the story of the Boy grown tall
And thoughtful, wise beyond His years, who stayed
Behind us in Jerusalem, and when
We sought Him sorrowing, so gently said:
"And know ye not that I must be about
My father's business?" Yet he came home with us,
Fulfilled His duty, learned His trade, and bore
The load of all the house and shop. Luke wrote
It down and wove it into perfect prose.
And I have read his words and lived again
Those long dead days that never more shall die.

THIS MUST WE KEEP

BY DOROTHY CANFIELD FISHER

Dorothy Canfield Fisher, from the very beginning of her outstanding and prolific career in literature and education, made a notable contribution to our culture. In a brief excerpt from This Must We Keep, *she tells how observance of Christmas links the past, present, and future through "the shining light, that shineth more and more unto the perfect day."*

[I have] an overwhelming feeling of gratitude and admiration for one exquisite element in our human life which has been sacredly preserved for us by the conservative instinct at its best— the ancient feast of joy and hope at the darkest period of each year. It was celebrated by man as long ago as we have the slightest traces of human life; we celebrate it anew every year, deeply moved by a beautiful symbol of a magnificent truth which we inherit from all our ancestors. We show our worthiness of it by preserving it and passing it on.

The celebration which to us is Christmas has been attacked again and again by one and another enemy. The Puritan radicals, confusing it with what seemed to them materialistic ceremoniousness, tried their best to throw it away as an outworn ancient piece of foolishness. The Romans, long before the coming of Christ, tried to lower a sacred festival to the level of a popular holiday with all license allowed. Our Scandinavian ancestors did their best, too, along the line. We ourselves are doing our best to cloud and darken its spiritual beauty by succumbing to the people who try to make Christmas only a shopping orgy.

But the perfect symbol of a mighty and radiant truth has always shone with a starlike beauty through the trash men heap around it. We moderns are irritated, weary and morose by the evening of December twenty-fourth because we half realize how shamelessly one of our most exquisite impulses is being exploited by the commercial instinct; and we sometimes think, "What a nuisance Christmas is! I wish we didn't have it—just a grab for presents." But on December twenty-fifth is there one of us who does not feel a pang, a shock of strange, secret, intimate joy such as we know on no other day? There is something preserved from the past which has golden worth!

The ancient symbol grows more richly encrusted with poetry and spiritual meaning as the centuries go on. Our cave-men ancestors probably rejoiced quite literally, quite materialistically, over the fact that the darkest days of the year were over, that they could turn their faces from blackness toward the hope of sunlight. The Romans felt the inner spiritual meaning of so turning from darkness to light—symbolizing it with their exchange of lighted candles and loving gifts, and with an even deeper piece of symbolism, only half understood but always a part of the joyous ceremony, when for a short time he who had been master and lord in the household became a servant, and he who had been a lowly servant put on fine garments and was humbly served by his master. Was not that a divination of a truth not yet expressed, and even now not grasped by us in its mystical significance, "For he that is least among you all, the same shall be great"?

And when Christianity came and found embedded in human life a symbol of such touching beauty, such unshakable hope, with what a profound wisdom did our faith lift this ancient vessel and pour it full of new wine! The coming of light after long darkness—that was the tenderness of the spirit of Jesus Christ. The old act of faith, to which man had clung with all his tortured, despairing, ever-hoping heart, of proclaiming with joy, at the very darkest period of the year, his sure and certain faith that light would come again—what better channel could be found along which to send forward the belief in the transformation of the world through the spirit of Christ? The new divination that men are to be valued for themselves, not for their outward place or class in society—what more popular expression of it than the ancient festival when servants became masters and masters servants—alas, that we have lost that!

Even the small oddities of custom found a place in this deepening of the meaning of one of the oldest of human institutions. The mistletoe of our Celtic ancestors under which, at Christmas, we still give and take harmless kisses, forbidden at other times—in its small corner this, too, is more than a harmless piece of gaiety; it reminds the meditative spirit of how much which is forbidden to the sensual and self-seeking can be safely done with a pure and loving heart.

Loftily mystical, homely, intimate, human, divine, wild with gaiety, solemn with the purest of thanksgivings for the best that God has given to man, Christmas is the exquisite universal expression of the faith which has kept us men and women alive through all errors and despairs—the faith that light will come again after darkness. That the celebration of this certainty that light will come again takes place at the very darkest of the year is for us, in our time of sorrow and anxiety, its most beautiful and moving aspect.

Let us keep this noble feast with joy and hope, and pass it on intact to those who come after us.

A FEAST IN KUWAIT

from *My Arabian Days and Nights*

BY DR. ELEANOR T. CALVERLEY

The locale of My Arabian Days and Nights *by Eleanor T. Calverley, M.D., is Old Kuwait at the western apex of the Persian Gulf. In this tiny but strategic oil state, a buffer among the Arab countries, "Dr. Pills," as she was lovingly called, and "Dr. Prayers," her husband, Reverend Edwin Calverley, served for twenty years from 1913. The first Americans to bring modern education and Western medicine to Kuwait, they accomplished incalculable good, which they attributed to the Divine Providence that led them to minister to this country in its poorest and most backward days. Here is Dr. Eleanor Calverley's spirited account of a family party in honor of Christmas at which august Shaikh Ahmed and later the Christian families of the Mission joined in the celebration of Jesus' birth.*

At the time of Miss Robertson's coming, Shaikh Ahmed al Jabir el Sabah was Ruler of Kuwait. He, like Shaikh Abdallah in later years, was to be knighted by Britain's sovereign and was thereafter called, "His Highness Shaikh Sir Ahmed." It was he who had, in the days of Shaikh Salim, been so calm and confident at the city's gate when others were nearly in a panic at the danger of attack by the *Ikhwaan*. After his accession to power, Shaikh Ahmed entertained, Western style, in his Desmaan Palace, situated in the desert beyond the town. He also came often to dinner in our home, as also in the homes of our colleagues.

I remember, in particular, one evening when we entertained Shaikh Ahmed at a dinner party in his honor, just before Miss Robertson's first Christmas in Kuwait. For weeks, Edwin and I had been listening to the sound of Christmas carols, which the children were practicing in the school room. The Shaikh, too, knew that Christmas was near. Always affable in his manner, on that occasion Shaikh Ahmed seemed unusually relaxed. His handsome, neatly bearded face was suffused with real enjoyment. We were chatting at the table about feast days, Muslim and Christian. Turning to me the guest asked,

"How will it be with you, on your feast day? Will you, like the Muslims, go about congratulating your friends?"

"Not exactly as you do," I answered. "In our family, first thing in the morning, we celebrate with carols, sung around a Christmas tree. Later, we give presents to one another. Because we have children, our British and American friends like to join us at that time. In the afternoon, all the Christians in our community come for a party around the tree. Then, for a week, Muslim friends come to see the tree and visit with us."

The Shaikh, smiling paused a moment. Then he asked, "May I too come to your family party?" We were surprised and delighted by his request.

"Of course!" we responded. We would be greatly honored by his presence. We told him the hour, after breakfast, when Colonel and Mrs. More would be arriving with the Mylreas and our other colleagues. We always waited, we said, until everyone had come, before opening the door of the living room where the tree stood. This year, we promised, we would all await his arrival before going in to see the Christmas tree.

With what delightful excitement Grace, Elisabeth, and Eleanor prepared for Christmas, that year! With their Aunt Iva's help they prepared presents for all the family and all the expected guests. Their eyes were big with some secrets they could not share with their parents. For Shaikh Ahmed they made fudge, which they packed in a pretty box and tied with a Christmas ribbon. By the time the great day arrived the carols had all been perfectly committed to memory. On Christmas Eve, after the girls were asleep, Edwin set up the tamarisk tree and helped Iva and me trim it with balls and tinsel. These had come, with many other lovely gifts for us all, in the wonderful boxes we received each year from friends in Flushing. Iva arranged the gifts her pupils had made. Before retiring we all filled the stockings hung in the nursery.

The joy of Christmas morning, I believe, was enhanced by our having to wait until after breakfast before going in to see the tree. Our colleagues arrived in the study, laden with parcels. Colonel and Mrs. More came in from their car with their arms full of daintily wrapped gifts. Last of all, His Highness the Shaikh drove up in his fine limousine, attended by an escort of retainers who remained outside when he came up the steps of the veranda. He wore a *chaffiya* of white cashmere with a border embroidered in colors, and a fluffy woolen *agaal*, filleted with broad bands of gold. Gold embroidery embellished the neck of the brown woolen *bisht* that hung from his shoulders to his brown leather oxfords.

"Merry Christmas!" the Ruler greeted us all in English, grinning at our surprise. We were all out on the veranda to shake his hands and inquire about his health, while he asked all the polite questions about ours. As he entered the house there came with him the fragrance of incense with just a hint of attar of roses. Thus are the handsome garments of Arabs, both men and women, perfumed for important occasions. Then the door of the living room was opened and guests and family, with expressions of pleasure, found places to stand around the shining tree.

Miss Robertson had charge of the program for which she had so carefully trained the children. First, there was the recitation by her pupils, in unison, of the story of the Angels and the Shepherds, from St. Luke's Gospel. Looking like golden-haired angels on a Christmas card, they recited in Arabic the story that Edwin and I had helped them memorize. Next, I accompanied them on the organ as they sang carols in English. "Joy to the World" rang out with accents of real joy in their childish voices. "O Little Town of Bethlehem" followed and then "It Came Upon a Midnight Clear." Last of all, they sang in Latin all the verses of *Adeste Fideles*, "O Come All Ye Faithful, Joyful and Triumphant."

No one had spoken a word during the girls' singing. The Shaikh knew the subject of the songs, although the words were in languages strange to him. Muslims also believe that Jesus was born of the Virgin Mary. Their sacred traditions tell stories of Him that Christians have never heard. Our Ruler could, without any disloyalty to his own religion, join in the celebration of Jesus' birth. The children's songs brought the program to an end.

The eyes of the little girls had not missed the sight of dolls and other toys awaiting them on the floor under the tree. But before any of their own gifts had been touched, Grace, as spokesman for her sisters, handed the box of fudge to Shaikh Ahmed. In response, the honored guest, reaching into his pocket, drew out a small parcel wrapped in muslin and tied with a string. He handed it to Grace. Perhaps we all held our breath while she removed the string and displayed the gift: one hundred pearls—we counted them afterwards—brought up by Kuwait's divers from the depths of the Persian Gulf!

That was a memorable Christmas! In the afternoon we welcomed the Christian families of the Mission, together with Israeel, Eesa, and Ravamoney. Yakoob and his wife, Esteer, had brought their boys and girls from Bait er Rabbaan, where they were well known as a Syrian Christian family. Shah Raza, a Persian Christian, with his Indian wife, Pretty, as young and attractive as the name implied, brought their little ones from their new home, built on the Mission property. Children of their family and ours played daily on the sand around our houses. Shah Raza had taken our girls shopping in the *sook*, together with his own daughters when they were all looking for Christmas gifts for their families and friends. The children of our guests that day were all dressed in their best and so were the parents.

Israeel, a promising young Syrian Christian, was proving a great help to Edwin in the Boys' School. Eesa, now hospital cook as well as water-carrier, was by this time quite at home in our gatherings. He was the only one of the group wearing a *chaffiya* and *bisht*. Ravamoney, the nurse, was radiant in a blue and gold *sari*, with a Christmas ornament stuck into her glossy, black hair.

During the remainder of Christmas week, while the tree stayed in our living room, we had many women callers. One day, after

I had read the Christmas story in Arabic to a group of women guests in our home, I overheard the following conversation.

"Why do Christians use a tree for celebration of their feast?" asked one of the women.

"I can tell you that!" answered a companion. "It's all written in our own books. Haven't you ever heard that the Prophet Jesus —on him be blessing and peace—was born under a date tree?" Perhaps it was just as well, I reflected with relief, that the question had not been asked of me! How could I have given a reasonable explanation of the phenomenon of a tree being used to express our Christmas joy?

THE SPIRIT OF GIVING

from *Christmas*

BY KATE DOUGLAS WIGGIN

We think of Kate Douglas Wiggin as an educator and author of juveniles, such as The Birds' Christmas Carol, Rebecca of Sunnybrook Farm, *and* Mother Carey's Chickens. *Full of light sweetness, with flashes of homespun humor, they disclose a deep understanding of human nature. In "The Spirit of Giving," Mrs. Wiggin presents her version of the Christmas message.*

When the Child of Nazareth was born, the sun, according to the Bosnian legend, "leaped in the heavens, and the stars around it danced. A peace came over mountain and forest. Even the rotten stump stood straight and healthy on the green hill-side. The grass was beflowered with open blossoms, incense sweet as myrrh pervaded upland and forest, birds sang on the mountain top, and all gave thanks to the great God."

It is naught but an old folk-tale, but it has truth hidden at its heart, for a strange, subtle force, a spirit of genial good-will, a new-born kindness, seem to animate child and man alike when the world pays its tribute to the "heaven-sent youngling," as the poet Drummond calls the infant Christ.

When the Three Wise Men rode from the East into the West on that "first, best Christmas night," they bore on their saddle-bows three caskets filled with gold and frankincense and myrrh, to be laid at the feet of the manger-cradled babe of Bethlehem. Beginning with this old, old journey, the spirit of giving crept into the world's heart. As the Magi came bearing gifts, so do we also; gifts that relieve wants, gifts that are sweet and fragrant with friendship, gifts that breathe love, gifts that mean service, gifts inspired still by the star that shone over the City of David nearly two thousand years ago.

Then hang the green coronet of the Christmas-tree with glittering baubles and jewels of flame; heap offerings on its emerald branches; bring the Yule log to the firing; deck the house with holly and mistletoe,

> "And all the bells on earth shall ring
> On Christmas day in the morning."

GIFTS FOR THE FIRST BIRTHDAY

from *This Way to Christmas*

BY RUTH SAWYER

Ruth Sawyer had a great love of folklore, myths, old ballads, and traditions. She traveled widely in countries near and far, collecting tales and songs. As a storyteller of broad experience and rare imagination, Mrs. Sawyer could retain the innate quality of all she heard and read, while contributing a fresh charm of her own. In "Gifts for the First Birthday" from This Way to Christmas, *she has recaptured the inner vision and grace of an ancient gypsy legend.*

It was winter—and twelve months since the gipsies had driven their flocks of mountain-sheep over the dark, gloomy Balkans, and had settled in the southlands near to the Aegean. It was twelve months since they had seen a wonderful star appear in the sky and heard the singing of angelic voices afar off.

They had marveled much concerning the star until a runner had passed them from the South bringing them news that the star had marked the birth of a Child whom the wise men had hailed as "King of Israel" and "Prince of Peace." This had made Herod of Judea both afraid and angry and he had sent soldiers secretly to kill the Child; but in the night they had miraculously disappeared—the Child with Mary and Joseph—and no one knew whither they had gone. Therefore Herod had sent runners all over the lands that bordered the Mediterranean with a message forbidding every one giving food or shelter or warmth to the Child, under penalty of death. For Herod's anger was far-reaching and where his anger fell his sword likewise. Having given his warning, the runner passed on, leaving the gipsies to marvel much over the tale they had heard and the meaning of the star.

Now on that day that marked the end of the twelve months since the star had shone the gipsies said among themselves: "Dost thou think that the star will shine again to-night? If it were true, what the runner said, that when it shone twelve months ago it marked the place where the Child lay it may even mark His hiding-place this night. Then Herod would know where to find Him, and send his soldiers again to slay Him. That would be a cruel thing to happen!"

The air was chill with the winter frost, even there in the southland, close to the Aegean; and the gipsies built high their fire and hung their kettle full of millet, fish, and bitter herbs for their supper. The king lay on his couch of tiger-skins and on his arms were amulets of heavy gold, while rings of gold were on his fingers and in his ears. His tunic was of heavy silk covered with a leopard cloak, and on his feet were shoes of goatskin trimmed with fur. Now, as they feasted around the fire a voice came to them through the darkness, calling. It was a man's voice, climbing the mountains from the south.

"Ohe! Ohe!" he shouted. And then nearer, "O—he!"

The gipsies were still disputing among themselves whence the voice came when there walked into the circle about the fire a tall, shaggy man, grizzled with age, and a sweet-faced young mother carrying a child.

"We are outcasts," said the man, hoarsely. "Ye must know that whosoever succors us will bring Herod's vengeance like a sword about his head. For a year we have wandered homeless and cursed over the world. Only the wild creatures have not feared to share their food and give us shelter in their lairs. But to-night we can go no farther; and we beg the warmth of your fire and food enough to stay us until the morrow."

The king looked at them long before he made reply. He saw the weariness in their eyes and the famine in their cheeks; he saw, as well, the holy light that hung about the child, and he said at last to his men:

"It is the Child of Bethlehem, the one they call the 'Prince of Peace.' As yon man says, who shelters them shelters the wrath of Herod as well. Shall we let them tarry?"

One of their number sprang to his feet, crying: "It is a sin to turn strangers from the fire, a greater sin if they be poor and friendless. And what is a king's wrath to us? I say bid them welcome. What say the rest?"

And with one accord the gipsies shouted, "Yea, let them tarry!"

They brought fresh skins and threw them down beside the fire for the man and woman to rest on. They brought them food and wine, and goat's milk for the Child; and when they had seen that all was made comfortable for them they gathered round the Child—these black gipsy men—to touch His small white hands and feel His golden hair. They brought Him a chain of gold to play with and another for His neck and tiny arm.

"See, these shall be Thy gifts, little one," said they, "the gifts for Thy first birthday."

And long after all had fallen asleep the Child lay on His bed of skins beside the blazing fire and watched the light dance on the beads of gold. He laughed and clapped His hands together to see the pretty sight they made; and then a bird called out of the thicket close by.

"Little Child of Bethlehem," it called, "I, too, have a birth gift for Thee. I will sing Thy cradle song this night." And softly, like the tinkling of a silver bell and like clear water running over mossy places, the nightingale sang and sang, filling the air with melodies.

And then another voice called to Him:

"Little Child of Bethlehem, I am only a tree with boughs all bare, for the winter has stolen my green cloak, but I also can give Thee a birth gift. I can give Thee shelter from the biting north wind that blows." And the tree bent low its branches and twined a rooftree and a wall about the Child.

Soon the Child was fast asleep, and while He slept a small brown bird hopped out of the thicket. Cocking his little head, he said:

"What can I be giving the Child of Bethlehem? I could fetch Him a fat worm to eat or catch Him the beetle that crawls on yonder bush, but He would not like that! And I could tell Him a story of the lands of the north, but He is asleep and would not hear." And the brown bird shook its head quite sorrowfully. Then it saw that the wind was bringing the sparks from the fire nearer and nearer to the sleeping Child.

"I know what I can do," said the bird, joyously. "I can catch the hot sparks on my breast, for if one should fall upon the Child it would burn Him grievously."

So the small brown bird spread wide his wings and caught the sparks on his own brown breast. So many fell that the feathers were burned; and burned was the flesh beneath until the breast was no longer brown, but red.

Next morning, when the gipsies awoke, they found Mary and Joseph and the Child gone. For Herod had died, and an angel had come in the night and carried them back to the land of Judea. But the good God blessed those who had cared that night for the Child.

To the nightingale He said: "Your song shall be the sweetest in all the world, for ever and ever; and only you shall sing the long night through."

To the tree He said: "Little fir-tree, never more shall your branches be bare. Winter and summer you and your seedlings shall stay green, ever green."

Last of all He blessed the brown bird: "Faithful little watcher, from this night forth you and your children shall have red breasts, that the world may never forget your gift to the Child of Bethlehem."

NAZARETH

from *The Light of the World*

BY GREVILLE COOKE

In The Light of the World *Greville Cooke has told anew and interpreted the life of Jesus and, while keeping as close to the Gospels as
possible, he has created a work of art, scholarship, and imagination.
As Vicar of Cransley, a quiet old town in the English Midlands, the
author spent seven years on this labor of love, writing not only from
his mind but from his heart. Everywhere in the British Commonwealth
and America the voices of leading clergymen have praised the tremendous impact of this biography. The first chapter, sounding the
keynote, follows.*

Jesus could never remember any home but the one in Nazareth.
There were times when He pressed His father and mother to
tell Him more about His early childhood; but often they would
turn away and change the subject, so that He never came to know
exactly the circumstances of His birth. Some of the Nazarenes
looked askance at Him and Mary whenever He spoke of His
birthday, as though they could have told Him a good deal if
they would—or if they dared, for Joseph was both a strong man
and a highly respected one, with whom it was always dangerous
to trifle, though a gentle man at heart.

But at night, when Jesus was asleep . . . Joseph and Mary
would sometimes sit and recall those strange far-off days and
their still stranger hints and omens. Zechariah's story, for instance.
He had been Mary's kinsman, having married her cousin Elizabeth. One morning, having just heard the triple blast upon the
silver trumpets blown from the pinnacle of the Temple in
Jerusalem, as the first rays of the early morning sun struck
over the far rim of the mountains of the Wilderness, he, the
officiating Priest for that day, had seen in the Sanctuary a vision
of an Archangel, who had promised him the birth of a son. He
had doubted the Angel's word, owing to the advanced age of
his wife and himself; whereupon he had been struck dumb and

emerging from the Sanctuary had been forced to describe by gestures his experience in the Temple. But Gabriel's prophecy had come true in due course, and John had been born to them.

Mary would recall, too, the visit to her cousin Elizabeth, following that ineffably strange experience she had undergone, here in Nazareth, six months after Zechariah's vision. But she could never be persuaded to talk about that; nor could Joseph. It was something sacred shared by them together, and only to be mentioned in the privacy of an evening talk, when the children were safely in bed, and the neighbours had shut-to their doors.

At such times Joseph would recall, with a shudder, that terrible journey to Bethlehem; and especially their passing of the tomb of Rachel, a monument to the tragic death of his ancestress, who died in childbirth there by the roadside, before Jacob could reach haven with her in Bethlehem. And things had hardly been improved by the failure to find accommodation in the khan, and Mary's consequent child-bearing in a stable. They often looked back wistfully to that night, seeing again the ass tethered close by, and the patient kine standing about moodily, their wet breath frostily visible in the dull lamplight. When the rough shepherds came with their strange tale of Angels singing and of the prophecy of the coming, that very night, of God's Messiah, it had seemed as though the cave had become suddenly the centre of the whole universe.

They would remember together, too, the visit to the Temple for the purification rites after childbirth, and the strange words of Simeon and Anna, both so old and so queerly inspired. It had seemed almost as though that visit were an ending and a beginning of vast epochs: as if prophecy had seen its final consummation in the song the old man had quaveringly sung—the swan song of a dispensation, and the opening of a new. Mary remembered the ominous words about the "sword that should pierce her heart," and how frightened she had been for Jesus, as she wrapped her arms closely about Him and hurried with Joseph out of the Temple. And that night, in a strange lodging, her eyes had filled with brimming tears, while Joseph listened helplessly to her weeping as the moonlight streamed slantingly through the shuttered lattice onto the sleeping Babe at her breast. Joseph often felt a great pity for Mary. She would muse and ponder deeply on those matters, and especially on the sayings uttered about her little Son. "Set for the falling and rising up of many. . . . A Sign that shall be spoken against." What could that have meant —or still mean—for her Son?

As for Jesus, He was beginning to take an interest in His fathers' carpentering business. He would hang about the workshop till Joseph gave Him some little job to do. He showed plenty of aptitude for the work, too. Joseph noted how carefully He would use the tools, how smoothly He was learning to plane, what an eye He was developing for the most suitable types of wood for different purposes. . . . Often Jesus would be sent down to the market place to buy the cheapest food obtainable. "Don't forget, you can get two sparrows for a farthing, or five for a halfpenny"—and the Boy would go off by Himself, clutching His tiny coins. Often, too, Mary would be hard put to it to know how to patch and darn the clothes. . . . There came a time when it was no longer practicable to patch a rent with new cloth. It only made the tear worse in the end. As she would sigh and put the torn garment wearily aside, she would see her Son's eyes upon her. He seemed to understand.

He would come and take her hand, too, when the cares and lets of life overwhelmed her, with their reiterated questions: what they were all to eat, what to drink, what to wear, and especially if a guest arrived unexpectedly and the larder was empty and Joseph was forced to borrow a loaf or two from a neighbour.

Jesus regularly attended the Synagogue services on the Sabbath. He had learned to love the Scriptures, especially the Psalms and the Prophets, and His favourite book of Moses, Deuteronomy. He loved, too, to hear Joseph tell the children clustered round him of the stirring deeds of Israel's heroes, of Samson and Barak and Gideon and David, and the stories of the Patriarchs, Abraham and Isaac and Jacob, and especially that of Joseph. Jesus liked nothing better than to curl up at His father's knee and to hear, enraptured, how God had looked after Israel and given her guidance and comfort in her sorrows. . . .

It had been His invariable custom to speak of God as His "Father." Indeed, He spoke of Him always as His "Abba"—the very first word He had learned to lisp at Mary's knee. His parents were deeply shocked and distressed, and tried hard to break Him of the habit, but in vain. The Rabbi in Nazareth got to hear of it and spoke seriously to Joseph of the necessity for reverence where the great Jehovah was concerned. But Mary thought it rather sweet . . . and a wonderful tribute—and a deserved one— to Joseph.

Whenever possible Jesus would slip away, especially in the cool of the evening, up through the sloping, winding streets, till the white-roofed houses were at last left behind; climbing still higher up the springy brown turf till the town sank down into the shadows far below and, with one last long stride, He would reach the very topmost level and could lie flat on the summit to rest and gaze and dream.

Almost all of Israel's long history was recalled to Him, spread out as on a relief map. To the southwest loomed the mighty shoulder of Mount Carmel, whence Elijah had thundered defiance to all the gods of the heathen and called down fire from Heaven. A little farther to the south rose Gilboa, rounded and strong, where Saul and Jonathan fought and fell. Closer at hand, arising out of the Plain, was the circular mound of Tabor, where Barak encamped before battling with Sisera. Down there, somewhere in the fields, Deborah the Prophetess had sung her wild and terrible song; where, all but hidden from view in its deep trench, ran the torrent Kishon, which, overflowing its banks suddenly, had swept away such of Israel's enemies as vere not bogged in the surrounding marshes. In yonder vale Gideon and his three hundred had upheld Israel's honour in an epic victory.

Beyond the huge bluff of Carmel lay the dark blue line of the Mediterranean, clearly visible from this hilltop. Away to the east rose the mountain range in the lap of which nestled the Lake of Galilee; while beyond, the arid heights of the Hauran hills marked the bastions of Arabia's vast desert. To the north rose the wooded brows of Lebanon, magnificent in splendid serenity, well watered, thickly afforested, remote and strange with uncharted uplands and wild beasts and great birds. Royally the ridges lifted their great shoulders into the sky, towering up towards the stars, crowned by the snowbound summit of Hermon, nine thousand feet high, colossal, exalted, halfway to Heaven. Was it not called "God's Throne" by the Prophets? A type, indeed, of God Himself—The government shall be upon His shoulder. This north country always deeply attracted Jesus, calling to Him, beckoning upward. . . .

But was not Jerusalem the true Throne of Jehovah? Swinging round on the warm, sweet-scented grass, He would gaze long and intently at the far mountains of Samaria, beyond which lay the Holy City, the centre of the whole earth, the Shrine of the Shekinah, the Holy Place of the Most High. There, streaking away to the swooning south, ran the caravan road along which, one day soon, He Himself would be taken by His parents (they went up every year)—and then He would see God's Temple and become a "Son of the Law" and worship His Heavenly Father in His own House. . . .

Though, to be sure, God seemed very near to Him up here on the hills. Jesus felt a peace stealing through Him whenever He lay here; almost as if God were enfolding Him in His arms, as a shepherd would a lamb. Just over there, as He now lay outstretched on the sun-warm grass, Jesus could see a shepherd leading in his sheep to their fold. He loved to watch and keep company with the shepherds, many of whom were His close friends. They were a simple kindly fellowship, devoted to their charges, going out in all weathers and in the face of any danger to seek a lost sheep or lamb; even at times lying themselves across the entrance to the sheepfold—literally the door of the sheep—rather than risk any harm happening to them. Jesus could see how one sheep farmer often possessed more than one sheepfold—there they were in front of Him, far down below—but they all belonged to one flock. Sometimes hired men were called in to give a hand at lambing time or when shepherds fell sick; and Jesus noted how the sheep would not follow them, coax they ever so hard; but when the real shepherds returned the sheep would run to them one by one as their names were called out.

Not long before, news had reached Jesus that a shepherd friend of His was missing. He had never come home after a night in the hills; search was made for him, and his dead body had been found in a ravine, mangled and torn by wild beasts—a kind, good shepherd whom Jesus had loved, giving his life for the sheep.

The shepherds also taught Him weather lore; how a red dawn, —terrible as an army with banners—over the far Arabian hills (their summits stark and black against the glowing sky) betokened a wild, stormy day, with, perhaps, one of those sudden tempests that, blowing down through the gaunt rock ravines, whipped up the waves of Gennesaret to a frenzy of foaming billows. Or, even worse, a blistering, searing sirocco from the Hauran, withering up the leaves before their time. But the gentle southwest wind, blowing from over distant Carmel, heralded the merciful rain, falling on fields and roads, on vines and olive groves alike, as did the sunshine when the showers were over.

And now the sun was fast sinking behind the hills of Naphtali, and long shadows were streaking over the northern uplands. Somewhere there, only a few miles away, was Sepphoris, the fiery sky that flamed above it reminding Jesus of a dreadful night that had scared Him only a few months before. He could not even now think of it without a shudder. For Sepphoris had been the storm centre of an insurrection against Rome, caused by the Syrian Governor's order for the taking of a census—for further taxation, of course. Judas of Galilee had raised the standard of revolt and had let loose the full flood of nationalistic passion, always strongly flowing in the north. Thither had swarmed all the young hotheads of the region. Along yonder highroad that wound round the foot of Nazareth's hill the eager groups of rebels had passed, till the gathering at Sepphoris had become a mighty army, fully ten thousand strong. Soon after, they all marched back again, singing the songs of Zion and watched by all the boys of Nazareth as they ran excitedly along the hilltops to keep the great army in sight as long as possible, till the dusty cloud was at length lost to view away to the far northwest. They were aiming for Tiberias, where Herod had reared his vast new palace—and where he kept his armoury, just ripe for pillaging. The plan had succeeded. The rebels broke in, seized the swords and spears, and marched on, singing and shouting, in order to fight with Rome and drive her hated legions into the Mediter-ranean or over Lebanon—anywhere so long as it was out of God's Promised Land, which would then be free forever.

But all this while the eagle of Rome was watching through narrow-slitted eyes, stealthily sharpening her claws. Then, silently, she rose in air, breasting the wind a moment, poised over her victim—and struck like a thunderbolt. From the encampments at Caesarea and Decapolis, Varus the Roman general had gathered his legions, and the rebellion was crushed like rubble beneath falling rock. Whosoever fell on that rock was broken; but on whomsoever it fell, it ground him to powder.

Then the legions marched against Sepphoris. Their grim ranks could be seen from the hilltop above Nazareth, the hems of their tunics swinging to their measured tread (no songs this time): an even greater—and very different—army, winding in reverse direction around the base of the hill. That night, the darkness was suddenly lighted up with an ever-growing red glow as a whole city was fired; and the flames leaped up and flared high to heaven till Sepphoris sank to earth in charred and embered ruin. All the inhabitants were sold into slavery, save some two thousand, who were ordered to be crucified. Crouched behind a boulder, Jesus saw for the first time the dread sight of condemned criminals moving to a terrible death and carrying their own crosses. He had been face to face with the horror and cruelty of war. It made Him feel lonelier than before, needing more than ever the company of His Heavenly Father out there on the hills. He missed, too, the friendship of His Judaean cousin John, who used to come every year for a holiday in the north. His parents were now dead and he had passed into the care of a relative somewhere in the south. They had enjoyed such jolly games together, especially that of "Weddings and Funerals," with the other children in the market place. Jesus had generally been chosen as the bridegroom, and John was always the bridegroom's friend. Would He ever see him again?

The sun by now was hidden behind the northern hills, and the air had suddenly become fresh and cold. It was time to go home. From far away came the bark of a fox. The grass was quite wet with the dew. . . .

ANNIVERSARY

BY MARGARET E. SANGSTER

Like her famous grandmother, whose name she bears, Margaret E. Sangster has had a distinguished career as a writer for radio and magazines. In Anniversary, as in many of her religious pieces, she shows a fertile imagination and adds new dimensions and interest to the tenderness of legend and tradition.

The boy sat quite alone on the hilltop, his shepherd's crook across his knees, his small square lunch basket beside him. He made an odd, distorted shadow in the white light of the moon, for even the fringed shawl that his mother had woven of lamb's wool could not hide the ugly hump that lay—a burden much too heavy for so young a lad to bear—between his shoulders.

Far below him, dotting the hillside with other irregular shadows, were the sheep. The majority of them slept, but a few wandered aimlessly up and down the slope. The boy, however, was not watching the flock. His head was thrown back, and his wide eyes were fixed on the sky.

"Perhaps it will happen again," he was thinking, "perhaps— though a third of a century has gone by. Perhaps I shall see the great star and hear the angel voices as my father did!"

The moon, riding high in the heavens, went under a blanket of cloud. For a moment the world was dark. The boy sighed and lowered his eyes.

"It is an omen," he breathed, "an omen! Though it is the time of anniversary, there will be no star this night. Neither will the angels sing. . . ."

The time of anniversary. How often the boy had listened to the story of the miracle that had taken place so long ago! The boy's father had been a lad himself then—he had been the youngest of the shepherds on that glorious occasion when an angel anthem sounded across the world and a star shone above the tranquil town of Bethlehem. The boy's father had followed the star; with the other shepherds he had come to the stable of the inn. Crowding through the narrow doorway, he had seen a woman with a baby in her arms.

"But—" the boy's father had told the story so many times that his family and the neighbors knew it word for word—"she was no ordinary woman! There was something in her face that made one think of a lighted candle. And there was a tenderness in her smile that the very cattle felt, for they drew close to her and seemed to kneel. It was not her beauty, although beauty she did possess! It was a shine from within—"

"And the baby—" the boy always prompted his father here— "*what of the baby?*"

The father's hand touched his small son's shoulder at this point —touched it, and drew away.

"The baby," he said, and his voice grew hushed, "was as unlike other infants as his mother was different from other women. Scarce an hour old when first I glimpsed him, there was a sense of wisdom—no, do not laugh—on his brow, and his tiny up-curled hands seemed—indeed, I do mean it!—to hold power. I found myself kneeling, as the cattle knelt, and there was the damp of tears upon my face, and—though I was a lad tall for my age— I was not ashamed."

Alone on the hillside the boy could almost hear the sound of his father's voice in the stillness. His father's voice telling the story of the marvelous infant and of the Wise Men who had come to the stable—following, also, in the path of the star. They had come bearing gifts, the fame of which traveled through all the land. Often the boy had heard of the gold and frankincense and myrrh; often he had shivered at the tale of the great cruel king who had ordered death to all male infants. Often he had thrilled to the saga of a worried mother—and her sober husband—who had stolen away into the land of Egypt with her child.

"Many of us thought," the boy's father finished, "that the child had been captured and slain by Herod. Until a decade passed and we heard rumors of a youth who bore his name, and who lectured in a temple at Jerusalem to a group of learned doctors. A few years ago we heard that this same youth, grown older, had organized a band of men, that with them he was journeying from place to place, preaching and teaching and aiding the needy. And—" here the boy's father had a habit of lowering his voice and glancing furtively around the room—"there are some who say that he has become a Messiah, and that he does more than champion the cause of the common people. There are some who say that he performs wonderful deeds, healing the halt and the blind and the lepers—even raising the dead."

Once, at this point, the boy interrupted. "I would that I might meet him," he had said with ill-masked eagerness. "I would that he might take the hump from my back and make me strong and straight like other children."

It was growing cold on the hillside. The child drew the shawl closer about his tired body and wished that he were not a shepherd. Shepherds led a lonely life—they did not fit into the bright places of the world. Rooms gaily lighted at eventide were for the men and boys who worked hard by day and earned their moments of ease; they were not for shepherds. But what. else could a crippled lad do to justify his existence—what else than tend sheep? A crippled lad who could not undertake physical labor and who had no talents.

Yawning wearily, the boy glanced at the sky. From the position of the moon he judged it to be middle night—it was still a long while before sunrise; still hours before someone would come to take his place and he could limp home. And yet middle night had its compensations! For at that time he could break his fast and partake of the lunch that his mother had packed so neatly into a basket.

As he reached for the basket, as he opened it slowly, the boy was wondering what had been prepared for his refreshment. He found, to his satisfaction, that there was a flask of goat's milk, and nearly a loaf of crusty dark bread, and some yellow cheese; that there were dried figs, sugary with their own sweetness. And, wrapped separately, he came upon a real treat. A cake made of eggs and sifted flour, with citron in it, and raisins!

He had expected the bread and the cheese and the milk. Even the figs he had expected. But the cake was a surprise, the sort of surprise that happened seldom. His eyes gleamed as he surveyed it, and some of the sadness went out of them. Carefully he set the basket down and spread on the ground beside him the square of linen in which his mother had folded the lunch. Carefully he laid out the flask of milk, the bread, the cheese—but not the cake, which he left tucked away in the depths of the basket. He left it there so that he might not be tempted to eat it first!

"It is good to be hungry," he said aloud. "Yes—and to have food!"

From somewhere just behind him a voice spoke. It was not a loud voice, and yet the music of it seemed to carry beyond the hillside.

"Indeed, yes!" said the voice. "It is good to be hungry. And to have food, and to—"

Startled, for he had thought he was quite alone with his thoughts and the drowsing sheep, the boy glanced back across his crooked shoulder. He saw a man standing upon the brow of the hill, silhouetted against the night sky. Ordinarily he would have known fear, for there were cruel robbers abroad often at middle night. But somehow the sight of this man, who was tall and muscular, failed to frighten him. He did not know why he instinctively completed the man's unfinished sentence.

"And to share it!" he murmured, as if in a dream. "You are a stranger, sir?"

The man came closer to the child and stood looking down upon him. "No, not a stranger," he said slowly, "never a stranger. As it happens, my journey started not far from this very place— started years before you, my lad, saw the light. I am by way of completing a circle."

Although he couldn't imagine what the man meant, the boy made swift response.

"I was about to eat my lunch," he said, indicating the square of linen on which he had arranged the contents of his basket. "One grows ravenous on the hillside. I am a shepherd, sir. I tend my father's flock, and each night my mother packs for me a simple repast. Will you be seated—you who have journeyed so long—and break bread with me? Perhaps—" he hesitated shyly— "you will talk with me as we eat? It grows lonely on the dark hillside—I pine at times for companionship."

The man continued to peer down from his impressive height. His eyes held a warm glow—it was as if a candle burned somewhere behind them, the boy thought, and remembered words that his father had spoken when he described a woman in a stable. He felt so comforted by the man's glance that he smiled up into the kindly face, and the man spoke again.

"It is a strange coincidence," he said, "the fact that you are a shepherd, for I also tend my father's flock! And I also—" his smile was luminous—"have often grown lonely waiting for the gates of dawn to open. Are you sure—" he seated himself upon the ground—"that you have enough for two? I should not like to deprive you of anything."

Gazing, fascinated, into the man's face, the boy replied:

"But, yes! I have a large flask of goat's milk, and some yellow cheese, and nearly a loaf of bread, and ten figs. And—" for a second he hesitated—"that's a great plenty," he finished lamely. He did not mention the cake, still wrapped in the basket. For a cake—a cake made of sifted flour and eggs and citron and raisins—was a rare delicacy. And it was not a very big cake.

The man bent forward to retie the thong of a sandal. The boy saw that the sandal was covered with dust. He tried to keep his eyes from glancing toward his lunch basket as he tore the crusty dark bread into fragments.

"Perhaps your feet are aching," he ventured as he placed the fragments in the center of the linen cloth. "This hill is hard to climb. I am close to being spent when I reach the summit of it, but I must sit high so that I can watch all the sheep."

The man said slowly: "I have climbed steeper hills than this one, my lad, and know that there are steeper hills to be. My feet do not ache. How long—" abruptly he changed the subject— "have you been crippled?"

Had it come from an ordinary person, the boy would have resented such a display of curiosity. From this man the question seemed a natural one, to be answered naturally.

"Why," he said, "I have never been without a hump between my shoulders. I hate it, but—" he was quoting his mother—"what must be, must be! Still—" his childish face was a trifle unchildish— "it is hard to go through life looking like one of the camels that the Wise Men rode when they came from the east—"

The man interrupted. "What, lad," he queried, "do you know of the Wise Men from the east? How does it happen that you should mention them to me on this night? It is—" he bit into a piece of the crusty dark bread—"very curious!"

Laughing softly, the little boy answered. "I suppose the Wise Men are in my mind," he said, "because this is the time of anniversary, and I have been thinking of the baby that was born in a stable. I was hoping—before you arrived—that once again the great star might shine and that the angels might sing. I have, in fact, been watching the sky rather than the sheep."

The man asked another swift question. "What," he queried, "do you know about these holy things—about the star and the song? You are so very young!"

The boy explained. "All Bethlehem," he said, "heard about the star, and about the infant who lay in the manger because there was no room at the inn. I know, perhaps, more than the others, for my father—a child then himself—was one of the shepherds who saw the light from the heavens and heard the angel music.

. . . Will you—" the boy had taken the flask of goat's milk into his hands—"will you share with me this cup, sir? For perhaps you thirst?"

The man took the flask from the fragile hands. His fingers were powerful and sinewy, but as gentle as a woman's. He said, "I will share the cup with you, my lad, for I do thirst."

As he watched the man drinking deeply, the boy thought, "It must be tiring to tramp from place to place."

He said on impulse, as the stranger set down the flask, "Will you tell me, sir, of some of the towns in which you have stayed?"

The man answered: "One town is very like another, my lad, with poverty and pain rubbing elbows against wealth, with greed taking toll, all too often, of humanity. With health on one side and illness on the other. With so few gracious deeds that one can do to help the sore distressed--" he turned his face away—"and a lifetime in which to do them so desperately short!"

In a low tone the boy said: "Sometimes, when I was a tot, I hoped that my life might be short, but already I am ten years old. How old, sir, are you? I feel older than my years. . . ."

The man's voice was muted as he replied, "I am more than three times your age, lad, but I, too, feel older than my years."

"You shouldn't, because you're so strong," the boy exclaimed. "When is your time of birth, sir? I was born when it was spring."

The man smiled his beautiful, luminous smile. "It's odd that you should ask, dear lad," he murmured, "for this is my day of birth. You, quite unknowing, are giving me an anniversary feast and never has a feast been more welcome. I was weary and for-lorn when I came upon you."

Weary and forlorn! As he stared at the man, the little boy queried:

"Haven't you any people of your own? People with whom you can make merry on your day of birth? When my birthday arrives, Mother prepares a *real* feast for me, and gives me gifts. This shawl I wear she wove for my last birthday. The year before she pressed a sheaf of bright flowers into wax. Once, when I was smaller, she made wondrous sweetmeats of honey and grain."

The man reached over and rested his hand on the little boy's knee. "I fear," he said, "that I have grown too old and large for birthday gifts. Furthermore, my loved ones are not near enough just now to make merry with me. But maybe, who knows, there will be a gift for me at my journey's end."

The boy's knee felt all atingle under the pressure of the friendly hand. He asked, "When, sir, will you come to your journey's end?"

The man did not meet the child's gaze. He replied, "Perhaps very soon!"

The boy was worried. He said: "You don't look happy about it. Don't you want to come to the end of your travels? Don't you want to reach home and see what gift they have in store for you?"

The man hesitated ever so slightly. "Yes," he said at last, "I want to reach—home. But the gift—it may be too beautiful to bear. Or too heavy for me to carry. I suppose—" his face looked drawn in the white moonlight—"I should be getting on. You have made this birthday very sweet, my lad!"

Peeping down at the white cloth with its remnants of bread and cheese, the boy thought: "There seems to be as much food as ever! He couldn't have liked it." Suddenly he was swept by a burning sense of shame. He spoke impetuously, one word tumbling over the other.

"You did not enjoy your food," he said, "and you have had no true birthday feast. That—though you have no way of guessing— is because I have been selfish and mean! I," he gulped out his confession, "have a cake in my basket—a cake that I was saving to eat alone after you left me. It is a cake of sifted flour and eggs and citron and raisins, *and I love cake*. But now," the boy's voice quavered, "I would not enjoy it if I ate it in a solitary fashion; it would choke me! Sir, I desire to give the cake to you as my gift. Perhaps you will munch it later, when the chill of early morn has set in and you are on the road."

The man did not speak, but his eyes were like stars—instead of candles—as he watched his small host lift the cake from the basket and display its rich goodness. It was only when the boy extended it toward him that he broke into speech.

"Ah, my lad," he said, "you have sustained me with your bread, and we have drunk deep of the same cup. So now we will share this cake, which shall be, through your bounty, my birthday cake. We will apportion it evenly and deftly, and we will eat of it together—you and I. And then you shall wait for the dawn, and I will be on my way. But as I walk along the road I shall see a little lad's face, and shall hear a little lad's voice, and shall remember a little lad's generosity."

Gravely—as if he were handling something infinitely precious—

the man took the rich cake into his fingers. Carefully, he divided it so that the two sections were equal. He said, "Bless unto us this food, my Father," and the boy was startled, because there was no one else upon the hillside. Then he said,

"This is the cake of life, lad. Enjoy it to the last crumb!"

So he and the boy ate the cake together, and the boy thought that he had never tasted such fare. It was as if the cake's richness were verily the richness of life! As he licked the last crumbs from his fingers he felt that he was gathering force and vigor and purpose. In his mind's eye, for no reason at all, he saw a picture of himself—robust and handsome and brave—striding down the road with his weakness cast from him and his chin high.

"It's like a vision!" he said, but when the man queried,

"What do you mean, lad?" he hung his head and was unable to answer.

Indeed, he was silent so long that the man's hand came to rest lightly upon his shoulder—lightly, but, oh, so firmly! There was something in the touch that made tears hang on the boy's lashes, that wrung from him quick words.

"Oh," he cried, "do not leave me, sir! We could be such friends, you and I. Come with me to my home and dwell with my family. My mother will bake many cakes for you, and my father will share with you of his plenty. And I—you may have my bed, and my waxed flowers, and even this fringed shawl that I wear. Do not journey on, sir! Stay with me, here in Bethlehem."

The man spoke. His voice was like a great bell tolling over hill and valley. "I must go on," he said. "I must be about my father's business—I must travel toward my destiny. But I shall never leave you, my lad, for all that. Lo, I am with you always—even unto the end of the world!"

Bowing his head in his hands, covering his misted eyes, the boy was aware of the man's firm fingers traveling up from his shoulder until they touched his hair. But now he couldn't speak, for a pulse drummed in his throat, and a strange rhythm was hammering in his ears. When he raised his head, finally, the man was gone, and the hillside was empty—save for the shadows that were the sheep.

The boy sobbed once, and sharply, with a sense of loss. He struggled to his feet. Only he didn't have to struggle, really, for there was a curious lightness about his body, and a feeling of freshness and peace—a peace that transcended the pain of parting. But it was not until he drew the fringed lamb's-wool shawl tighter across his back that he realized how straight he was standing—*and how straight he would always stand.*

JOURNEY TO CHRISTMAS

by B. J. CHUTE

Journey to Christmas *by B. J. Chute, author of the best-selling novels* The End of Loving, Greenwillow, *and* The Moon and the Thorn, *is poetic in its theme, beautiful and intimate in its touches of nature's aspects, vivid and sympathetic in its characterization. This heartwarming story which takes place in a time of desperate hardship shows how Christmas revives the spirit of loving and giving.*

The world had never been so deep in snow.

Rom swore at the little donkey when it stumbled into a drift of the wicked whiteness, and it shook its head and looked back at him sorrowfully as if its master ought to know it was doing its best.

"Get up, you beast," said Rom between his teeth. They were making such a slow way that it would be evening before they reached the great town, and, by that time, someone else might have laid claim to the miserly bit of a job that Rom was after.

"Get up, you beast," he said again and glared about him fiercely, hating the fields that lay so still and bound, the fields that had panted and scorched all summer long under the cruelest sun he had ever known in his eighteen years.

There had been bad times before, when the flour bin was scraped to its bottom and potatoes and old cabbages did for a daily diet, but there had never been bad times like this in the memory of the oldest. Now it was every man for himself in a world that had once seemed loving, and if he could only reach the great town in time, he would slit the throat of any man who came to take the bare promise of work away from him.

He looked at the donkey's sides, caved in like a broken barrel, and all he could think of was how slow its little hard hooves plodded. Months since the animal had known the treat of a carrot or even good hay under its nose, and there would be none tomorrow, the next day nor the long day after.

Only, tomorrow was Christmas Day.

"God's curse on it," said Rom, and the sound of the words was quick and dreadful in his ears but he could not take them back. His eyes stung with the tears whipped up by the icy wind, and he shook the stinging away and looked up the long road ahead.

Someone was walking the middle of it, someone shapeless as a huge bundle of blown rags and plodding even slower than the donkey. The thin jingle of harness must have reached the walker, and the haystacky figure turned heavily and watched the cart come.

It was the peddler woman that he remembered from childhood, thinner by pounds than when he had seen her last but still as broad as an oak beam. She threw up one hand out of her tatters, the other clutching a worn brown sack, and cried a greeting as if she was met up with a saint.

He pulled the donkey up alongside her, grudging even the moment of delay. She grabbed at the bridle rein, and the donkey puts its nose on her shoulder, nuzzling hopefully.

"God be praised," said the peddler woman. "All the other carts are traveling east. You'll take me where I'm going." She trundled around to the side of the cart and leaned on the high wheel. "Give me a hand up, lad. I'm that bent with the crippling."

He had an impulse to push her away, but it would take as long to argue as it would to let her clamber on. "I'm following the road straight to the great town," he said sharply. "I'll not turn an instant off it, not for the Devil himself. Lay that to your mind."

She gave a short laugh and heaved her bulk up the step which creaked its protest. "The Devil'd not be walking in this weather," she said. "I'm going to the Kestery house."

"Not by me you're not going," he told her. "I'll take you to the crossroads because it's on my journey, but you'll walk the rest of the distance in your own two shoes." He slapped the reins across the donkey's back, and the cart lurched ahead.

The peddler woman gave him no heed, grumbling and settling herself about. "Been going there for a month's time," she said, a little pleasanter now she was in the cart. "Each day I've put it off, telling myself there'd be tomorrow and I'd not walk so lame and the snow and cold would go. I might have known for myself that nothing good like that would happen this year."

"I'll take you to the crossroads," said Rom again.

"We'll talk that between us when I get my breath back." She went right on. "There's a doll in my sack for the little Kestery girl," she said, "the first doll she'll ever be having. They'd promised it to her from the day she was born, I think. Not born natural, she wasn't, you know. Her arm withered, poor mite, like a bird with one wing, though she's quicker than most, even so. Word came to me through the preacher that the Kesterys had the money all laid by, and I've had the doll for them since autumn. Would you like to see the doll, lad?"

She fumbled at the sack's drawstrings, mumbling to the knots.

"No," said Rom. "I would not." Money for dolls, some had, money to throw away even in the bad times with not two coins to rub together for most. With the doll money in her pocket, the peddler woman would be able to see a little ahead, if only around the next corner.

"I can draw breath easier for a bit," she said, reading his thoughts. "Wood on the fire, at least, and a bit of food without fighting for it, and maybe an extra or two."

"You're fat enough," said Rom.

She did not take it in bad part. "I'm not so bad off as your donkey," she admitted. "Poor beast. It'll lie down where it walks one day, by the looks of it."

"It's not laid down yet," said Rom grimly.

The peddler woman shrugged and looked at the sky, half-closing her eyes. "There's another storm up in there. It'll be a bad Christmas Day if the clouds mean anything."

"There'll be no Christmas this year," said Rom.

"God's truth," said the woman heavily. "Do you mind how it was other years, the lights in the windows and the little trees inside with their glitters on them? People buying my trinkets wherever I went, and the churches with their warm stoves and the pine boughs and the singing. They were fine, the churches were, before the bad times. The floors are so cold for kneeling now, it reaches up through your bones and into your heart."

"The Lord's not so long remembering as He was once," Rom said bitterly.

"That's blasphemy for a lad to think," said the peddler woman.

"I'll think it and I'll say it," said Rom. "There's precious little good left in the world."

The woman sighed heavily and fell silent. The cart jogged and lurched on its journey, turning wheels muffled by thick snow. The little sharp donkey-hooves shushed through it, and the road unwound, white and with no seeming end.

When they came at last to the crossroads, Rom pulled the donkey up. It stopped and stood with its legs spread and its head drooping, as it had stood in the oven of summer, under a sky like metal. Rom spoke over his shoulder. "This is your turning-place," he said. "I'm going on."

There was no answer, and he glanced back. The old fat bundle of rags had fallen into sleep on the floor of the cart, hand still clutching the sack. He leaned from his seat and shook her by the shoulder. "Get up and get out," he said. "This is as far as you go."

She woke with a cry, and it took her a moment to find where she was. Then she looked about and up the road she would have to travel alone, the snow not even broken along it. She gave a whimper. "It's a long ways yet," she said, "and I'm that crippled—"

"Your feet carried you to where I found you," said Rom coldly. "They can carry you again. Get out, and don't be keeping me. There's work waiting for me in the great town, and I'll not be kept from it."

"I'll fall," she said, sitting up and swaying back and forth. "I'll fall, and the snow will cover my bones."

"You'll not fall, a great lump like you. Get out."

"No," said the peddler woman, making a rock of herself.

Anger swelled up inside Rom. He could taste it bitter on his tongue, and he almost liked the taste of it. "Get out!" he said.

She held herself tight in her own arms, against the cold and his voice. "With the cart it's only a bit of a way to the Kestery house. I'll stumble forever and never get there."

"It's time out of my road coming and going," said Rom fiercely, "and I could lose what I must be having if I'm late to the town. The way's been slow enough. Get out of my cart!" He raised his hand, almost as if he would strike her.

She scrambled to her feet and climbed over the cart side and down into the snow. She stood so, for a long moment, staring at him, and then she drew in a long sigh and turned away.

He watched her. She was getting along all right, and she did not look back, thanks be for that. He muttered a curse and turned back to the donkey. It was still standing, patient as the eternal, its head down but one long ear pointed back to listen for the voice that would tell it to go on.

"Poor beast," said Rom suddenly and shook the reins. The little donkey must be aching for rest, but it moved forward without question. Rom had a quick memory of it, all through the hot summer and the dry autumn and the icy days. Its belly had not been filled in a long time and its fur was patchy with bad feeding and the rub of the harness, but it never even asked to rest a moment longer. It was old, too, old donkey, and tired half to death. Like the peddler woman.

Rom hunched himself up and pushed away the thought. The peddler woman would reach the Kestery house and there was money waiting for her there, money saved up and put aside for the child's doll. She had more ahead of her, she and the child both, than he could even hope for. The road was not so long but the old woman would reach the money.

"Who ever eased *my* way?" said Rom aloud, angry, and then he looked at the donkey.

He told himself not to be a fool. Just because a poor bag of donkey bones served him so willingly, that was no reason to risk his hope in the great town ahead. Others could look after themselves, others could—

"Ah, the Devil take it!" Rom cried out suddenly, and he pulled hard on the reins, turning the donkey about in its tracks. The donkey ears waved as if the creature was surprised, but the cart circled.

"It's God's own fool I am," said Rom despairingly, and he slapped the reins across the donkey's back so that it broke into a shambling trot.

The peddler woman was plodding along up ahead, bent over against the pain in her back and the bite of the wind, but she heard them coming and faced about. From the look on her face, the donkey cart might have been a gold chariot and six white horses. "Get in," said Rom. "Get in, and be still. I'm a fool."

She looked at him queerly and got in, and there was not a word out of her until they came in sight of the Kestery chimney. Then Rom stopped the cart once more and she climbed heavily over the side. She started to speak but Rom would not listen, so she only gave him a look before she turned away.

But it was such a look that it stayed with him as the cart rolled him back down the road, and it seemed as if the wind was a little less cold after all.

Mrs. Kestery had seen the cart and came running out of the small house. The cart was gone before she reached it, and there was only the peddler woman, standing still.

She was a little body, Mrs. Kestery, young and once pretty, but the bad times had put the scar of lines on her face and her eyes were too big. She said, "Come inside, come out of the cold," and led the way back into the small house, with the peddler woman lumbering behind.

"It's a wonder I'm here at all," said the peddler woman, spreading her bulk on a chair and puffing with relief. "But today it had to be, or never, with Christmas Day almost upon us. I got your message from the preacher in the autumn, and I'd have come sooner, only—"

Mrs. Kestery put the back of her hand to her forehead as if she had lost something in her mind. "The preacher?"

"Surely, the preacher." The peddler woman looked suddenly canny and glanced around her. "The little one's about?"

"In her bed," said Mrs. Kestery, and her own glance darted like a bird toward the closed door. "She's warmer so."

"Ah, then, we'll do our business at once and I'll be off, and the little one will never know how it came." She undid the string of the sack lying on her lap and put her hand inside. "The doll," she said proudly and pulled it out.

Mrs. Kestery gave a small cry and held out her hands like a child herself, wanting to touch and stroke the pretty thing.

"I found you the best," said the peddler woman proudly. "See— the dress and the little shoes." She held the doll in the air, twirling it around gently, and then suddenly she looked at Mrs. Kestery. "What is it? What's wrong?"

Mrs. Kestery stood there, twisting her hands inside her apron and looking everywhere in the room except at the peddler woman. "I can't—" she said. "We can't—" She looked at the doll with terrible longing and said, fast and quick. "We can't buy the doll. I'm sorry you've had the journey."

The peddler woman sat the doll up on her lap and blew out her breath in a great puff. "What's this nonsense?" she said. "The preacher himself gave me your message, and I went to get the doll at once. It was not my fault I was so late coming, and even so I'm not too late. The child will have her doll on Christmas Day, that's what you wanted." She looked sharply at the mother. "You've not been and bought another doll?"

"No, no, it's not that." Her apron was all screwed tight in her hands.

"Well, then." The peddler woman sighed her relief and danced the doll on her knee. "The preacher said you'd laid the money by before you sent your message, and—"

"The money's gone," said Mrs. Kestery, very low.

The peddler woman gaped at her. "Gone?"

Mrs. Kestery's hands dropped the tormented apron, and she lifted them to hide her face. "I thought from day to day things would be better," she said, very close to the edge of tears, "and then, when it got so near to Christmas and you not come, I made certain you knew—"

"But the money! The preacher said you had the money."

"Oh, we had it all right. We put it away in the brown teapot for the child's Christmas, and we'd take it out at times and smile at it, my husband and me, thinking how the little one would care for the doll. She's been planning a home for it all year—Oh, dearie, dearie," she said and sobbed outright, letting all the held-back tears spill over the drought of her grief.

"You had the money," said the peddler woman dully, "you must have it still. The preacher said it was all laid by and would not be touched." She got to her feet, suddenly outraged. "You wasted it. You wasted the money for the child's doll that I came all this way through the snow to bring her! And all the weary way back to go and—" She stopped. And nothing at the end of it for herself, except the fireplace without enough wood and the cupboard without enough food and the bad times grinning at her from every shelf and cranny. "Oh!" she said. "You could not have wasted the money so!"

Mrs. Kestery raised her head, and suddenly she began to dart about the kitchen like a little mad creature. For a moment the peddler woman thought her brain was turned, but all Mrs. Kestery was doing was to throw open bins and cupboard doors and even the door of the oven itself.

"Look," Mrs. Kestery said. "Look there, and there. Not enough to get us through the cold days, not enough of anything. See, there's so little flour left in the bin, it's no more than a scraping. I made the last loaves yesterday and how will they last all the while we need them? Cabbages and potatoes, half of them gone bad, and never a bit of meat anywhere. You don't know what it's been."

The peddler woman shook her head, not able to believe. "But you had the money," she said again, and again. "The preacher said you had the money. Your man was working and doing well. I know it's bad times for most, but you were able to set money by for such a thing as a doll without fretting. The preacher said you had done it."

"My man's got no work," said Mrs. Kestery, her hands fallen loose to her sides. "The fever came on him, and the blood in him went bad. That was how the money went, the money we'd saved for the doll, and all the money we scraped up later. The medicine and the doctor and all the things. We prayed the bad times would end—"

"No money," said the peddler woman, seeing only the reflection of her own money lost to her. You couldn't use a doll for food or heat.

"He's out gathering wood now, my husband is," said Mrs. Kestery, suddenly timid, looking at her pitifully. "When he comes back, he'll tell you how it was. We should have got a message to you, but I put it off and kept hoping. She wants the doll so, she's talked of nothing else, and this year we were so sure—Oh, I'm sorry you've had the long journey." She made a gesture. "If there's anything I could offer—"

The peddler woman got to her feet, her mouth set tight. The long journey, indeed! And all the way back. And none of the little extra things to look forward to, to be bought with the money that would have carried her ahead for a little while. She looked down at the doll in her hand, and a counting look came into her eyes. If she went to the great town now, surely there would be someone wanting a doll. And there would be carts coming back from the town to bring her home. It would not be like hoping for someone to take her up the road to the Kestery house. Perhaps she could get more, even, for the doll in the great town.

"Well," she said at last, "it's not so bad but it might be worse. I'll find someone to take the doll and make my money from them. But another time you might take more thought to others," she added sourly.

"I'm sorry you had the journey," Mrs. Kestery whispered, her eyes on the doll. Suddenly she stretched out her hand. "May I hold it for a moment?" she said and, without waiting for an answer, she took the doll into her hands.

The peddler woman reached to snatch it back and then paused, struck by something odd in the way the doll was held. Crooked in one arm, instead of cradled in two. She frowned for a moment, and then it came to her. The mother held the doll as the child would have held it, one arm withered. Poor wounded wing.

"Give it me," said the peddler woman sharply and reached out her hand.

For just a moment Mrs. Kestery laid her cheek against the doll's cheek. "It's so sweet," she said. "Such a little love it would have been for our baby to hold. I wish I'd never told her it was going to be Christmas Day tomorrow."

"There's no Christmas this year," said the peddler woman grimly and took the doll, gave it a quick shake to straighten its dress and thrust it into the sack. "There's no Christmas for anyone, and I've miles to go. I hope to God there's a traveler on the road who'll go my way." She turned, stumping toward the door. "I'll be off before the child wakes."

"Yes," said Mrs. Kestery.

The peddler woman pulled her cloak tight about her shoulders and, without looking back again, she went out. She hoped she would not meet up with Kestery himself coming back from the search for firewood. She hoped she would not meet up with anyone else unless it was another cart going her way which led toward the great town. She would do better selling the doll there, no doubt of that.

It would be a sore Christmas for the Kestery child, but there was Christmas for none this year and no helping it. Time taught you not to expect good things. Who ever did a kindness for an old peddler woman?

Then she remembered the lad in the donkey cart, it coming into her mind without her asking it. Well, she admitted, that had been a kindness. He'd chanced his job for her, and now it was all for nothing, since the doll was still to be sold.

She braced herself stolidly. Sold it would be, then, and some other young one would be well pleased with the world at sun-up. Not a young one with a wounded wing, but someone.

"He turned off his way for me," said the peddler woman aloud.

"It was not so much to do," she said. "Only a mile or so."

She walked ten paces very briskly. She walked another ten.

But he had risked his job, had he not?

She stopped. She opened her sack and took out the doll and stood looking at it very fiercely. She shook it a little as if it had done something wrong to her, but it only looked back calmly out of blue china eyes.

"I'm a fool," said the peddler woman, and she turned about in her steps and marched back to the house, opening the door without a knock or a by-your-leave. Mrs. Kestery was sitting at the table, just sitting, her hands idle.

"Here," said the peddler woman and thrust the doll into her hands. "Give it to the child in the morning. You can pay me when there's money again, and Christmas again, and the bad times over. If that day ever comes."

She turned and was gone, off again down the road she had come by. The snow was not quite so deep perhaps as she had remembered it.

It was past dark when the knock came at the Kestery door. Husband and wife, sitting together by a faint glimmer of light so as not to waste the lamp, looked up startled, each from private thoughts. The little one was sleeping, her last awake words of the doll she would have in the morning. Kestery had been greeted with the news of the doll the instant he came back from the woods, and the slow smile that had not shown for months broke across his face.

The doll lay on the table between them now, and the joy of it had lasted through twilight. But they had spent the time since in trying to see ahead, and there was little to see that was not darker than the night itself. With carefulness, their food would last a few weeks, not more. The bread baked with the last of the flour would be gone in a week's time.

"If the spring would come early," said Kestery heavily, "and I would be stronger."

"You're mending," his wife said as she had said it so often, but she felt a pain in her heart, knowing so well what he meant. The rising sap, and the summer birds coming back, and the sky blue again, they would be healing. He could look for work. But, if the winter held, how long would it be before their little girl would shrink and pinch and pale beyond saving?

"The times have never been so bad," Kestery said hopelessly, and then there was the knock at the door.

Mrs. Kestery went to open it, and the small skinny creature that stood there grinned ingratiatingly, mouth stretched over skeleton jaw. She knew him at once—Barren the Mean Man, come to beg. There was nothing for him in this house, and she all but got the door shut in his face before he slipped inside.

"There's nothing for you here," she said.

He stood, still grinning, so thin his clothes hardly touched him at all, looking like a shivering dog. "I'm hungry."

Kestery rose to his feet. "Get out. There's nothing to share."

"I'm starving," said Barren, whining but telling little less than the truth.

"The world's starving with you," said Kestery.

"You've food."

"None to spare."

"A rind—a scrap of bread—all the doors have been closed in my face. Tomorrow is Christmas. In the sweet name of Jesus—"

They knew Barren from years back, he had never said thanks to anyone and he had never reached out a hand to a person in the world. If he died, no one would be poorer, and if he lived, no one would be richer. The name of Jesus had never lain in a mouth that treasured it less.

"Get out!" said Kestery again, and raised his hand.

Barren shrank back. "Only a little crust, only a moment's help—"

"There's none has helped us," said Kestery.

Barren's eyes ran to the doll on the table. Mrs. Kestery reached out and tried to cover it away from his look and make it safe. "It took money to buy that," said Barren.

"It was left us in kindness," said Mrs. Kestery quickly, and then she put her hand to her breast and looked sideways at her husband. Then, "It's God's truth, there was one who helped us, there was the peddler woman," she murmured. "I could give him a crust."

"Not while I stand here," said her husband, but he looked at the doll too.

"If I'd strength to get to the great town," Barren whined, "I'd go there and beg. But without food, I'll fall in the snow."

"Fall then," said Kestery. "There's none will miss you." But he could not take his eyes from the doll or his mind from the thought of the peddler woman's kindness. She had been going to sell the doll in the great town, that was what his wife had told him, but she had left it behind. And the man Barren was skin and bones.

He jerked his shoulders as if something lay on them heavy, and he made a gesture with his hand. "Give it him then," he said. "Give him the crust."

Barren said, "Aaaah," hungrily.

Mrs. Kestery went to the place where the bread lay hidden away and took out a round loaf and the knife to cut it. She lay the bread on the table and she measured her knife's edge just against the heel of the loaf. Then she looked up at her husband. "Like this?" she said.

He nodded, and she was about to draw the knife across when suddenly he came over and took it out of her hand. Barren sucked in his breath with sudden fear that he was to go empty-handed after all.

But Kestery had set the knife to the very center of the loaf and cut it into two equal parts. He lifted the one half in his big hand and held it out to the beggar.

"Here," he said. "Take it and be on your way." He hardly dared to look at his wife for shame of the fool's thing he had done, but when he did look he found he need not have been anxious. Her eyes were so full of love.

Barren the Mean Man never stayed to say his thanks. He scuttled to the door and was out faster than a thieving rat, and he ran into the snow and away from the house before they could change their minds, the half-loaf held to his chest like a dear thing.

Not until he was safe in the woods did he stop running, and then he sat down on a log, his breath coming fast and the loaf clutched tight. "Slowly," he said, "slowly," and broke off a corner and stuffed it into his mouth and tasted the sweet taste of grain.

The wind had died down, and the woods were quiet. The storm clouds had gone over, and the moon was up. There were stars in the sky, one of them so bright in the darkness that its rays were like torchlight. A great fir tree stood in the center of the space where Barren had come, its boughs friendly and wide and sweeping down to the ground. One year such a tree had stood in the square at Christmas time, with tinsel and glitter and a huge star at the top made of something silvery. There had been singing of carols, and even Barren the Mean Man had not been turned away. That was back in the time when Christmas was real.

Now all that was real was the half-loaf of bread, and Barren tore off another chunk and chewed it slowly, savoring the smallest crumb. Bit by bit, the hunger dying in him a little.

It was then that the birds came.

Perhaps they had been already there, and he had not noticed them in his hunger, but likely not. Birds coming out at night made a strange sight, and Barren looked twice, before he made sure his eyes were not tricking him. Small handfuls of feather and beak, scrawny as plucked chickens, all of them. What seeds or scraps lay about for birds in bad times?

Barren looked at them very cunningly and held the loaf tighter. "There'll be no crumbs," he said maliciously and laughed to himself because all the crumbs were his. The birds came a bit closer. He had never seen birds by moonlight before; birds were day-walkers, except the owls and such.

They pecked at the snow and gave little cries and fluttered their wings, hopping toward him and then away. He waved his hand and shouted angrily, and some flew off, but even those came back to the near branches of the fir tree and watched him.

"Get out, get away," said Barren furiously, wishing the moon would find a cloud to hide behind so he could not see his strange audience.

They would not go, and the moon would not either. And the

star had grown so terribly bright that he almost covered his eyes against it. "There's scarce enough for one," said Barren to the birds, "let alone all you things. Get away!"

Still they would not go, though he half-rose, threatening, and then he pulled off another chunk of bread to thrust it in his mouth and show them he would have it all.

They watched him with their bright eyes, and they pecked at the empty snow. "The Devil take you!" Barren shouted. He made a sudden move and hid the bread away from them, under his coat where they could not see it, though he wanted to hold it in his hands and eat and eat.

One little sparrow came closer. It was so thin a man could take it up and crush it like a handful of tiny twigs. Barren huddled himself around his half-loaf of bread, as if a little bird would tear it away from him, and anger shook him like wind.

Why should the little birds come begging to Barren? Barren the Mean Man—he knew very well how they named him. Begging to him, the birds were, as if he ought to do for birds what no man had ever done for him, share of his very life.

And then the memory of Kestery came to him clear with the knife in his hand, and he remembered how the promised crust had grown under that knife and become half a loaf of bread. There had been precious little to share in the Kestery house, a beggar's eye had told Barren that.

The sparrow pecked snow, and it might better have pecked air for all the food it got.

Slowly, Barren drew the loaf out from under his rags. He nipped a tiny crumb off between thumb and finger and flicked it toward the sparrow. The bird moved so quickly it scarcely seemed to move at all, but it was on the crumb in an instant and the crumb was gone. A flutter ran through all the birds, and a little talking asking noise like a cry.

He pulled off another crumb and then another, and then, before he could stop his hand from what it was doing, he had torn off a great hunk of his bread and was crumbling it up in his fingers and scattering the bits all over the snow.

"I'm a fool," said Barren, half sobbing it. "God's truth, I'm a fool if there ever was one."

It seemed as if he could not stop himself. The fir tree was all at once alive with more birds and such a singing of carols that it was like the old days in the square.

Barren looked up, his eyes going from wide branch to wide branch, until they came to the top branch of all. Caught there at the very tip, blazing against the sky, the great star shone with its rays streaming down to the earth.

He could not know it, having no way to tell the hour, but midnight had just gone by and it was the morning of Christmas. He stood still, holding what was left of his half-loaf of bread, and something stirred inside him as if a hand had been laid on his heart.

No one ever knew afterwards just when the bad times had passed. But pass they did that winter as if they had never been, and that was God's truth, and no one ever rightly knew why.

THE SONG OF THE HEAVENLY CHORUS

from *Raphael, the Herald Angel*

BY DAVID APPEL AND MERLE HUDSON

Raphael, the Herald Angel *is a rare fantasy imparting rich significance to music as a center of the glory and joy of Christmas in heaven and on earth. With gaiety and enthusiasm, but with tenderness, the story relates how after countless generations of devoted service in heaven, Raphael receives an order from God to train and lead all of the immortal choral groups in proclaiming to mankind the miracle of the Nativity. But there is so little response to their celestial carols that he retires to the Silent Grove where he remains, lamenting his failure for almost 2,000 years. At last, in the selection below, victory comes to Raphael and his singers.*

"Raphael!"

"*Raphael!*"

Had the choirmaster really heard his name called? Or was it only a trick of his imagination? Who could be interrupting his meditations in the Silent Grove? Didn't every angel in Heaven realize that here no one was to be disturbed?

The Herald Angel raised his eyes in astonishment—and found himself peering into the smiling face of Lemuel. The tenor nodded at him pleasantly. "Come, Raphael," Lemuel said as if there were nothing the least bit unusual about his presence. "Come with me."

"Do not disturb me, old friend," answered the choirmaster. "I am thinking."

"And so you have been," Lemuel readily agreed, "for more than nineteen hundred years."

"Years? Centuries? Days? What are they to us? Nineteen hundred years are less than a moment on the eternal calendar," Raphael replied with some annoyance. "If I still feel the need to remain in silence, please observe the rules and allow me to do so. No one else has interrupted me at any time for any reason. You, my closest friend, should know better than to do so!"

The smile left Lemuel's face. "I have been commanded to come here, Raphael. I have been ordered to take you with me."

"Where are we going?"

"To earth."

"To *earth!*" exclaimed Raphael, springing to his feet in alarm. "No, that I cannot do! See here, Lemuel, you know that I have remained here in the Silent Grove since the night we sang for man. I have spoken to no one. I have listened to no one. During all that time, my thoughts have been concerned with just one question—how did I fail in bringing news of the Gift to mankind? What did I do wrong? And only this morning, Lemuel, only this morning did I at last realize the answer!"

Lemuel gazed steadily at his friend, but did not speak.

"Yes," continued Raphael, "today I came to see that the fault was not mine, nor that of the music we sang, nor that of the words of our hymns. The fault lies in man himself! Mankind did not *want* to understand. Men are hopeless."

The choirmaster returned to his seat. Every determined line of his body made it plain that he would not budge. "Yes," he repeated, "men are hopeless. I will have nothing more to do with them."

Lemuel gently placed his hand on Raphael's shoulder. "You have explained why I am here. Our Father knows the path your thoughts have taken. That is why He has commanded me to lead you out of the Silent Grove. Tonight, Raphael, is the anniversary of the journey we made together on the night the Child was born. And tonight we must return."

The Herald Angel knew there could be no further delay. Without even a backward glance, he followed Lemuel out of the Grove, through the streets of the Beautiful City, past the Rainbow Field where the cherubim play, and through the Majestic Gates. Into the darkness the two angels flew.

In that limbo between Heaven and earth, Raphael wanted to linger. There, between star and satellite, there where the past, the present and the future all meet, he wished to tarry. But Lemuel refused.

"We travel far tonight," he said. "There is much for you to see."

"I am ready," Raphael replied. "But before we go further, Lemuel, please tell me one thing. How did it fare with the Child on earth?"

"All but a few men rejected Him," said Lemuel. "After only a short time He was slain."

The Herald Angel covered his face with his hands, and slowly shook his head.

"I will go with you. *Why* we are going I cannot understand—but I will go. I am ready."

Swiftly, soundlessly, the two angels continued their journey until at last they paused to rest on a cloud which hovered just above the flickering lights of a city.

"How high they make their buildings!" said Raphael.

"Some of those buildings reach all the way to Heaven," answered Lemuel. "Mortals call them churches. They have been built to honor God, and to worship His Gift to mankind."

"Impossible!" declared the Herald Angel. "The Son of God was not accepted. You yourself just told me that."

"You have been in the Silent Grove for almost twenty centuries, dear friend. You have much to learn tonight. Come close with me to this building, and read the words that are carved above the door."

Raphael peered at the inscription. *For thine is the kingdom,* he read, *and the power, and the glory, forever.*

"Does this mean," he asked, "that there are still a few men and women on earth who love our Father and His Son as we do?"

"Far more than a few!" answered Lemuel. "Look around you, Raphael—this is a city, one of the biggest that man has ever

built. Now look far over, far far beyond that river, to where
only a few lights are glimmering in the night. Raphael, both
this giant city and that tiny town have made buildings dedicated
to the Son of God.

"He was a healer. They have built hospitals in His name on
earth, where the sick are housed and cured. He was a teacher.
Man has built many places of learning, again in His name and
glory.

"Look, Raphael, look at the window of this school for children.
Do you see all the paintings and pictures the children have pasted
to the panes? These are all symbols of the Gift. These snowflakes,
these trees, these wreaths, these gaily colored balls—and here,
Raphael, here's a drawing of an angel!"

The Herald Angel laughed. It was the first time he had laughed
in almost two thousand years. "Why, Lemuel!" he said, "this
angel looks like you!"

The tenor snorted. "Please—I'm not quite as plump as that!"

"Oh, this is a wonderful visit!" cried Raphael. "More—please,
let us see more."

"We will. Come, let us walk along their streets."

"Oh, no—no, dear friend, we'll frighten them."

"This time they shall not see us. But," the angel added, "look
at those crowds! Be sure they do not frighten *you*!"

In an instant the two friends were separated. Raphael found
himself being pushed along, pulled, jostled; girls, their faces
shining, their arms piled high with multicolored packages, loomed
up before him. Laughing children were under-foot and under-
wing. "Merry Christmas," he heard them say as they bumped
into one another. "Merry Christmas! Merry Christmas!"

It was too much for the Herald Angel. He darted above the
street to the safety of a low-hanging cloud. "Lemuel," he called,
"Lemuel, come and get me!"

"I'm right here," his friend answered from the other side of
the cloud. "I'll be out as soon as I can straighten my wings."

As Lemuel finally emerged, adjusting his robes and halo, he
said: "I was caught in a crowd in front of a toy store. A dangerous
place for angels—a toy store on Christmas Eve."

The Herald Angel did not understand.

"You see," the tenor explained, "men and women celebrate the
Birth of the Son by exchanging gifts. At this time of the year
they remember people they have never even seen, and never

will. On this day, as on no other, they find joy in giving. And most of all, Raphael, they give presents to their children.

"But that is not the only way they celebrate the Giving of the Gift," Lemuel continued. "In their churches they meet to pray by the light of many candles. Look below, Raphael, through the open doors of that little church; you will see how vividly people remember each moment of that night almost two thousand years ago."

Raphael's face glowed with happiness. "Yes—there is the Mother, the Child, Joseph, and three shepherds. Are they speaking, Lemuel? Or are they singing?"

"You will have your answer, Raphael. Let me take you into one of their homes."

It was a modest home on a starlit street that the two angels selected. As they approached they could see a rainbow of colored lights reflected in the windows; from within they heard voices, young voices.

There were three children in the room, and with them their mother and father.

All were gathered round a large tree that reached to the ceiling, and glowed with small lights and ornaments. Raphael looked questioningly toward Lemuel. "It is a symbol of this holy day," Lemuel replied. "It is called a Christmas tree. And Raphael, don't look so worried. These mortals can neither see nor hear us."

One of the little boys was tugging at his father's arms. "Read us a story before we go to bed," he begged. "Please read us a Christmas story, daddy!"

The husband looked at his wife, and a smile passed between them. "This is the time," the father said, "to read the best Christmas story of all." He walked to the side of the room where a case held many books, and selected a large one from the shelves. The place for reading was already marked.

Slowly, with deep feeling in his voice, he read from the book: "And it came to pass in those days . . ."

The children grew silent as they heard ancient words that were ever new.

"And she brought forth her firstborn son, and wrapped him in swaddling clothes, and laid him in a manger . . .

"And there were in the same country shepherds abiding in the field, keeping watch over their flocks by night. . . ."

Raphael listened and watched, and was carried back twenty centuries. He strained for every word.

"And the angel said unto them, 'Fear not: for, behold, I bring you good tidings of great joy, which shall be to all people. For unto you is born this day in the city of David a Saviour, which is Christ the Lord.' "

Now the Herald Angel could contain himself no longer. "Your words, Lemuel!" he whispered to his companion. "Those are the very words you sang as you walked through the clouds!"

But before the tenor could reply, new sounds filled the air—laughter, and from the house glad cries of welcome. There in a semi-circle on the snow-covered lawn were children, laughing children, tall and short, thin and chubby, their eyes as bright—yes, Raphael decided—as bright as those of the cherubim.

"They have come to sing Christmas carols," Lemuel explained. "It is the custom."

The children's faces glowed with the twinkling red, green, blue, yellow and white lights of the Christmas tree. The tallest boy stepped forward. He raised his arms high in a signal for quiet; higher, higher—and then he brought them down, and led the group in song.

"Glory to God in the Highest," they sang, "and on earth peace, good will toward men!"

This was the first time in almost twenty centuries that Raphael had listened to a group of singers. With the interest of a professional musician, he observed the way the young voices blended, and watched the confident gestures of the young conductor. "They have a pleasant freshness in their voices," he thought. "They stay on key. I could do much with them."

Then, suddenly, the Herald Angel became aware of the *words* of the carol. They were *his* words! It was the song of the Angel Choir on the night the Child was born!

"Lemuel," he shouted, and tears of joy streamed down his face, "they are singing the song of the Heavenly Chorus. It wasn't lost—our songs were never lost! Our message was heard! They heard us, Lemuel! We did not fail!"

He closed his eyes tight shut. He raised his arms toward Heaven. "Father," the Herald Angel whispered, "Father, I thank Thee!"

And from above—Raphael heard a high note, a low note and

a middle note. Three cherub voices, voices bubbling with happiness, picked up the refrain. And then they were joined by others—by the Hallelujah Choir, the Vesper singers, the Jubilee Chorus, the Angelus Choir, and by all the pure sweet voices of all the cherubim.

The magnificent sound rose. Slowly the choirmaster turned, rapture lighting his face—his left side to Heaven, his right side toward the children on the lawn. The voices of the two spheres blended into a joyous carol that resounded through the skies.

And Raphael, the Herald Angel, led the mighty chorus.

THE WAITS

BY MARGARET DELAND

The Waits, originally public musicians, were hired to perform for entertainments. Still active in England, they are usually a group of children, but sometimes street or rustic carolers, who play or sing outdoors for small gratuities, especially at the Christmas season.

At the break of Christmas Day,
　　Through the frosty starlight ringing,
Faint and sweet and far away,
　　Comes the sound of children, singing,
　　Chanting, singing,
　　　"Cease to mourn,
　　　For Christ is born,
　　Peace and joy to all men bringing!"

Careless that the chill winds blow,
　　Growing stronger, sweeter, clearer,
Noiseless footfalls in the snow
　　Bring the happy voices nearer;

Hear them singing,
    "Winter's drear,
    But Christ is here,
Mirth and gladness with Him bringing!"

"Merry Christmas!" hear them say,
    As the East is growing lighter;
May the joy of Christmas Day
    Make your whole year gladder, brighter!"
        "To each home
        Our Christ has come,
All Love's treasures with Him bringing!"

III   The Hearts of Children

*Suffer the little children to come unto me, and forbid them not;
for of such is the kingdom of God. (Mark 10:14)*

Among the sublime elements in the Christmas story, we revere
the love of a father and mother for a heaven-sent baby. Since
that birth, throughout the world, the message has been spread
that love is a law of life, and love in the home is a wellspring of
human happiness and well-being. When we commemorate the
mission of the Child humbly born in a manger, we discover anew
how the hearts of the parents turn to the children and the hearts
of the children to the parents.

✳   ✳   ✳

INCARNATE LOVE

BY CHRISTINA ROSSETTI

Love came down at Christmas,
        Love all lovely, Love Divine;
Love was born at Christmas,
        Star and Angels gave the sign.

Worship we the Godhead,
        Love incarnate, Love Divine;
Worship we our Jesus:
        But wherewith for sacred sign?

Love shall be our token,
        Love be yours and Love be mine,
Love to God and all men,
        Love for plea and gift and sign.

THE KINGDOM

from *Christ in Poetry*

BY THOMAS CURTIS CLARK

"Where is the Kingdom?" asked the solemn priest,
Weighted with lore and spent with fast and feast.
The happy Christ at his pretensions smiled
And simply said, "In the Heart of a child."

A DIFFERENT CHRISTMAS

from *How Dear to My Heart*

BY EMILY KIMBROUGH

*The books of Emily Kimbrough have attracted a large and loyal
readership for their freshness, information, and whimsicality. How
Dear to My Heart describes scenes of her childhood in Muncie, In-
diana, at the turn of the century. "A Different Christmas," an excerpt
straight from the heart of a little girl, will awaken nostalgic memories
for parents and grandparents and make doubly joyful the hearts of all
who keep to the celebration of birthdays, especially the anniversary of
"a little Boy of Heavenly birth."*

There were so many different things about Mother that it was
hard to think how Christmas, as she had said it would be, could
be more different than she was.

When I got home from school that day, I asked her again about
the Christmas being different this year. Why had she said it
would be? She was reading, all curled up on one end of the
couch in the sitting room. I lay down on my stomach beside the
fire; then I sat in the big green velvet armchair where Grandmother Wiles always rocked me, and then I went over on the
couch with Mother while we talked.

She told me a great many things that day. She said I mustn't
be disturbed about things being different. That we mustn't hold
on to things just because we were used to them.

"Open your casements wide."

By that she meant, she explained, to pretend to open my
windows, and look out to see what was all around; to let things
from outside come in, and welcome them, no matter how strange
they might seem. Then she laughed, and said,

"I was misquoting, you know. Don't ever do that." . . .

The night before the school entertainment I thought I would
never go to sleep. All the parents would be there. And, except for
that moment of obscurity as the middle Wise Man, I would be
doing a great deal in the entertainment. Furthermore, there would

be real presents under the tree this year. The box for the poor children was separate and already prepared. The ones in view, though mysteriously wrapped, would all be for us children. So it was just like two Christmases. Zoe and I talked about it while I got ready for bed, and she agreed that it would be hard for me to sleep, but I must just try. I said that Mother and Daddy would certainly be excited about the presents I was making, and excited about the entertainment, too. She said they would, she knew, and left me with the dimmer glowing in the hall, to drift off in a haze of the sights and smell and jingle bell sounds of Christmas.

There were other sounds that woke me sometime in the night— quick footsteps as if someone were running, and people talking, and someone at the telephone. I called and called Zoe, but she didn't come. I thought of getting up to see what was the matter, but my room was very cold, my bed warm, and I only half awake. I listened to the sounds again, and then slid off once more to sleep.

The next morning I heard about the cause of the disturbance, but I had no chance to tell anyone about it until we reached the school. Daddy evidently told Miss Richey when she came for me, because she seemed to know about it when I started to tell her. When we came onto the landing, however, for our morning exercises, she said to Mrs. Ball, as soon as we had sung "Good morning to you,"

"Emily has something to tell you, I think, Mrs. Ball."

"Well," I began, looking around at all the other children to make sure that they were with me in my excitement, "I did have something happen this morning."

"Yes, dear," Mrs. Ball said, from over the balcony. She didn't sound very interested. I felt sure, however, that she would be when she really heard what it was.

"Well," I began again, "this morning I ate breakfast all by myself at the table, and"—I paused, because the real denouement was coming—"I didn't have cream of wheat, I didn't have oatmeal; I had a whole cake of shredded wheat hot, and I crunched it in my hands myself."

There, it was out. The breath-taking event. I laughed to myself about Mother's surprise for me and things being different, and getting used to them.

"Tell Mrs. Ball," Miss Richey said, "why you had breakfast alone. What else happened this morning?"

"Oh," I said. If asked, I would oblige with the details. "I expect it was because I had a baby brother early this morning. And Zoe said everyone was busy."

Mrs. Ball stood stock still—looked over my head at Miss Richey. "Lottie?" she asked. Miss Richey nodded, I guess.

They talked so fast over me I could hardly hear what they were saying, and I wasn't listening particularly. I was still thinking about the shredded wheat.

Suddenly what they were saying, and what I had said, did reach down to me. I had a baby brother. That was what was really different. It wasn't the breakfast food.

There would be someone else in the house all the time, doing things like me. And Mother had known there would be. But she had decided to make it a surprise. . . .

There wouldn't ever again be just Mother and Daddy and Zoe and me. It wouldn't be just a different Christmas. It would always be different.

I put my tongue between my teeth to hold back the crying. That is, I started to. Fortunately I remembered just in time not to put my tongue there. I remembered, too, exultantly, that I had something different to tell Mother, myself—something I knew was going to happen, but that would be a surprise to her. It was like her knowing about my brother and keeping it a surprise for me.

This very morning, on the way out to school, I had lost an upper middle front tooth. I had waggled it out while I was riding on the trolley, and had gotten blood on the floor but not on me. The week before, when it was first loose, Uncle Frank had told me that if, when it came out, I kept my tongue away from the hole, a miracle would happen. He said what the miracle would be, but I had kept it secret. I had never dreamed that anything so beautiful could happen to me, and I had made up my mind instantly, to guard my tongue day and night, in order to bring this about. A string tied around it at night, the end held in my hand, would protect the hole while I slept. And when this miracle appeared, it would stay forever, just like a baby brother.

I broke into Mrs. Ball's and Miss Richey's conversation. I urged the children to listen, too.

This was my moment. I would reveal my surprise just like Mother.

"I'm going to have," I announced my triumph simply, "something more different than a baby brother. It will be"—I paused, choked up by the beauty of the vista—"a front tooth of solid gold."

The Christmas entertainment was over. Mother hadn't come. Neither, to my astonishment, had Daddy. When the entertainment began, and I realized that they weren't there, I felt suddenly as if I were in a strange place and didn't know anybody there. But afterwards, when the singing was over, all the parents crowded around me, so that I felt familiar again. They wanted to know about my baby brother and about Mother, but they had liked King Wenceslaus very much, too, they said; and I told them about my gold tooth. I decided not to keep it a secret any longer. Everyone was very interested. I decided to tell Mother, too, as soon as I got home, and not keep it from her.

Miss Richey dropped me at my house, earlier than usual, but she called me back to say again to be sure to give Mother her love, and to hug the baby for her. I said yes, I would, but I was in a hurry to get in. I ran up the front steps and pushed open the front door, which was heavy.

The whole family was in the sitting room—Grandfather, Grandmother, Aunt Helen, Uncle Frank, Aunt Huda, Uncle Lloyd, even Grandfather's brother, Uncle Jervis, and Aunt Wilmina from Wilmington, Ohio. I knew they would come over for Christmas, but I didn't expect them so soon. I was very excited. It was like a party, almost like Christmas itself, only it was at our house. They were all talking at once. It was so festive. I said:

"Hello, everybody. I'm home."

Nobody said anything to me. They went on talking. I waited a minute, but they didn't seem to see me. Once before it had been like that, the time Grandfather had bought his automobile, and I had followed Daddy and Mother up the street to see what was happening. They hadn't noticed me for a long time that evening. But there was certainly no automobile here. I decided to push through all of them, go to my own room, find Zoe, and get her to tell what Grandfather had bought now. I squeezed past Uncle Lloyd and Aunt Wilmina, who were talking together; edged around Uncle Lloyd and Grandmother, and was almost at the door to Grandmother Wiles' guest room, with my room beyond it, when Grandfather did notice me.

"Oh, Emily," he said, "I didn't see you. Mustn't go in there. Out of the way, dear, and be very quiet."

My Grandfather himself said that, and in a booming voice besides. He always talked with a booming sound, but he had never in my life said "Out of the way dear" to me. He went on talking, as if he hadn't seen me.

"*Little* Charles, little *Charles*. Charles, the second. Wonderful! Wonderful! Gives me a fine feeling, that does, Jervis."

Grandmother said,

"Hush, Charles. Not so loud. You'll disturb her. And you know she's going to call him Wiles. Wiles Kimbrough, to keep her family name."

"I am not for a moment," Grandfather told her, "questioning what Lottie is going to call him. I am only saying what I am going to call him. For me, he will be Charles, the second."

Aunt Huda asked him why he hadn't named one of his boys Charles, since it meant so much to him.

"Never thought of it," he told her. "Never knew it *would* mean so much to me."

The door from Grandmother Wiles' guest room opened. Grandmother Wiles herself stood there, with Grandfather Wiles and Daddy just behind her. I started to run to her and shriek. This was a surprise. But she looked as if she had been crying and that embarrassed me. I hung back. Grandfather went over to her and started to lead her, in a very courtly way, to the green velvet rocker, where she had always sat with me before this, to tell me stories. He was saying as they walked toward it,

"Mrs. Wiles, I was just saying that I have never felt so proud as I feel on this day, to have my first grandson, and to have him a second Charles will fill my cup. If you would permit me to share his name with you?"

Grandmother nodded her head graciously, and sat down in the green velvet chair.

"I should be happy to," she said, "and proud. Charles Wiles is, I think, a good combination."

That would be another surprise to tell Mother, except that surprises seemed to have lost their zest. Daddy had gone back into the guest room immediately. He didn't see me either.

I slipped out the side door. Once, long ago, last Spring, I had slipped out that door, and hidden behind the syringa bushes to see what was going on. But the syringa bushes were heavy now with snow, and I knew what was going on.

I wandered into the back yard. The hole was still there in the shingle on the house where they had cut out the picture of Mother, which the burglar had pasted there. I went over to my swing, brushed off the snow absent-mindedly, and began to swing back and forth, back and forth. I could, I supposed, go over to see Mitchell Woodbury, without even asking. Nobody would even pay any attention. But I didn't seem to want to much. I could probably lie down in the snow and make an angel and get wet, without anybody minding. But I didn't seem to want to. I dragged my feet on the ground and scraped off the snow. I had on my heavy arctics and they made wide tracks. I went on swinging, back and forth, back and forth, thinking about things that were different, and about surprises.

"Open your casement wide," Mother had said. And I thought about Christmas coming, and how the other Christmases had been as I swung back and forth.

Zoe was calling me. I could hear her around on the front porch, and then from up the street past the Vatets'.

"Emily, Emileee!" . . .

"Is Emily here? I can't find the child. Her mother is asking and asking for her."

I almost fell down I ran so fast. Up the back steps, through the kitchen, across the back hall where the telephone hung on the wall, and through my bathroom. The door of the bathroom closet was open. Just inside was the dirty clothes basket where I prayed. But I hadn't had time to pray about this. It had happened so suddenly, and just now they hadn't—all the family out in front—let me in to do any praying. I was at the door to my own room, looking in.

Mother was in my bed. It was higher than when I slept in it because there were several bricks under each leg. I looked and looked at them.

A minute before I had been scrambling to get to her. Now I didn't want to come any nearer. I didn't feel comfortable about looking at Mother. I didn't feel well acquainted with her, and it was not because she was lying in bed, though I wasn't used to that. Perhaps she was different, but I couldn't run to meet her until I was sure, and if she really were different, I didn't seem to want to. I kept on looking at the legs of the bed.

"Ommy," she said—that was my baby name, and hadn't been used for a long time—"the something different is over there by the fireplace. It's a baby brother. Go over and look."

She didn't say come to her. She knew I didn't want to. My heart choked me suddenly. I walked over to the fireplace. She kept on talking.

"They moved me down here this morning. It's handier for Mrs. Lothan to be near the kitchen. Will you sleep upstairs next door to Daddy to take care of him?"

I stood looking down at the baby in the crib. He didn't seem very much to look at. Smaller than I had thought he would be—not much bigger than my baby doll. He was pinker. He didn't have so much hair. He was more wrinkled. My doll had only two creases in its neck.

The crib had always been kept up at the big house. It was the one Daddy had slept in when he was a baby. Grandmother Kimbrough let me rock my dolls in it when I had them there on a visit. Now this baby was asleep in the crib.

Mother said, "Christmas is going to be just the same, Ommy, up at the big house. Only I have to stay here in bed for a little while."

She wouldn't be there to get her surprise make-believe shirt-waist from Grandmother. She wouldn't get her beautiful pin that was Daddy's surprise for her. He was still working for it every night, late, putting in the lights at Mr. Myers' store. And my book of shaving papers for her.

"Will you and Daddy bring me my presents from the big house, after you've had yours, and help me open them? And then everybody is coming back here to our own house for Christmas dinner. The very first time in your own house. But at the big house, sing loud 'For He Cometh, For He Cometh.' Uncle Frank will play it on the piano. And Ommy—all His jewels, precious jewels, are the little children, you know, His loved and His own. We have a new one for Him."

The baby in the crib opened his eyes. They were blue. He jerked his hand up in the air. It was shut tight in a fist.

"Slip your finger down through his fist," Mother said.

I put my hand to my mouth and slowly pulled off my mitten

between my teeth. My mittens were attached to a cord which went through the sleeves of my coat, so I let this one dangle. I slipped my first finger into his fist, and the baby held it as tight as I could squeeze hickory nuts in my hand to crack. I thought that perhaps, later, when he walked around with me, he would hold my hand like that, and I would say to people,

"This is my baby brother."

I looked quickly across at Mother for the first time. She was smiling at me, and I smiled back.

"BUT THE GREATEST OF THESE IS CHARITY"

from *A City of Bells*

BY ELIZABETH GOUDGE

Elizabeth Goudge, daughter of a distinguished Canon of Ely Cathedral, is especially suited by training and temperament to write of the spiritual and of family love and loyalty. In A City of Bells she frames beautiful pictures of life among the people of a cathedral town. "But the Greatest of These Is Charity," an incident from this novel, illustrates with understanding, affection, and gentle humor what happens when children learn that works are the outward evidence of faith.

The day after the party was the day chosen by Grandfather for the children's annual lesson on the connection between Faith and Works, and it was a black day. Faith, as understood by Henrietta and Hugh Anthony, was saying your prayers and going to church and this they had no objection to, but Works was giving away your toys to the poor and that was another thing altogether. What connection was there, they demanded indignantly of each other, between kneeling in your nightgown at the side of your bed at night and saying "Our-Father-witchard-in-heaven," followed by "Now-I-lay-me," and parting next day from the dolls' perambulator and the tin helmet? . . . There seemed none.

The giving away of the toys always took place in the afternoon, and in the morning, as soon as breakfast was over, Grandfather and the children withdrew to the little room halfway up the tower where the toy-cupboards were kept. They toiled up the stone stairs, carrying two large baskets and the oil-stove that was to warm them during their melancholy employment, in a depressing silence.

The little room had been given to the children because it was like a room in a fairy tale. It was nearly at the top of the tower and its mullioned window, set in the thickness of the wall, had a lovely view of the Cathedral towers, the Tor and the jumbled roofs of the city. It was quite empty, except for the children's treasures, and in it they were never required to tidy up.

They had a cupboard each whose state, Grandfather thought, was typical of their owners. In Henrietta's cupboard her dolls, together with their garments, furniture, crockery and cooking utensils, were laid out in neat rows on the top shelf. Her books were on the second shelf and treasures such as ribbons, tinsel off the Christmas tree and boxes of beads were on the third shelf. You could see at once where everything was, and what it was, and when you opened the cupboard door nothing fell out.

With Hugh Anthony's cupboard it was not so, for as soon as the door was opened an avalanche descended. Jumbled up among engines with their wheels off, cricket bats cracked in the middle, headless soldiers and a moth-eaten golliwog who had seen better days, were chestnuts, bits of silver-paper, birds' feathers, the skin of a defunct snake, a mangel-wurzel and, most horrible of all, a baby chicken with two heads which had been preserved in a bottle of spirits and given to Hugh Anthony by Bates two Christmases ago. . . . Hugh Anthony with his scientific mind adored this chicken and could never understand why everyone else averted their eyes when it was produced.

Having lit the oil-stove Grandfather sat himself down on the old rocking-horse and proceeded to superintend. Each child was required to fill a basket but they were not required to give away anything they had received this Christmas. They chose themselves what they should give away and Grandfather only interfered when he considered the choice unsuitable.

The cupboards were opened, the avalanche fell and work began.

Hugh Anthony always started by picking out the things that he really did not want, the heads of the soldiers, for instance, and the moth-eaten golliwog, but Grandfather's voice would thunder out behind him, "No, Hugh Anthony! Rubbish must not be given to God's poor!" Then Hugh Anthony, after getting no answer to his "Why not?" which Grandfather considered a rhetorical question unworthy of answer, would be obliged to choose instead the soldiers that were very neatly intact and the least beloved of his engines, pistols and bricks. The things that he cared for most deeply, such as the two-headed chicken and the skin of the snake, Grandfather mercifully considered unsuitable.

Henrietta was the stuff of which martyrs are made, for when she had to give away she always gave what she loved best. Grandfather, as he watched her dark head bent sadly over the basket and her dainty fingers slowly placing her treasures side by side inside it, understood her and suffered agonies. Yet he never interfered with the suggestion that Gladys Hildegarde, the least-loved of Henrietta's dolls, would do just as well to give away as Irene Emily Jane the worshipped and adored. . . . No. . . . For who knew what spiritual strength and beauty might not pass from Henrietta to the sawdust bosom of Irene Emily Jane, and from thence to the little girl to whom she would be given?

But the sacrifice of this lady had taken place a year ago and she was now forgotten, for time heals even the worst of wounds. Henrietta had this year, so her conscience said, to part from the snowstorm that Miss Lavender had given her on her birthday. It was an incomparable toy. It consisted of a glass globe inside which a red man in a yellow hat stood on a green field. His cottage stood in the middle distance while to the right was a fir-tree and to the left a dog. This in itself was amazing, for how in the world did the red man, his cottage, his dog and the fir-tree get inside the globe? But there was a greater marvel yet to come for when the globe was held upside down it began to snow. First a few flakes fell, then a few more, then they fell so thick and fast that the man and his house and his dog and the fir-tree were hidden from sight. Then you turned the globe right way up again and the storm ceased. . . . It was amazing. . . . Henrietta took it out of the cupboard and held it in her hands, her head bent. Then for the last time she held it upside down and watched the snow fall. Then she placed it in the basket and turned her back on it.

Grandfather watched her with painful attention and her action seemed to him to take on a mystic meaning. The globe was the world itself, containing all creation, trees, animals, man and his works, the earth and the sky, and Henrietta, it seemed, was one of those rare beings who, like Catherine Earnshaw, are prepared for love's sake to see "the universe turn to a mighty stranger."

After she had parted with the snowstorm it seemed to Henrietta quite easy to part with other things; with her necklace of blue beads, her set of drawing-room furniture made by herself out of chestnuts, with pins for legs and pink wool twisted round more pins for the backs of the chairs, her toy sewing-machine and her Dolly Dimple, a cardboard person with twelve sets of cardboard underclothes, and ten hats.

When the baskets were packed they went downstairs and Grandfather read to them to cheer them up, and after that there was a rather penitential dinner of boiled cod and rice pudding at which Hugh Anthony did not behave well.

"Will you have skin, Hugh Anthony?" asked Grandmother, for she did not make the children eat milk-pudding-skin if they did not want to.

"No," said Hugh Anthony shortly.

"No, what?" asked Grandmother, who was punctilious about "thank you" being inserted in the proper place.

"No skin," said Hugh Anthony.

A LETTER FROM SANTA CLAUS

BY MARK TWAIN

from *My Father, Mark Twain*

BY CLARA CLEMENS GABRILOWITSCH

Few authors have been so well and universally beloved as Mark Twain. Although his pen ranged with wit, wisdom, and humor over almost every conceivable subject, he struck especially responsive chords with joyful stories involving family fun and loyalties, his own boyhood and playmates in Hannibal, Missouri. In her biography My Father, Mark Twain, *Samuel Clemens' daughter describes his gay and loving qualities. His sympathetic understanding and fondness for children pervade the following Christmas letter in which he gives a definitive answer to the famous query, "Is there a Santa Claus?"*

> "Palace of St. Nicholas
> In the Moon
> Christmas Morning.

"MY DEAR SUSIE CLEMENS:

I have received and read all the letters which you and your little sister have written me by the hand of your mother and your nurses; I have also read those which you little people have written me with your own hands—for although you did not use any characters that are in grown peoples' alphabet, you used the characters that all children in all lands on earth and in the twinkling stars use; and as all my subjects in the moon are children and use no character but that, you will easily understand that I can read your and your baby sister's jagged and fantastic marks without any trouble at all. But I had trouble with those letters which you dictated through your mother and the nurses, for I am a foreigner and cannot read English writing well. You will find that I made no mistakes about the things which you and the baby ordered in your own letters—I went down your chimney at midnight when you were asleep and delivered them all myself—and kissed both of you, too, because you are good children, well-trained, nice-mannered, and about the most obedient little people I ever saw. But in the letter which you dictated there were some words which I could not make out for certain, and one or two small orders which I could not fill because we ran out of stock. Our last lot of Kitchen-furniture for dolls has just gone to a very poor little child in the North Star away up in the cold country above the Big Dipper. Your mama can show you that star and you will say: 'Little Snow Flake' (for that is the child's name) 'I'm glad you got that furniture, for you need it more than I.' That is, you must *write* that, with your own hand, and Snow Flake will write you an answer. If you only spoke it she wouldn't hear you. Make your letter light and thin, for the distance is great and the postage very heavy.

"There was a word or two in your mama's letter which I couldn't be certain of. I took it to be 'a trunk full of doll's clothes.' Is that it? I will call at your kitchen door about nine o'clock this morning to inquire. But I must not see anybody and I must not speak to anybody but you. When the kitchen door bell rings, George must be blindfolded and sent to open the door. Then he must go back to the dining-room or the china closet and take the cook with him. You must tell George he must walk on tiptoe and not speak—otherwise he will die some day. Then you must go up to the nursery and stand on a chair or the nurse's bed and put your ear to the speaking tube that leads down to the kitchen and when I whistle through it you must speak in the tube and say, 'Welcome, Santa Claus!' Then I will ask whether it was a trunk you ordered or not. If you say it was, I shall ask you what *color* you want the trunk to be. Your mama will help you to name a nice color and then you must tell me every single thing in detail which you want the trunk to contain. Then when I say 'Goodbye and a Merry Christmas to my little Susie Clemens,' you must say 'Goodbye, good old Santa Claus, I thank you very much and please tell that little Snow Flake I will look at her star tonight and she must look down here—I will be right in the West bay-window; and every fine night I will look at her star and say, 'I know somebody up there and *like* her, too.' Then you must go down into the library and make George close all the doors that open into the main hall, and everybody must keep still for a little while. I will go to the moon and get those things and in a few minutes I will come down the chimney that belongs to the fireplace that is in the hall—if it is a trunk you want—because I couldn't get such a thing as a trunk down the nursery chimney, you know.

"People may talk if they want, until they hear my footsteps in the hall. Then you tell them to keep quiet a little while till I go back up the chimney. Maybe you will not hear my footsteps at all—so you may go now and then and peep through the dining-room doors, and by and by you will see that thing which you want, right under the piano in the drawing-room—for I shall put it there. If I should leave any snow in the hall, you must tell George to sweep it into the fireplace, for I haven't time to do such things. George must not use a broom, but a rag—else he will die some day. You must watch George and not let him run into danger. If my boot should leave a stain on the marble, George must not holy-stone it away. Leave it there always in memory of my visit; and whenever you look at it or show it to anybody you must let it remind you to be a good little girl. Whenever you are naughty and somebody points to that mark which your good old Santa Claus's boot made on the marble, what will you say, little Sweetheart?

"Goodbye for a few minutes, till I come down to the world and ring the kitchen door-bell.

"Your loving
SANTA CLAUS
"Whom people sometimes call 'The Man in the Moon.' "

MAMA'S NICE LITTLE MAN

from *A Time To Remember*

BY LLOYD C. DOUGLAS

At first a Lutheran minister, later a Congregationalist, Lloyd Cassell Douglas served in the church for more than twenty-five years. When he was over fifty, he became one of the most widely read novelists of all time with the publication of his first story The Magnificent Obsession. *In addition to modern books such as* Green Light *and* White Banners, *he later brought out* The Robe *and* The Big Fisherman, *both of which traced the progress of early Christianity. While love interest, lucky happenings, and the expected ending characterize his works, the teachings of the Gospel are everywhere paramount. An unsuspected sense of wry humor permeates* A Time To Remember, *Douglas' autobiography, which abounds in entertaining anecdotes, among them recollections of Christmas and the role played by his matchless parents.*

It is nearing Christmas, and there are to be "exercises" at our Monroeville church in celebration of the enchanted night when Shepherds and Kings, indifferent to such trivial matters as social caste and protocol, knelt together in a stable.

Mama had consented to plan the program for our Christmas entertainment. There were plenty of poor folks in Monroeville, and Mama spread the word that something would be done for the ragged children of our town; something more substantial than candy and popcorn. She canvassed the merchants for donations. She even had the nerve to approach Mr. Redelsheimer. He reminded her, with his usual courtesy, that he was a Jew.

"Christmas is not a feast day with my people," he said.

"But you do believe that Jesus was a kind man, who went about doing good; don't you, Mr. Redelsheimer?"

"Yes," agreed Mr. Redelsheimer, "Jesus was a good man; but he was not a God. There is only one God."

"Well," said Mama, "the birthday of a good man is worth a celebration; don't you think?"

Mr. Redelsheimer grinned and asked her what she wanted him to do. She told him what the church was trying to do for poorly clad children, and he said he would think it over.

On the afternoon of Christmas Eve, while a score of the church people were beautifying the tall pine tree with gay baubles, Mr. Redelsheimer came, in person, with twenty-five new suits of boys' clothes and as many woolen dresses for assorted sized girls, together with warm underwear, socks, stockings and shoes.

The Christmas Eve entertainment was an immense success. Papa made a short talk, and so did Mama, who put in a good plug for the Jews in general and Redelsheimer's General Store in particular. Mr. Amasa (Macy) Robinson, the Sunday School Superintendent, also made a little speech.

Monroeville boasted a Ladies' Band. There was one man in it, Gilt Cruszon, who played the big, battered tuba. Every blast he blew puffed his cheeks, and after each piece played he tugged a U-shaped section from its small intestines and poured out a heaping mugful of a dark brown fluid which Papa, when queried about it, surmised might be tobacco juice; for many men chewed tobacco in those days, no matter what else they were doing at the time. The Ladies' Band did very well, I think. Sometimes two or three of the instruments would be unable to finish a number quite as promptly as the others; but, eventually, they all got through it, and received hearty applause. There were all sorts of pieces spoken. Occasionally a long line of kids would take the platform, carrying large half-concealed cards. Each performer would stammer through a quatrain and hold up his or her card. When they were done, they had spelt MERRY CHRISTMAS.

Mama's nice little man spoke a piece which, like his pants, was much too small for him. As I have told you, it was not customary, in our home, for children to beg for things, after having been refused; nor was it permissible to beg not to be forced to do things; much less stage a revolt. But, that time, when Mama handed me the rather longish poem I was to memorize and recite, I pleaded with tears to be let off. And when my tears were unavailing I got mad. I forget what the babyish doggerel was. Happily for me, I have always been able to forget the details of events that have caused me much suffering. I have even forgotten the names of people who, through the years, have wronged me.

But the Christmas poem I was to recite belonged in the same age-group as "I am Jesus' little lamb." I told Mama I couldn't do it—and, By Golly, wouldn't do it! I made a last-ditch stand, but it was no good. Mama cried. Here she was working her fingers to the bone to make this Christmas thing successful, and her own nice little man was letting her down!

Then Papa happened in on the scene. Mama and I both tried to state our cases, but the prosecution had the better of it. Papa took me aside and said gently that Mama had been working day and night to bring this affair off. She was tired, he said, and you know how it is. Don't upset her, my boy. Do what she wants. You'll feel better about it, in the long run. . . . So—I capitulated.

On the night of the entertainment, when my name was called, I marched bravely up the steps of the gallows and spoke my piece; but I thought I heard some kids giggle, midway of the torture, and I omitted a stanza that had seemed particularly loathsome. When, after a few eternities, I finished and climbed down, Mama said, loudly enough to be heard by the first ten rows, "You left out one verse!" My pride nearly bled to death.

It was not until many years afterward that I understood this well-intended matriarchal tyranny. Mama had dedicated my life to the Lord, somewhat in the same manner that the boy Samuel had been trained, from his early childhood, for holy orders. Mama was determined to prepare me for the ministry. In her opinion it was, at its very highest and best, a life of self-abnegation and sacrifice. In her zeal to arrive at perfection in molding my character, and setting me apart from the rough and tumble of ordinary boyhood, she had made me a solemn, moody, lonely child.

Mama's nice little man made no defense, nor did he exhibit any signs of annoyance when later, at home, the matter was brought up, as he had feared it might be. Mama was exultant over our smash hit performance; but, in all affairs where the nice little man was involved, she was a perfectionist. She began to chide me for putting on a poor show: I was easily the worst performer of the evening.

At that point, Papa came to my rescue! The whole entertainment, he said, had been fine! If Lloyd hadn't shown much enthusiasm in speaking his piece, it was not to be wondered at. It was much too babyish for a lad of his age. In any case, it was now Christmas Eve, and nobody was to be made unhappy.

It was on that occasion that I made a new acquaintance, whom I loved, ever afterward, with a devotion akin to worship, my Papa.

WHEN THE WISE MAN APPEARED

BY WILLIAM ASHLEY ANDERSON

Every year millions of people all over the world hear the Gospel story of the Magi and the Star which guided them from Jerusalem to Bethlehem. When the Wise Man Appeared *by William Ashley Anderson throws light on a modern miracle when a boy with Christmas in his heart brought comfort and renewed belief to some sorrowing mountain folk.*

It was a bitterly cold night, vast and empty, a ringing void doomed with icy stars. Over Hallett's Hill the evening star danced like tinsel on the tip of a Christmas tree. The still air was resonant as the inside of an iron bell; but within our snug farmhouse it was mellow with the warmth of three cherry-red stoves.

The dinner things had been pushed back, and I was feeling relaxed and content, lazily smoking a cigarette, when Bruce entered the room.

He was dressed in a long white nightgown with a purple cloak of Tintexed cotton over his shoulders. In one hand he held a tall crown of yellow pasteboard and tinsel. From the other swung an ornate censer. On his feet were thin flapping sandals.

"What in the world are you supposed to be?" I laughed.

My wife looked at Bruce critically, yet with concern and tenderness in her eyes.

"He's one of the Wise Men of the East," she replied indignantly.

Her remark was an urgent reminder that I had promised to get Bruce to the schoolhouse in town in good time for the Christmas pageant. I shuddered and groaned at the thought of the cold and went out into the night pulling on a heavy coat, Bruce trailing after me.

The battery in the old car had gone dead, but by one of those freaks of mechanical whimsey that baffle man, its maker, the engine caught at the first turn of the crank, and off we went with a bang, bouncing and roaring across the rough frozen field.

That was a trick of the devil, for at the turn by the barn the engine suddenly died. My heart sank. I looked out the side of my eyes at Bruce, sitting there saying nothing, the crown and censer clasped in his arms, staring down that long endless lane that disappeared in the lonely hills.

It was a moment of deep breathless silence. The hills walled us in from all hope of neighborly assistance. Hallett's place was more than a mile and a half away, and the nearest turn of Route 90, even with the thin chance of a lift, was more than two miles away.

Well, I thought, it's not tragically important. Bruce said nothing, but his eyes were wide, staring now at the big star twinkling just over the ragged edge of the mountain. Then a strange and uneasy feeling stirred in me, because I knew the boy was praying. He had made his promises too, and he was praying that we would get to the schoolhouse in time for him to be one of the Three Wise Men.

I got out and strained and heaved at the crank, but it was useless. The still air cut like a knife. The cold metal clung to my hand. Every deep breath rasped my lungs until I sputtered. I rummaged through my pockets for my cigarettes. When I struck a light with fumbling hands and looked up through the smoke, Bruce was scuttling down the lane, one hand holding his skirts, one hand swinging the censer, the high golden crown perched cockeyed on his head. I hesitated between laughing at him and yelling for him to stop. I began once more to crank. Finally the engine began to cough throatily and I scrambled frenziedly into the car.

Just about where Fifth Street enters Stroudsburg, I overtook Bruce. My heart went out to that small figure trudging along with the cockeyed crown on his head and the censer hugged to his stomach. He turned his face into the lights with a white-lipped grin. His gown was torn and he shivered violently.

"You shouldn't have gone off that way," I growled. "It's terribly cold!"

"I put twigs in the censer," he said, "and made a fire. I kept warm enough. I took a bearing on the star and made a short cut across Lasoine's farm. I came out right back there by the new cottage."

"But look at your feet! You might have frozen them!"

We arrived at the school on time. I stood in the back and watched.

A good many years have passed since I last saw the story of Bethlehem and the homage of the Three Wise Men presented by children at Christmastime. It had become so old a story to me that it seemed strange to realize that to them it was new.

When I saw Bruce walking stifflegged on cut and chilblained feet with his two companions on the stage, kneeling by the creche, declaiming his studied lines, I regretted my laughter at the dinner table, then an uneasy awe rose up within me. I couldn't mull it out.

Going home Bruce showed me where the short-cut came out.

"That's where the Thompsons lived," I said, "before the place burned down."

"I know," said Bruce; "where the boy was burned to death."

As we passed the Lasoine farm there were lights burning. I thought this was strange, because since George Lasoine had gone off to war the old grandmother, who had lost her youngest son in the first war, had sort of shriveled up, and a gloom lay over the house; but as I slowed down I could see Lou Lasoine through the kitchen window, smoking his pipe and talking with his mother and wife, and so I sensed everything was all right.

So far as I knew that was about all there was to the evening; but on Christmas Day, a farmer's wife, a neighbor of ours, came by with gifts of mincemeat made from venison and a jug of sassafras cider. She had shaken off her customary pessimism and was full of bounce and high-pitched talk. She went into the kitchen where my wife was supervising the Christmas feast. Since I have a weakness for the racy gossip of the countryside, I drifted toward the kitchen too.

"You must hear this!" said my wife, drawing me in.

The farmer's wife looked at me with a glittering but wary eye.

"You hain't agoin' to believe it either," she said. "Just the same I'm tellin' you, folks up here in the hills see things and they do believe."

"What have you been seeing?"

"It was old Mrs. Lasoine. Last night when she was a-feelin' awful low she thought she heard something back of the barn and looked out. Now I'll say this for the old lady—she's got good vision. That she has! Plenty good! There warn't no moonlight, but if you recollect it was a bright starry night. And there she saw, plain as her own husband, one of the Wise Men of the Bible come a-walkin' along the hill with a gold crown on his head, a-swingin' one of them pots with smoke in them—"

My mouth opened and I looked at Rosamunde and Rosamunde looked at me; but before I could say anything, the woman hurried on:

"Now don't you start a-laughin'—not yet!—'cause that hain't the long and the short of it! There's other testimony! Them Thompsons. You know the ones whose oldest boy was burned in the fire? Well, the children heard him first. They heard him a-singin' 'Come All Ye Faithful' plain as day. They went runnin' to the window and they seen the Wise Man a-walkin' in the starlight across the lane, gold crown and robes and fire-pot and all! Well, my goodness, they put up such a shoutin' and a yellin' that their parents come a-runnin'. But by then it was too late. He was gone. Just disappeared. Afterward they went out and looked but they couldn't find hide nor hair—"

"Did they see any other signs?" I asked faintly.

The farmer's wife scoffed.

"Old folks and children see things which maybe we can't. All I can say is this: Lasoines and Thompsons don't even know each other. But old lady Lasoine was heartsick and lonely and a-prayin' about her lost boy, and the Thompsons was heartsick and lonely because this was the first Christmas in the new house without Harry, and you dassent say they wasn't a-prayin' too! Maybe you don't believe that amounts to anythin'—but I'm tellin' you it was a comfort to them to see and believe!"

I swallowed hard, recalling the look on Bruce's face as he stared at the star, when I knew he was praying that he might not fail his friends. Well, not daring to look at my wife, I said with all the sincerity I can feel:

"Yes, I believe God was close last night."

The farmer's wife looked at me in disbelief, for she knew I was not a very religious person. She stared as if an even greater miracle had been performed before her very eyes.

CHERISHED AND SHARED OF OLD

from A *Christmas Booklet*

BY SUSAN GLASPELL

The literary career of Iowa-born Susan Glaspell was distinguished and varied. Co-founder of the Provincetown (Cape Cod) Players with her husband, George Cram Cook, she wrote plays that are continuing favorites with little-theater and amateur groups. Her novels, appearing at frequent intervals, attained great popularity. In a huge sheaf of short stories, as in her other writings, Miss Glaspell presents us with interesting segments of life and its aspirations. "Cherished and Shared of Old" takes us close to one meaning of our childhood Christmases.

"Thank goodness for the snow," thought Addie Morrison, as she watched the two children racing round the barn. And she was thinking it was nice there were some things that were everywhere—most everywhere: like sun and rain, like the wind and the snow, so's when you were sent far from your home there were these things—like the stars—to make you feel a little more at home in a distant land.

"Not a soul here they ever knew before," she would think of these two little Dutch children she'd taken into her home. They were warm now at night—not wandering on a road. They weren't hungry now—mercy no, she'd seen to that, but what are they thinking she'd wonder, as at times they'd sit there so gravely. She wished they'd do more things they shouldn't, for when you're too good you must be a little afraid.

She hadn't been able to stand the pictures in the papers—so many tired children wanting to get back home. Her daughter Emmy, in the East, was working for little ones who had been turned out into the world. "Mother dear," she wrote, "I can't get home this Christmas—just can't. But i could send you two children for whom you could make a Christmas—the way you used to for me and Jack. You'll be so sorry for Johanna and Piet, and come to love them; perhaps you'll want them to stay on there with you in our old home. There were always children on the Morrison place."

So once more there were children on the old Morrison place, but could she make a happy Christmas for this little girl and boy bereft of their own? She could say "Merry Christmas," but could she make their hearts glad? And what is Christmas if there is not warmth within?

"Maybe you'll help," she was saying to the turkey she crammed with savory stuffing. "And what about you?" she thought, regarding with favor the mince pies on the shelf.

She didn't even know what they were used to for Christmas. She wished, for just five minutes, she could talk to their mother. "What would they like?" she'd ask. And their mother would reply—eagerly, so anxious: "Oh, if you would give them—" But this mother couldn't speak up for her children—struck down trying to hurry them to safety.

Germans did that. The Schultzes were Germans—over there in their fine house on the hill. And so her heart hardened anew against Emma Schultz—and that was good, for she found it not so easy to hate Emma at Christmas.

Never a Christmas they hadn't shared—all those years they were growing up. In this very kitchen they'd hung around sniffing and tasting. And when they weren't here they were at the Schultzes'. She had two homes—her own and Schultzes'. And Emma had two—her own and the Morrisons'.

And then they had to act like that! Just to get a piece of land that didn't belong to them at all they'd fought John Morrison, best friend they'd had since they came—greenhorns—into this country. Country where the Morrisons had been since first there were white men in Iowa! Not to her dying day would she forget her father's face that late afternoon he came back from town, and standing by this very table said: "Well, they've won. The court has given them the strip. Don't ask me why. I don't know why. But I do know this! They've won the land—but they've lost the Morrisons. Never again—do you hear me, Addie?—never again can a Morrison be friend to a Schultz."

Oh, she heard him all right, and never forgot. How could she forget, when she saw him change from that day? The land wasn't so very important. But the defeat—bitter words spoken—from that day he began to brood, until soon people were saying: "Why Addie, seems like your father is beginning to fail."

But Emil Schultz—he didn't fail. As the Morrisons began to

have less and less, the Schultzes had more and more. Emma Schultz's land-grabbing father lived on till just last year—and many a snow had fallen since they carried John Morrison to the last land he would know.

So a fine daughter she was—letting into her heart memories of those long-ago Christmases with Emma Schultz. Memories were tricky things—come Christmas-time. Maybe it was because you went on doing the same things. You made the cranberry sauce, trimmed the tree—doing alone the little things you'd done with someone else—with the dearest friend you'd ever had.

For no one had ever taken Emma's place. Who could take the place of the friend with whom you'd shared all those good years of your life? Emma helped her make all her wedding things. Emma was there when her first baby was born. She'd named that daughter Emma. Later she'd thought of changing it—but not easy to change a name, and anyway she had an aunt named Emma—she got around it that way. And Walter. Emma was to have married Addie's brother Walter. But Walter went away to war—that other time the Germans tried to wreck the world—and he never came back. And they had comforted each other then.

Yes, laughter and sorrow they had shared. And how divided now! That fought-over land connected the Morrison and Schultz farms. Connected only to divide. It wasn't land—it was a gulf, a gulf that had widened with the years. Feeling—that is what lives on. You might even have forgotten what caused it, but it has come to have a life of its own, regardless of what it flamed from long ago. That is why there is hate in the world—(she half knew this, tried not to know)—hate unreasoning, living on because, one way or other, it got there in the first place; and when a thing has existed a long time it gives you the idea you can't change it—even makes you think you don't want to.

The smells of Christmas brought Emma close to her—Christmas smells trying to make her betray the legacy of hate to which she had been so bitterly loyal! "And what if we did get many a Christmas dinner together," she thought. Remember the words— those very words they spoke!

Yes—the words. How cruel—and again how blessed—were words. They could carry testimony of love, the sympathy that brought heart closer to heart and warmed the world. And they could blast and wound and kill like those contraptions of the devil man used against man in war. And their life was as long as the life of man.

Longer. For the men who had fought for that land were gone now—her father and Emma's. Walter was gone, and Addie's husband. Her children were in homes of their own and she lived on here at the old place—running down now, and she couldn't do anything about that—and over there on the hill, in her fine new house, lived Emma Schultz. She had a frigidaire, they said—a vacuum and everything to make life easy. She wore a sealskin coat and was proud and cold—how she'd laugh if she knew poor old Addie Morrison was thinking of the days they'd made the Christmas candy together—remembering how Emma's stocking hung at the Morrisons', and Addie's at the Schultzes'.

"Come in and get warm!" she called to the children. "Stamp hard! Shake!" she cried gaily. They got in a mix-up getting off Piet's ski pants. "You take one leg and I'll take the other," she said to Johanna. Johanna was the little mother, two years older than Piet, who was four. Addie made a great fuss about this, pretending she couldn't pull so hard, letting on she was going to fall over backward, until Piet laughed out loud and Johanna smiled—her grave little smile that seemed to be feeling its way. "It will take time," Addie told herself. Tomorrow they'd have their presents—sleds and skates, toys and new caps and mufflers and mittens. And tomorrow the Allen children were coming over to play with them. Once she heard them break out in laughter that came because it couldn't help itself—how happy she'd be, as if a little of the weight of misery had lifted from the world. Perhaps Christmas could do that. That was what Christmas was for. She wanted them to be happy as she hadn't wanted anything in years. That would be her Christmas present—a smile not uncertain, a laugh that was happy clear to the inside. People like Schultzes running little children out of their homes! As for her, she was an American. She didn't hold with such things. (And way in her heart Addie Morrison knew Emma Schultz didn't hold with them either—but this she couldn't let herself know.)

Well, if that little fellow wasn't edging up to the cookie-jar. Good! You must think it's *your* house when you go after the cookie-jar.

Johanna said, in her new careful English, "Thank you," for the cookie; little Piet said something she didn't understand, but he smiled and she knew it was "Thank you."

What funny little cookies the Schultzes used to make for Christmas. Cut in all sorts of shapes—a rabbit, a star, a St. Nicholas and something called a grampus, and supposed to be for the bad child, but it had currants and nuts in it just the same, so who cared? Perhaps Johanna and Piet were used to cookies like that. Yes, Emma might know more than she did about what these children were used to. But Emma—warm in a fine sealskin coat—what did *she* care?

"Oh—pret-ty," she heard Johanna murmur, and turned to find her fingering a length of red ribbon that was to be tied on the tree. Addie stood stock-still watching her, for the little girl's fingers moved over the bright stuff so wistfully, as if—as if she had once loved something like this. "Oh you poor little thing," she thought, in a new wave of sympathy and tenderness—anger too. All the little fineries left behind. Only what you needed—not the pretty things to make life gay.

"Time to dress ourselves up for Christmas," she said, slipping the bright broad ribbon under the collar of Johanna's sweater and making a fine red bow.

And then she began to laugh—Emma running after a pig, trying to catch the pig to tie a red ribbon round his neck. That was one of the crazy things they did together—dressing up the animals for Christmas. Well, Emma caught the pig, but fell down doing it and Emma and pig rolled over and over together—the pig squirming and Emma clutching. Addie could see them now and she went on laughing, until the children, thinking there must be something very funny indeed, politely joined in.

The snow continued to fall softly, knowing it was Christmas and the world should be white, and after the dinner things were cleared away Addie wondered whether they'd like to be bundled up and go out again. That was the trouble—it was still hard to know for sure what they would like, for it wasn't *their* house yet.

But suddenly it was! What in the world were they looking at out that window—dancing up and down, catching hold of each other and squealing and pointing?

Oh—dear. Now what? For there he was—that miserable Schultz dog who came bounding over as if he didn't know a Schultz shouldn't come to the Morrisons'. She started for the door to go chase him away but the children thought she was going to let him in, and they were right upon her, all excited and happy— *natural*—for the first time they really were children. And all because of that ugly Schultz dog—for some crazy reason called Doc—was standing there wagging his tail as if waiting for them to come out and play with him.

"Bad dog," she said. "German. Bad German dog"—though she knew she shouldn't be doing this.

But they didn't care. It didn't seem to make any difference to them that Doc was German. And then Addie knew. It wasn't only the ribbons and the toys had been left behind. The dog had been left behind too. . . .

"We'll get a dog," she said. "A nice dog. This is the homeliest dog ever lived."

And Doc *was* a very funny-looking dog. He wasn't any kind of dog—just Doc. He had a bulldog face and crooked legs, but he was sort of a dog of all nations, and Addie knew in her heart that the kindness of all nations came together in Doc, and that Doc was a good dog. But he was a Schultz.

She tried to interest them in the dog they would have, but they wanted Doc and wanted him right now; and as Addie saw that first flare-up of joy begin to die down into disappointment, of course she couldn't stand it and there began a mad gay scramble to get them into their clothes so they could rush out and play with Doc Schultz.

Then she remembered they were used to having dogs draw things—pictures of Holland always had dogs drawing little carts —so she hurried into the shut-up front room, where the presents waited in secret, to get the Christmas sled—she might as well be killed for a sheep as a lamb, she thought.

Oh they were so delighted! They could scarcely wait to get out —and then they were all in a scramble together, Doc jumping on them and waving his silly tail—and for goodness' sakes if the dog didn't seem to be grinning—and the children were laughing and screaming and they all went tearing away together.

And Addie Morrison sat there thinking it was strange—so very strange—that their first happy moment on the Morrison place came through Emma Schultz. She sat there alone remembering her dogs and Emma's—new sleds—and other mad scrambles in the Christmas snow.

Emma Schultz was remembering something herself. She was again a little girl not eight—new to America, a greenhorn. And the children at school stared and laughed at her because she talked funny and didn't know their ways. But little Addie Morrison—so pretty then—came up and hooked her arm through Emma's and said: "You and me, lets us be friends."

More than anything else in the world she would like to walk over to Addie Morrison now, open the kitchen door just as she used to, and say—"You and me, lets us be friends."

At Christmas it was so hard not to remember. And this Christmas most of all, because again—after all these years—Addie was befriending the stranger. How good of Addie! How good of America! And she wondered if anyone could love America as did the one who had come here a stranger and been taken in.

She was the one to do something for these children, for who could know better than she what it was to be a child among things not familiar.

She was putting in a big jar the Lebkuchen, German Christmas cookies she made every year. She wouldn't have had the heart to make them this year, but her mother hadn't many Christmases left and clung to the things she was used to. Next week Emma's Sunday-school class would come for their party, and they'd have these cookies and their presents. But it was lonely here today.

Ten thousand times she'd wished that land in the bottom of the sea. What is land, compared to the love of friends? How gladly she would have given it back. It had changed things for the Schultzes. Her father grew hard after that and wanted to make money and didn't care about friends. And she herself had to pretend she didn't care, and that made one hard too. The Schultzes didn't like being told they weren't Americans, being shouted at they weren't honest. They'd show them who the Schultzes were! But it had been lonely business, and at Christmas especially she knew there still lived in her heart all she and Addie had loved together, dear things shared. She'd like to cross that strip—and abolish it in crossing—open the kitchen door and see if there wasn't something she could do for those little children against whom a wicked wrong had been worked. But what nonsense. You couldn't change the way things were, and Addie had grown more bitter with the years. She'd shut the door—shut it in Emma Schultz's face.

"Emma! I hear Doc barking," her mother called out to her. "He wants to come in."

She opened her own kitchen door, and yes—there stood Doc. But—what in the world? He was all decorated for Christmas. Red ribbon was wound round his collar and tied in a big gay bow. Now who could have done that?

And suddenly Emma Schultz sat down—so sure there was only one person in the world could have sent Doc home decorated for for Christmas. She and Addie used to do that together. The dogs always had their big red Christmas bows. Addie had not forgotten! Oh, she had sent a message saying she remembered. And Emma Schultz began hurrying fast as she could—getting the cookies—presents for those she had for her Sunday-school class— for couldn't she get others for them?—filling a big basket, hurrying into her boots, her coat, and out into the snow. It was Christmas! She ran across the strip giving it scarcely a thought, so eager to get to the Morrisons'.

But at the kitchen door she paused. So many years . . . Then she knocked, and Addie opened the door.

"Why—why Emma Schultz," she said, as if she didn't know what to say.

"Merry Christmas, Addie," said Emma—timidly, bravely.

"Why—why—" And then all of a sudden Addie cried: "Merry Christmas yourself!"—and swiftly added: "For pity sakes come right in out of the snow!"

A little later they were all sitting round the kitchen stove, nibbling the cookies Emma had brought, Emma and Addie drinking tea and the children their cocoa—so cozy in the Morrison kitchen. Yes, Johanna and Piet knew cookies like these, and great fun they had picking out now a new moon, now a little man— Johanna hugging the doll Emma had brought and Piet dangling the baby panda.

"Emma!" Addie burst out with a laugh—"do you remember the pig?"

While they were laughing came a barking and scratching at the door and Johanna and Piet ran to let in their friend Doc.

As the children were busy brushing him off, Emma said, very low: "Oh, Addie—when he came home all fixed up for Christmas—and I knew you had remembered—were telling me you remembered—"

Addie had been sitting with her back to Doc. She turned now, and saw that the bow she had tied on Johanna at this moment adorned Emma's dog Doc.

And Emma thought she had done this! A Schultz thought a Morrison had made the first move.

Ah, there was danger in that moment—danger the world has faced time and again. Old bitter loyalties—resentments of many years—right there, ready to rush in.

But something else came flooding into that moment: It was the children had done this. The children whom hate had driven here—brought love. How strange that this could be. Like a miracle it seemed.

She was afraid she was going to cry, so when Doc came sniffing up to the stove she said, almost crossly: "Why, Emma Schultz— that dog's hungry."

"I'll tell you, children," she went on, "what do you say we give him our beef stew, for tomorrow we'll have turkey."

Doc knew it was to be for him and was dancing all around, his big bow bobbing. "Say Merry Christmas!" cried Addie, holding high the plate. Doc waved a hearty "Merry Christmas"—and they all watched Doc Schultz devour the Morrison stew.

The children clapped their hands at the speed with which he cleaned the plate. Emma and Addie smiled at each other—so much alive and warm between them. Dogs of other years were wearing their Christmas bows and cleaning the plate. In a changing world of many sorrows it can be sad to remember alone. But when friends share dear memories—a fire in the cold, light in the darkness.

And right there the children began a great clatter, running round in circles with Doc. Why, they weren't a bit afraid—for all the world as if they knew something had happened there amongst them. Whether they knew it or not, it was true—how blessed and true—that fear flew out through the window when love came in by the door.

CHRISTMAS EVE

from *For Our Vines Have Tender Grapes*

BY GEORGE V. MARTIN

*For Our Vines Have Tender Grapes by George V. Martin takes the
reader to a small Norwegian farming community of some time ago.
In this picturesque framework transpire the episodic happenings of a
quiet year among a community of sturdy, stable, honest people. Nine-
year-old Selma Jacobson sees and interprets their life as it unrolls and
finds a deep response in her heart. The love, simple dignity, and
spirituality of Selma and her parents reach a peak in their observance
of "Christmas Eve."*

All right. And so Christmas Eve was here. No company and
no visiting on this night, and snowing and blowing and swirling
out of doors, and the branches of the orchard trees whistling
through the air like whips and the chimney sucking noisily and
the stove sighing. . . .

Selma skied out and hunted for the tree that was to be the
Christmas tree. With a hatchet in her belt, and with an eye to
symmetry and lightness in weight, she'd hunted till she found
one unquestionably suited. She chopped it down and dragged it
home.

The tree had stood outside against the house till this evening
when Pa set the much hacked stump of it in a box of hard-packed
earth in the parlor. He and Selma were trimming the branches
with pop-corn strings, tinsel, sugar-coated Christlings and silver
snow, and Ma was playing the organ with the thumb and fore-
finger of her right hand. Ma had on her purple taffeta, Selma a
new red velvet dress, and Pa his fine shiny blue serge suit. They
were singing carols, and it was all very gay.

"We should sing like this more," Selma said. They'd just
finished singing *Noel*, and Ma was hunting through the book for
a song that had practically all whole notes, and that was written
in the key of C. "Whenever we're sad about anything, we had
oughta come in the parlor and sing like this," Selma said.

She wasn't having any luck in making the candles stand up straight on the branches. "Will you help me, Pa, please?" she said, and Pa did the job. Then Selma lighted them with a long spill, and Pa put out the lamp.

This was the best moment of the long, long year. Right now when the candles were just lighted, and with all the Christmas joys ahead, and packages in white tissue paper tied in red silk ribbons tumbling over each other in her brain. Packages and small glittering Christmas trees spinning head over heels in the crystalline lens of her mind's eye, like a strange merry-go-round in a happy dream, resembling, somehow, the pictures in the catalogue when you flipped the pages quickly off your thumb. It was everything good in life spinning in review in a Christmasy mist, and you couldn't know how or why you achieved the good feeling or why Christmas should be as it was: so lovely and soft and gently glorious and all. And the three Jacobsons looking at each other and sort of smiling and Pa and Ma chuckling soundlessly with great satisfaction.

"And now what about the presents?" Pa said. "I ain't going to be able to wait much longer for that handkerchief you got for me, jenta mi."

"Me neither," Ma said eagerly, "so let's everybody get what he's got for the other one."

Selma walked on winged feet through the house into the summer kitchen, returning with the gifts for Ma and Pa. But as quick as she had been, they already had their contributions beneath the tree and were standing side by side, pretending to be very calm and unconcerned. Ma was a little out of breath.

"Now put yours under the tree with all the rest," Ma said. Selma did, and then they all bowed their heads and Pa gave thanks.

"Now, by golly," Pa said, clapping his calloused hands, and then rubbing them together with a dry hard sound, "I think we better get busy here. Selma, you read the names."

Selma sat on the floor. "Let's all sit down on the floor, too," she said. So Ma and Pa sat down.

"Now ain't this swell?" Ma said, her eyes soft, and her lips pulled into a faint smile. She sighed: "Ain't this just swell?"

It was very swell, all right. Selma had Pa's packaged knife in her hand, but she set it slowly down among the other gifts again. She and Ma and Pa looked up at the tree. They sat cross-legged and looked up at the flickering candles through the hazy spirit of Christmas Eve and felt the coziness, sureness, aware-ness and mystery of what it was they felt. They were right on that ridge that straddled laughter and tears because of the spirit that was a pressure on their throats and inside their chests and that was Christmas Eve.

All right. Here was Selma. And as the spirit sometimes leaves the body, so Selma's body left her sitting all naked without a body and spirit soft with something that fused with the meaning of Christmas Eve. With one eye, her spirit focused on the scene in the parlor. Another eye but smaller, and in the back of her head, roved subconsciously but purposely over the world striking analogies and making comparisons. This eye observed Lake Thursday frozen and snow covered and the roads hard packed and trees wet black, cold and brittle.

Pa broke it: he started singing Noel—No-ho-elll, mmmm—No-ho-elll . . .

"Should I give the presents now?" Selma said, and Ma and Pa nodded. She handed Pa the knife.

"This is pretty heavy for a handkerchief," Pa said, hefting the little package and scowling perplexedly at Selma. And Selma felt much as she felt when Pa slid an icy cold fingertip down the back of her neck.

They never opened their gifts all at the same time at Christmas. First one would open a package while the others watched, and then another, turn by turn, each thrilling to the thrill of giving and receiving, stretching the joy into many dove-tailed install-ments. Pa opened the package, then held the knife in his hand, turning it over and over before even opening any of the blades or tools.

"My, my, bärn, what a pretty thing," he said again and again. Then after a while he laid it down on the floor before him, and that was the signal for Selma to hand out another gift.

"This is for you, Ma," she said, giving Ma a big square package.

Ma hadn't known that Selma had ordered a lamp for her, but she dared not open the package immediately. The rules were that one must first weigh it and turn it around and ponder as to its contents.

"Now I wonder what in the world this can be," Ma said. She

looked very thoughtful. "N-no, it couldn't be that; the box is much too big for that." A pause. "N-no, it ain't that either."

"Well, I guess maybe you better open it," Pa suggested after a while, and Ma opened it.

"A lamp!" she cried. "Oh, Selma, Selma, how beautiful! I ain't seen a more pretty lamp in all my whole life!"

"Thank you, Ma," Selma said, so happy that it hurt, "and maybe you want to fill it up and light it now so we can see how it looks?"

"Would you wait that long?" Ma said dubiously.

Selma and Pa certainly would, and so Ma went into the kitchen to fill the lamp from the kerosene can. Pa picked up his knife and admired it some more, and the first thing they knew Ma came back again. She had the lighted lamp in her hand, and there were tears in her eyes at the heavenly beauty of it. Both Pa and Selma exclaimed aloud at the sight, but Selma forced herself to be silent after her first explosion; it would not do to praise the gift that she herself had bought.

"Look," Ma said, brushing the roses with her fingertips, "the flowers come up so high, just as natural." She brought the shade close to her face: "I can almost smell them," she said, sniffing, and shaking her head in genuine wonderment. "Red roses on a frosty shade."

"It's a bedroom lamp," Selma said. "It's for the bedroom."

"Not this lamp," Ma said firmly. "The other one's good enough for the bedroom, but this lamp ain't going to get out of my sight."

"Thank you, Ma," Selma said fervently.

"I shouldn't have it lit while the Christmas tree's lit, I suppose, but . . ." Ma said tentatively.

"Sure we can," Pa said. "And I think it's even prettier than the tree."

So Ma brought the table real close to the tree and set the shining lamp on it.

"It'll be Christmas the whole year now," Selma said to herself.

"Now take that big one there," Ma said to Selma. "Now it's your turn to get something."

It was a black plush coat, and when Selma put it on it reached a little below her knees. Then there was the doll's head that was called Minerva in the catalogue, and a sled, and, of course, home-knit mitts and stockings. But the black plush coat! Soft as a kitten's fur and . . . A symphony in a small heart, and only a fervent Jeepers to tell about it: "Jeepers, Ma! Jeepers, Pa!" She threw herself upon them, hugging both their heads to her breast: "Jeepers . . . !"

It doesn't end there. It goes on and on in the form of a formless something eternal in the vital being. Thank is such a meagre word, and deep down inside there's a voice crying thanks for life and the good feeling, and thanks for life everlasting of which this tonight is just a sample. But you can't put your finger on it and you can't tabulate and catalogue and describe nor tell its number of dimensions nor state its color and composition. Try as you will, there's only Jeepers!

That night before they went up to bed, they kneeled and prayed. It was very easy to believe in God.

HOW CAN THE WORLD BE REDEEMED
BY A CHILD?

from *The Lost Gospel*

BY ROBERT E. LUCCOCK

A modern short story, expertly summarized, introduces each of the novel and effective sermons in Robert E. Luccock's helpful, informative book, The Lost Gospel. *In this collection, originally designed for preachers as a vital method of sermon preparation, every discourse, derived from a Bible text, whetted the interest of his congregation and the result was book publication. The swiftly told stories are analyzed to illuminate the universal truths emphasized by Dr. Luccock. Among the selections, all of high literary merit, he has chosen Selma Lagerlöf's* The Christmas Guest, *and a passage in George Eliot's* Silas Marner *to point out the great lessons of the Nativity.*

How is it that the birth of a little child in Bethlehem can redeem the world? Selma Lagerlöf tells a beautiful Christmas story in a modern setting which, taken as a parable, reveals a deep meaning of Christmas—the redemption of the world by a baby.

At Ekeby, in Sweden, many years ago, a band of musicians lived as pensioners to a wealthy man. One of these was little Ruster, who could transpose music and play the flute. "He was of low origin, and poor, without home and without relations. Hard times came to him when the pensioners were dispersed." His profession was to copy music, but he was no longer welcome in the homes of Löfdala, for "there was the odor of dirt and brandy about him, and if he had only a couple of glasses of wine he grew confused and told unpleasant stories. He was the torment of the hospitable houses."

One Christmas, in acute misery and distress, he came to the home of Liljekrona, the great violinist, seeking work. Liljekrona gave him a little copying to keep him busy. At this his wife was furious—now Christmas would be spoiled, for the unpleasant little Ruster would surely stay for Christmas. Ruster caused everyone a suffocating disgust. Moreover, the family feared that under the influence of the irresponsible Ruster their master would leave home again, a victim of the artist's wanderlust.

By the noon of Christmas Eve, Ruster, being finished with the copying, hesitantly said something about leaving. He said there were many rich homes that would welcome him for Christmas. He was proud. But everyone saw through this as a sham. Nevertheless, Liljekrona answered, "Very well, you may go if you will." So the master harnessed the horse to a sleigh and sent the little man out into the night with a driver to take him where he wanted to go, though they knew he had no place to go. They were glad to be rid of him.

That is, all except Liljekrona were glad. He retired to his room and commenced to play on his violin, music of longing and revolt, hate and scorn. His wife knew this meant a foreboding of evil things. "Tomorrow he is gone," she said, "if God does not work a miracle in the night. Our inhospitableness has brought on just what we thought we could avoid." In the meantime it was a most lamentable Christmas Eve in the household. "The wife grew uneasy, the children were discontented, everything in the house went wrong. The porridge turned sour; the candles sputtered; the wood smoked; the wind stirred up the snow and blew bitter cold into the rooms. The stable boy who had driven Ruster did not come home. The cook wept; the maids scolded."

During the hours of Christmas Eve little Ruster drove about in the snowstorm. From every door he was turned away. "Drive to the next neighbor," they said. He grew disconsolate; no welcome anywhere for little Ruster. "It is the end," he thought. "No one on earth needs me; no one has compassion on me." He no longer thought where he was being taken in the sleigh. Instead he gave himself up to thoughts of despair. It seemed that he rode in the land of death. "He understood that it was the end of him on this Christmas Eve. Hunger and cold would destroy him. He understood nothing, he was good for nothing, and he had no friends."

Suddenly the sleigh stopped. In the dim half-consciousness of the freezing cold he was aware of a light around him, and friendly voices. He vaguely awakened to the fact that he was back in Liljekrona's house again. It puzzled him that he was so warmly received. After warming him before the fire, the mistress lost no time in setting Ruster to work. "You hear, I suppose, that Liljekrona does nothing but play all evening, and I must attend to setting the table and the food. The children are quite forsaken. You must look after the smallest."

Ruster knew little about children. Their ways and interests had always been beyond his experience. But he set about giving them a lesson on the flute. They enjoyed it; but as he began to tell them the notes on the flute: A and then C, they ran for their alphabet books. "No, that is wrong," they cried. "It is A. B. C." And so he heard their alphabet. Soon Ruster made a game of it, and the children laughed as they had not laughed in a long time. But they learned. However, in the midst of the merriment, Ruster grew sorrowful. He could not dismiss the thought that it was the end of him. He began to cry. Liljekrona's wife spoke to him kindly.

"Ruster, I can understand that you think that all is over for you. You cannot make a living with your music and you are destroying yourself with brandy. But it is not the end, Ruster. Do you see that to sit as tonight with the children, that would be something for you? If you would teach the children to read and write, you would be welcomed everywhere. That is no less an important instrument on which to play, Ruster, than the flute and violin. Look at them, Ruster!"

She placed two children in front of him, but it seemed as if he could not look into the eyes of the children, which were big, clear and innocent. "I dare not," said Ruster. It was like purgatory to look through the beautiful child eyes to the unspotted innocence of their souls. "Then you must accustom yourself to them, Ruster. You can stay in my house as schoolmaster this year."

On hearing the conversation, Liljekrona had come in. He was amazed at what his wife had said. "Do you dare?" he questioned. "Has he promised to give up—?"

"No," said the wife; "Ruster has promised nothing. But there is much about which he must be careful when he has to look little children in the eyes every day. If it had not been Christmas, perhaps I would not have ventured; but when our Lord dared to place a little child who was his own son among us sinners, so can I also dare to let my little children try to save a human soul."

Everyone had a happy Christmas at Liljekrona's house.

This story is a parable, a parable of the way a child can redeem the world. The great message of Christmas is that with the coming of the Christ child there came a love with the power to transform a weary and broken world into one of hope. Granted that the world's redemption was effected, not by a baby in Bethlehem, but by a man on Calvary, nevertheless there is an important sense in which a child can reclaim life from darkness. For nineteen hundred years Christmas has remained the symbol of this hope. The greater message of Christmas is that in the birth of every child, wherever he may be born, there is likewise a love sufficient to bring our own souls out of darkness to light. In the messianic prophecies of Isaiah we read this promise: "And a little child shall lead them." Originally these words were spoken to declare that the Messiah would come as a little child, and that in the Kingdom of God the spirit of a little child would have pre-eminence. But Isaiah's words are a spoken promise to each succeeding generation at Christmas: a little child shall lead your world from death to life.

Little Ruster had come to the end of his rope, no longer wanted by anyone as either teacher or companion. He was through, a human wreck. But then two little children climbed upon his knee. He looked into their eyes and felt the thrill of the greatest purpose he had ever known. In the lives of these children he could hear music again. Here was a greater instrument than he had ever played on. . . .

One of the great passages in English literature occurs in George Eliot's *Silas Marner*. Because his life had been framed by evil circumstances Silas Marner had become a thoroughly selfish man. In his loneliness and humiliation hoarding gold was the only pleasure he had left. Then one winter night a lovely child found her way to his fireside. And looking into Eppie's eyes he beheld such beauty and wonder as he had never seen before. He was shaken out of his selfishness and pride. Nothing else had ever been able to destroy his selfishness, but a little child captured his heart and took away all the possessiveness and self-concern. George Eliot writes of the transformation in these words: "In the old days there were angels who came and took men by the hand and led them away from the city of destruction. We see no white-winged angels now. But yet men are led away from threatening destruction: a hand is put into theirs, which leads them forth gently toward a calm and bright land, so that they look no more backward; and the hand may be a little child's."

With what better words could we describe the meaning of the birth at Bethlehem? In Bethlehem a hand was put into ours, to lead us forth toward a brighter land, so that we look no more backward. It was the hand of a little child.

"WHO GIVES A CHILD"

from *The Everlasting Mercy*

BY JOHN MASEFIELD

In The Everlasting Mercy *John Masefield tells the dramatic story of brutish Saul Kane's regeneration through Christ. This magnificent study of religious conversion moves from climax to climax, interspersed with passages of rare power, beauty, and wisdom which culminate toward the end of the narrative. Throughout, the poem reaches to the depths and heights of a debased life reclaimed by faith. The following lines express Masefield's insight into the heart of the home, the Child of Christmas.*

And he who gives a child a treat
Makes joy-bells ring in Heaven's street.
And he who gives a child a home
Builds palaces in Kingdom Come.
And she who gives a baby birth,
Brings Saviour Christ again to earth.
For life is joy and mind is fruit,
And body's precious earth and root.

IV   The Bosom of the Family

Neither do men light a candle, and put it under a bushel, but on a candlestick; and it giveth light unto all that are in the house. (Matthew 5:15)

Christmas can be a happy time anywhere; but to keep it well, it should be spent in sharing, especially in making others happy, in being with those we love, under the roof, however humble, that we call home. "Our feet may leave, but not our hearts." We all long to be home at Christmas, and we should all go there to take and give something of the spirit of the day. Where else can we find the warm and joyous welcome of family and friends, the security of constant affection, the delightful memories of other precious days? In the bosom of the family at its best and dearest is a sanctuary for body and mind, for the joy, the Light, and the blessings of the Christmas holiday.

❄ ❄ ❄

SO LONG AS THERE ARE HOMES

from *Light of the Years*

BY GRACE NOLL CROWELL

So long as there are homes to which men turn
At close of day;
So long as there are homes where children are,
Where women stay—
If love and loyalty and faith be found
Across those sills—
A stricken nation can recover from
Its gravest ills.

So long as there are homes where fires burn
And there is bread;
So long as there are homes where lamps are lit
And prayers are said;
Although people falter through the dark—
And nations grope—
With God himself back of these little homes—
We have sure hope.

CHRISTMAS ON THE PRAIRIE

from *A Lantern in Her Hand*

BY BESS STREETER ALDRICH

*In a number of short stories and several novels Bess Streeter Aldrich
has written about Christmas, a day which always meant home to her.
"Christmas on the Prairie," from her outstanding novel A Lantern in
Her Hand, tells of two such days in the life of a pioneer woman
who made the barren prairie an abiding place for her family.*

Every one was in want that year of 1874. In the early fall people
began going past the house. "Going home," they all reported.
Many times parties of them stayed all night. They had their own
quilts and would arrange their beds on the main-room floor. They
were beaten, they said. One could stand a few disappointments
and failures, but when everything turned against one, there was
no use trying to fight.

"Nebraska hasn't turned against us," Will would argue stubbornly. "It's the finest, blackest land on the face of the earth.
The folks that will just stick it out . . . You'll see the climate
change . . . more rains and not so much wind . . . when the trees
grow. We've got to keep at the trees. Some day this is going to
be the richest state in the union . . . the most productive. I'll
bet anything next year . . ."

Always "next year"! It was a mirage, thought Abbie, an
apparition that vanished when one came to it. Six times now they
had said, "Next year, the crops will be fine."

And so she could not throw off the blue mood that had
descended upon her, a horde of worries that had come upon
her even as the horde of grasshoppers had come upon the land.
The thought that there was nothing to do with; that they could
scarcely keep body and soul together; that she probably would
never be able now to do anything with her voice; that another
child was coming,—they all harassed and tormented her. All fall
there was in her mind a tired disinterest over things. In spite of
what he said, that surface courage which he pretended had
returned to him, Abbie detected that Will, too, was morose. To
her keen eye he seemed dull and stoical, underneath an assump-
tion of cheerfulness.

Before cold weather, the old grasshoppers were gone, but first they had taken infinite pains to leave a reminder of themselves in the newly broken prairie everywhere,—holes the size of lead pencils in which they laid one to two dozen eggs in a sack. In a six-inch square of ground, Will testing their number, found a double handful of the next year's hatching. There seemed not even a hope for the following crop.

It was in November that the barrel and box came from the folks back home. Will drove up to the soddie with rattling announcement of their arrival. A letter from Grandpa Deal had been the forerunner of the donations and already Abbie knew that an old brass horn of Dennie's was among the things for Mack. She determined to slip it out without his knowledge and put it away for Christmas. They all gathered around the barrel while Will pried open the top. Mack and Margaret dancing about in an ecstasy of excitement. The first thing to be taken out was an envelope marked "For Abbie," in Grandpa Deal's handwriting. In it was twenty dollars. Abbie cried a little, tears of love and homesickness, happiness and relief, and put it away with secret thoughts of the desired organ. She sensed that Grandpa had slipped it in with his one hand the last thing, so Grandma would not see it.

There were flower seeds and sugar and beans, seed-corn and dried apples in the barrel. Mother Mackenzie had tied and sent two thick comforts. Regina Deal sent an old soiled white silk bonnet with a bead ornament and a cluster of three little pink feathers on it,—"tips," Abbie told the children they were,—and a pair of dirty white "stays" and some old white hoop-skirts. Abbie laughed until she cried at the sight of them.

"Maybe I could put the hoops over some stakes next summer and keep the setting hens in them," she suggested. She put them on over her work dress, the hoops and the stays both, and perched the dirty bonnet on her red-brown hair, dancing about in them, the three noble tips nodding with uncertain dignity as though, like their former owner, they had no sense of humor. She pushed Will and Mack and Margaret into position for a square dance and showed the children how to "whirl your partner" and "alamand left." The four of them pranced around in the impromptu dance, the children in their patched dingy clothing, Will in his denim work things, and Abbie in the foolish soiled cast-offs which Regina had sent with so little thought. The two older children laughed and clapped their hands and shouted that they had never had so much fun in their lives, and little John toddled in and out and between them in an ecstasy of bubbling spirits.

It broke something in Abbie, some tight-bound band around her heart and throat, which had not been loosed for months. She hid the old brass horn of Dennie's in the bedroom. She put away the precious dried apples and pop-corn, the seed-corn and the big solid Greenings from the orchard behind Grandpa Deal's house. She hugged the huge warm quilts as though they were the fat pudding-bag body of Maggie Mackenzie. The bad luck was temporary. They were young and well. The children were all healthy youngsters. Why, how wicked she had been! She was only twenty-seven. She mustn't let her voice rust the way she had done this summer. In another year or so she could have an organ and maybe even get to a music teacher. She mustn't let youth slip away and her voice go with it. She was ashamed of herself that she had not sung for months.

> "Oh! the Lady of the Lea,
> Fair and young and gay was she."

Her voice rose full-throated, mellowed now with tribulations and sympathy. The children clapped their hands that Mother was singing.

> "Beautiful exceedingly,
> The Lady of the Lea."

She replenished the fire of twisted hay and corncobs in the stove with the four holes and the iron hearth in front. She cooked cornmeal mush for supper and set the table. Several times she sang the same verses over.

> "Many a wooer sought her hand,
> For she had gold and she had land."

The teakettle sang and the children chattered happily at the window. She lighted the coal-oil lamp with the red flannel in the bowl and washed her hands in the tin basin. The prairie twilight came on. The winds died down.

> "Everything at her command,
> The Lady of the Lea."

Will came in from doing the chores.

"It's the nicest time of day . . . isn't it, Will . . . the red fire of the corn . . . and the steaming teakettle . . . supper ready . . . and the children all alive and well . . . and you and I together?"

Will put his arm around her for a brief, rare moment.

"It's the nicest time of day, Abbie-girl."

Yes, the coming of the barrel seemed to put something back into Abbie which had been gone temporarily,—laughter and hope, courage and faith. She began planning right away for Christmas. Mack was nearly eight, Margaret six and little John two. They were going to have the finest Christmas they had ever known. To Abbie's pleasure, Will entered in the preparations, too. He was as glad to see Abbie come to life as she was to see him throw off a little of his moroseness.

She told Gus and Christine Reinmueller their plans.

"*Ach!*" Christine snorted. "So? *Gans narrish* . . . voolish."

"A heck of a Christmas we'll have," was Gus's equally enthusiastic response.

But Abbie found sympathy in Sarah Lutz,—Sarah, with her little black beady eyes and her cheerful, energetic way.

"You know, Sarah, I think every mother owes it to her children to give them happy times at Christmas. They'll remember them all their lives. I even think it will make better men and women of them."

"I think so, too, Abbie. We're going to have a cedar tree hauled up from the Platte. Henry can get you one, too."

All day long Abbie worked at the tasks that demanded attention, washing, ironing, patching, mending, baking, churning, caring for the chickens,—all with meager equipment or no equipment at all. Two wooden tubs, three heavy, clumsy flat-irons, a churn with wooden dasher, scissors, needles and thread, and a baking board with a few heavy dishes and utensils. But from them, clean clothes, sweet butter, neatly made-over suits and dresses and food that was palatable. The tapering Mackenzie fingers were calloused and burned and pricked. As tired as all these tasks left her, she would get the children to bed early and then bring out the Christmas things and begin working on them.

She got out the precious paints Mrs. Whitman had given her and worked on a picture for Will when he was away. It was a scene of the prairie with a clump of cottonwoods in the foreground. She tried to get the afterglow of the sunset but even though she worked faithfully, she could not get it. "If I only had some one to help a little," she would say. "Some day I want to take some painting lessons again. If I could just make a picture as I want to,—it would satisfy something in me."

From the barn she got clean husks and made a family of dolls for Margaret. She made the bodies, heads and limbs from the husks and braided the corn-silk for hair. A man, a lady and a baby, she made, and dressed them in corn-husk clothes. Will built a small bedstead for them. Out of one of the coats in the barrel she made Mack a new suit and concocted a bonnet for Margaret out of the old one Regina had sent, trimming it with a little wisp of the pink tips. With her paints, she marked off a checkerboard for Mack, and Will whittled checkers from the circumference of some small cottonwood branches. She cut a pattern and made a calico dog for little John, stuffing it with corn-husks, and covering it with knotted ends of carpet rags to give it a woolly appearance. She ironed out brown wrapping paper, tied the pieces with yarn and drew waggish-looking cows and horses on it for him, too.

Margaret laboriously hemmed a handkerchief for her father and Mack made him a box for his newspapers. There was a State Journal now, and as scare as money was, Will had subscribed. "We can't drop out of touch with other parts of the country," he had said. "And we must know what the rest of the settlers are doing."

The children could talk of nothing but the approach of the wonderful day. The word "he" had only one meaning in their vocabulary,—a portly gentleman with a white beard and a sack on his back.

"Are you sure he'll come this year, Mother? Heinie Reinmueller said he wouldn't. He said his mother said so."

"Of *course* he'll come," Abbie assured the three. "Because Father and I are making things, too, to help him when he comes."

With Scotch-Irish cleverness, she could think of a dozen things to do with her meager supplies to add to the festivities. She ran tallow in tiny molds for the candles. She made a little batch of molasses candy and baked cookies in star and diamond shapes. She boiled eggs and painted faces on them and made little calico bonnets for them.

Christine was contemptuous toward the unnecessary festivities.

"For dot . . . no time I haf. You learn 'em vork . . . cows milk 'n' pigs svill . . . 'n' dey for foolishness no time haf."

"Oh, don't let us ever get like Reinmuellers," Abbie said. "We're poor. If we were any poorer we might as well lie down and give up. But we can fight to keep civilized . . . can fight to keep something before us besides the work."

On the day before Christmas the snow lay deep on the prairie and the children's greatest anxiety was whether "he" would find the little house which was half buried. Margaret, with the characteristic ingenuity of the female of the species, suggested tying a piece of bright cloth where "he" would notice it. And Mack, with the characteristic daring of the less deadly of the same, got on top of the low house via a crusty snow bank and tied one of little John's red flannel shirts to the stove-pipe.

At lamp-lighting, they all hung up their stockings, even Will and Abbie. The children were beside themselves with excitement. By their parents' stockings they put the little presents they had made for them. They danced and skipped and sang. They cupped their eyes with their hands, pressing their faces to the little half-window and looking out into the night. The gleam of the stars was reflected in the snow, and the silence of the sky was the silence of the prairie.

"I see the Star."

"So do I. Right up there."

"It looks like it was over a stable."

"Yes, sir. It looks like it was over a manger-stable."

"Now it looks like it's stopping over us."

"Yes, sir, it looks like it's stopping right over *our* house."

Wide-eyed, they went to bed. The three faces in a row on the pillows, with the patchwork quilts tucked under the chins, were flushed with anticipation.

"Always keep the Christmas spirit going," Abbie told them. "Promise me, that when you get big and have homes of your own, you'll keep the Christmas spirit in your homes."

"We will," they promised in glib and solemn accord.

When at last they slept, Will brought in the little cedar tree. The morning found it trimmed with popcorn and tallow candles. And a marvelous flock of butterflies had settled upon it. Their bodies were of dried apples dipped in sugar and their antennae were pink and feathery, looking surprisingly as though they had once adorned Regina Deal's bonnet. Will had made and painted Abbie a corner what-not with four shelves, secreting it in the stable behind some straw bedding. And he had constructed a monstrous hobby-horse for the children, the body and head of cottonwood chunks, real horse's hair for mane and tail, reins and a bit in the steed's cut-out mouth. The wooden horse of

Troy never looked so huge. And then the old brass horn was unwrapped.

"I'm so excited," Mack said, in solemn ecstasy. "I'm so excited . . . my legs itch."

Historians say, "The winter of 'seventy-four to 'seventy-five was a time of deep depression." But historians do not take little children into consideration. Deep depression? To three children on the prairie it was a time of glamour. There was not much to eat in the cupboard. There was little or no money in the father's flat old pocketbook. The presents were pitifully homely and meager. And all in a tiny house,—a mere shell of a house, on a new raw acreage of the wild, bleak prairie. How could a little rude cabin hold so much white magic? How could a little sod house know such enchantment? And how could a little hut like that eventually give to the midwest so many influential men and women? How, indeed? Unless . . . unless, perchance, the star *did* stop over the house?

It was a half century later and Abbie made her usual extensive preparations for Christmas that year. The daughters and daughters-in-law said a great deal against her using up so much energy. "But you might as well talk to the wind," Grace wrote to Isabelle. "There's something stubborn about Mother. She is bound to go through with all that mincemeat, doughnut, popcorn-ball ordeal even if she's sick in bed afterwards. Margaret wants us to come there to save her all that work, and Emma and Eloise have both offered their homes, too, but she won't listen. 'No,' she says, 'as long as I'm here, the Christmas gathering is here.' I've tried to tell her over and over that conditions have changed, that we don't live out on an isolated prairie any more; that she doesn't make one thing that she couldn't buy, but she just won't catch up with the times. 'They're not so full of the Christmas spirit when you don't fix them yourself,' she says. Isn't that the last word in old-fashioned ideas?"

So the clan came once more to the old farmhouse behind the cedars. Grace was the first to arrive in her own roadster, coming over the graveled highway from Wesleyan University. The others arrived at various times, before Christmas Eve. Mack and Emma, Donald and Katherine came. Only Stanley was missing from the Mack Deal family. Having married, Stanley had discovered that a wife's people must also be reckoned with. Margaret and Dr. Fred Baker, Dr. Fred, Jr., and his wife and two little boys came. Isabelle and Harrison Rhodes got in from Chicago on the afternoon train, the road boasting a flyer now instead of the old baggage-and-day affair of the time when the children were small. John and Eloise, Wentworth and Laura and Millard, who was eight now, all came over from their home on the other side of Cedartown in time for the evening meal. Every car was loaded to the doors with packages.

Abbie had an oyster supper. That, too, was a hang-over from the days when sea food was scarce and expensive. No matter that the bi-valves were on every menu placed before the various members of the Deal family these days, Abbie continued to have an oyster supper each Christmas even,—bowls of crackers alternating down the long table with celery, standing upright in vase-looking dishes, like so many bouquets from the greenhouse.

Jimmie Buchanan came over later in the evening and brought Katherine a gift. Jimmy was rather astounded at the sight of so many relatives.

"Every one has to be here," Katherine told him. "In all the wedding ceremonies, whenever a Deal is married, the question is asked, 'Do you solemnly promise to spend all your Christmases at Granny Deal's, forsaking all others as long as you shall live?' And if you can't promise,—out you go before you're in."

Abbie Deal was embarrassed beyond words. To speak so to a young man with whom you were keeping company!

Katherine went on, "No, sir,—it wouldn't be Christmas without the wax flowers in the parlor and the patent rocking-chair and the painting of the purple cow and the *whutnut*. Grandma makes us all animal cookies yet. Can you beat it? When I was big enough to read love stories by the dozens, she gave me 'A Frog That Would A-Wooing Go,'—not but that it had its romantic appeal, too. We always stay two nights and we have to have beds everywhere. Granny puts us in corners, on couches, sinks, bathtubs, ironing-boards . . . and not one of us would miss it. Donald passed up a dance at the Fontanelle for it. You can't tell the reason, but the minute you see those old cedar trees and come up the lane under the Bombarded poplars with snow on 'em, you're just little and crazy over Christmas."

There were some very lovely presents the next morning,—the

radio in its dull-finished cabinet for Abbie, jewelry, a fur, expensive toys and books,—an old musty smelling one for Emma, who had gone in for first and rare editions. Margaret gave her mother the painting of the prairie with the sunshine lying in little yellow-pink pools between the low rolling hills. "For I think you made me love it, Mother, when I was a little girl. I learned to see it through your eyes," she told her.

In the afternoon, Mackenzie Deal, the Omaha banker, in an overcoat and old muffler that had been his father's, spent a large share of his time out in the barn cracking walnuts on a cotton-wood chunk. John Deal, the state legislator, went up into the hay-loft and potted a few pigeons with an old half-rusty gun. Isabelle Deal Rhodes, the well-known Chicago singer, called her husband to help her get the old reed-organ out of the storehouse. She dusted it, and then, amid a great deal of hilarity, pumped out, "By the Blue Alsatian Mountains." One of the keys gave forth no sound at all, so that whenever she came to it the young folks all shouted the missing note.

By evening the younger members of the group had gone,— Fred Jr. and his family back to Lincoln, Donald and Wentworth to Omaha, while Katherine was off somewhere with Jimmy Buchanan. But the others, in the early dusk of the Christmas twilight, gathered in the parlor with the homely coal-burner and the lovely floor lamp, with Abbie's crude painting of the prairie and Margaret's exquisite one, with the what-not and the blue plush album and the tidy on the back of the patent-rocker.

"There was one Christmas we had, Mother," Mack said, "that I always remember more than the others. I can see the things yet, —my old brass cornet, a big wooden horse made out of logs, a tree that looked . . . well, I've never seen a tree since look so grand. Where in Sam Hill did you raise all the things in those days?"

"I think I know which one you mean," Abbie was reminiscent. "It was the year after the grasshoppers. Well, my son, your father and I made all of those things out of sticks and rags and patches and love."

It brought on a flood of reminiscences.

"Remember, Mack, the Sunday afternoon we were herding hogs on the prairie and that Jake Smith who kept the store at Unadilla, came along with his girl in a spring wagon, and threw a whole handful of stick candy out in the grass for us?" Mrs. Frederick Hamilton Baker, well-known artist and club woman of Lincoln, was speaking.

"Do I? I can see them yet, red and white-striped,—and looking as big as barber-poles to me. I wondered how any one in the world could be that rich and lavish," Mackenzie Deal, a vice-president of one of the Omaha banks, was answering.

"And do you remember, John, how scared you were . . . the time we chased the calf and you grabbed it by the tail when it ran by you and the tail was frozen and came off in your hands?"

When they had all laughed at the recollection, Isabelle put in, "But I'll bet he wasn't as scared as I was once . . . the time a man came to the door and told Father he was drawn on the jury. You all stood around looking solemn, and I took a run for Mother's old wardrobe and hid in behind the clothes and cried."

"Why . . . what did you think?" They were all asking.

"Well, I knew 'jury' had something to do with law and jails and penitentiaries. And I had heard of 'hung,' 'quartered' and '*drawn*' so the inference was that Father was going to be hung in the penitentiary."

"That's as bad as I was." It was John. "Remember that preacher who used to stop at our house, the one with the beard that looked as though it was made out of yellow rope?"

"Who could forget it? He tied it up like a horse's tail when he ate." They were all answering at once.

"The first time he stopped, he said to Mack, 'What's your name, Son?' Mack said, 'Mackenzie.' 'And what's yours, little man?' he said to me. I was so scared I said 'Mackenzie,' too. Can you beat it? I'll bet there isn't a kid living to-day as bashful as that."

And so they went on, recalling their childhood days,—days of sunburn and days of chilblains, of made-over clothes and corn-bread meals, of trudging behind plows or picking up potatoes, of work that was interwoven with fun, because youth was youth. Prairie children never forget.

Far into the evening they sat around the old coal-burner, talking and laughing, with tears not far behind the laughter,—the state legislator and the banker, the artist, the singer, and the college teacher. And in their midst, rocking and smiling, sat the little old lady who had brought them up with a song upon her lips and a lantern in her hand.

CHRISTMAS AT PEACE-PIPE

from *And Now Tomorrow*

BY RACHEL FIELD

Rachel Field was an author of poetry, stories, and novels containing large and small delights for old and young alike. And Now Tomorrow, one of the popular books about her beloved New England background and characters, deals sensitively with the spiritual development of Emily Blair, heiress to the Peace-Pipe Industries. It also converges on the problems of social justice, of labor and its rewards. A Christmas celebration for the out-of-work employees at Peace-Pipe moves Emily, when only a child, to realize that good will to mankind can never be served by the throwing of crumbs to the poor.

Thanksgiving was hardly over and the last of the mammoth turkey making its exit in hash before snow fell and we began to practice Christmas carols.

Janice, young Jo, and I wavered in eager, ill matched chorus as we played in the winter-shrouded garden or poured pails of water on a slope behind the house to turn it into a glassy, frozen slide. We sang "O Little Town of Bethlehem, how still we see thee lie," and "It came upon a midnight clear" and my favorite "O Tannenbaum." Father always used to wake up with that one on Christmas morning. Only now the German words had been banished. But I knew the new ones by heart:

> O hemlock tree! O hemlock tree! how faithful are
>   thy branches!
> Green not alone in summer time,
> But in the winter's frost and rime!
> O hemlock tree! O hemlock tree! how faithful are
>   thy branches!

I loved those words because I could understand them. Standing there under our snowy hemlock where young Jo had fallen on my birthday, I felt almost that I had made the words up myself. They seemed so true and right as I stared up through branches darkly green against the clear December skies. All the maples and beeches and elms were swept bare of leaves, and the old apple trees behind the garden looked more twisted than ever in their wintry nakedness. But the hemlock was richly alive in every needle. It was good that this should be so, and that there was a song to fit it.

Young Jo Kelly and I were united by a tremendous secret. We knew that there wasn't any Santa Claus.

Janice still believed that he came with his reindeer and squeezed down chimneys. We were hardened realists and knew better. But we also knew that to the adult world our faith in the legend was appealing. Older people thought they deceived us with their sly references to the jovial Saint and their hurried hiding of presents when we appeared. Young Jo and I discussed it seriously and decided not to disillusion them even though it required constant watchfulness to keep up our end of the fantasy.

"I've known for a whole year," he boasted when I dared to voice my suspicions. "I kind of thought Gran'pa was fooling me, so I fixed a way to find out for sure; and I did all right."

"How, Jo?"

"Oh, I hung up one stocking same's he said to. Then I hung the other one where Gran'pa didn't know. I figured if there really was a Santa Claus he could find it anywhere."

"Well," I persisted, "and was it empty in the morning?"

"You bet it was."

"You two stop whispering," Janice complained when we compared notes in skepticism. " 'Tisn't polite to whisper in front of people, and I'll tell Maggie and Aunt Em on you."

"All right. Go ahead and tell them," I urged her. "And then I'll tell who dropped the silver spoon they can't find down the hall register."

Two days before Christmas Aunt Em and I walked home through the winter twilight after the exercises at my school. There had been Christmas carols and a tree, and I had recited a French poem without faltering once. Aunt Em said she was proud that I remembered every word, and that I could be heard to the back row of chairs. She said it was a pity when children were shy and mumbled their words. I can remember exactly how she looked that afternoon, tall and straight in her sealskin coat. In spite of the cold air her long face stayed the color of my white coral beads and her smooth brown hair exactly matched the fur of her collar and the small toque she wore. She seemed years older than the other children's mothers, yet she must have been only thirty-five. Our school exercises had taken on importance simply by her presence. I noticed that the teachers looked to her for approval when each carol or poem had been safely accomplished. Used to her as I was, I had had a sense that day of her place in the community. She did not need to wear bright colors or stylish clothes to be the most distinguished visitor.

"There will be another Christmas tree for you to see tomorrow," Aunt Em told me as we turned in at our gate. "It's going to be over at the mills, and you can go with me if you'd like to."

"Across the river?" I was instantly curious.

Janice had run out to meet us.

"Doesn't Santa Claus cross the bridges?" she wanted to know.

"Of course, dear," Aunt Em explained. "But so many more people live over there that we must try to help him."

"But," Janice broke in, "he remembers everyone except the bad children. Are there more bad ones over there?"

"Certainly not!" Aunt Em answered hurriedly. "Now run upstairs, both of you, and get ready for supper."

That other Christmas tree across the river, I shall remember as long as I recall anything out of those years.

It stood on a wooden platform that had been raised in the center of the mill yard with the long brick buildings on all four sides. On that day before Christmas the closing whistle had blown at four-thirty instead of six o'clock. When Aunt Em, Uncle Wallace and I reached the gates all the machinery was silent, and the great open space was already teeming with workers and their families. I found myself peering into old faces wrinkled as walnuts under shawls or shapeless caps. There were women with babies in their arms and children of all sizes pressing at their skirts, and trooping from the buildings where machinery loomed gigantic against lighted windows, came the mill hands, men, women, and young girls. Although the workers chattered together in languages I could not understand, they smiled at me and stepped back to make room for us to reach the platform.

"This is Elliott's older daughter," Aunt Em introduced me to the group of men on the platform. I made my curtsy and stood quietly beside her, secretly glad that Janice had been considered too young to take part in such an occasion. I tried to stand as straight as Aunt Em in my blue broadcloth coat with the squirrel fur and the round muff that kept my hands warm.

A band with banners that bore the familiar Indian's head and Peace-Pipe name had begun to play a march, and over the deep rhythm of the drums I asked Uncle Wallace when the tree would be lighted.

"Pretty soon now. Want to turn on the switch?"

I nodded eagerly, and he lifted me on a chair and put the electric button attached to a long cord in my hand. I wasn't to press it, he cautioned, till he gave me the signal. I suppose that wait could not have lasted more than ten minutes, but it seemed hours to me perched high above the close-packed crowd, hoping that nothing would go wrong in my part of the ceremonies. First the Catholic priest rose and made a prayer in Latin, and then our minister followed him with another that had to do with Bethlehem and with Peace-Pipe and the Blair family. After that the mill band played "Adestes Fideles," and then it was my turn to make those green and fragrant branches come to life.

As I pressed the button a deep murmur rose in admiration, and heads were lifted to the tree. All the faces were touched by the light from that glowing pyramid of quivering tinsel and colored bulbs like miraculous fruit. I tilted my head back till I could see the topmost star, set so high that it cleared the smoke that still hung low over the yard and mill buildings.

"Now for the presents," I heard Aunt Em say to Mr. Parker, who was the twins' father and also the mill manager. "I must say I'll be glad when they've been distributed."

"Don't worry, Miss Blair," he promised. "We've got more than enough, and everything's well in hand."

Just then a big red-coated Santa Claus appeared, jingling bells and shouting to invisible reindeer that were supposed to have been left outside the gates. He carried a pack on his shoulders, and his white beard waggled unsteadily with every word he spoke.

"Merry Christmas, one and all!" he began. "This here tree's not big enough to hold what I've brought for the folks at Peace-Pipe. So you'll have to line up and come and get your presents. No pushing, *if* you please. Plenty for all, and keep your places in line. Strike up, boys." And he waved to the band leader.

He took his place just below the platform, and though I could not see much of his face there was a familiar ring to his voice that puzzled me till I recognized it as belonging to Mr. Dolan, the big Irish night watchman. The band was playing another march, and the distribution of gifts had begun. The hand trucks that wheeled cotton from the storehouse, had been loaded with filled baskets and hundreds of red mesh stockings that each contained an orange and an apple, a bag of chocolates, a sugar Santa Claus, and a striped peppermint cane. Baskets, with chicken legs and celery tops protruding, as well as each red stocking were identical as pins in a paper. I turned to Aunt Em with shocked surprise.

"But where are the presents?" I asked under cover of the music and the noise of marshaling the long lines into military order.

"Why, right here," she whispered, and then turned back to her place. She was bowing and smiling as the long line moved forward below the platform.

I stared dizzily down at the hands that reached out for the baskets and the stockings, moving along in an endless stream. I felt cold and disappointed and hollow under my coat. All the magical glow of Christmas had slipped away into monotony. It might have been a grocery store, I thought, except for the lighted tree that everyone seemed to have forgotten except me.

"Aren't there going to be any *real* presents?" I tried once more to distract Aunt Em.

Mr. Parker heard me, and they exchanged an amused look.

"What's the matter with these, Emily?" He bent down and pinched my cold cheek. "A chicken dinner and' plenty of candy looks pretty good to me. How about you? Want me to get you one of those stockings?"

But I shook my head. My feet had, turned to chill clods, and my eyes swam with weariness. Even if I closed them I could still see the stockings and baskets being handed out. The band had paused to rest, and only the drum thumped on to keep feet moving in time. I drew closer to Aunt Em and plucked at her sleeve. She turned to speak to me, and as she did so a sudden commotion began below us.

There was a break in the slow-moving, orderly line. Then something thudded against the platform. More thuds and ripping sounds followed. One of the candy-filled stockings came hurtling and spilled open at my feet. I saw a man's arms gesturing darkly above the crowd. His voice came hoarse and shrill above the drumbeats.

"Merry Christmas—yah—I rather have job back, not this—"

I could see the man who spoke. He was dark and thick-set, and his black hair had fallen across his eyes. Beside him stood a woman tugging at his waving arms and a little girl and boy. The girl's face was buried in the woman's skirt, but the boy did not turn his face away. His lips were pressed together in a thin line, and his eyes looked directly at me from below the platform. Something about his unflinching look terrified me more than the man's strange, wild voice crying out again in broken, accusing words.

"You give charitee for Christmas—no want—I rather work—" For a moment the voice was muffled, then it broke out again. "No eat your dinner—we starve first. Chicken an' candy—yah—an' other time you throw me out an' no care!"

They overpowered him at last. . . .

The band struck up loudly and drowned out the rest of his words. Aunt Em's hand tightened on mine. I could feel its cold tenseness through her gloves. Below us the line had closed in again as if nothing had interrupted the ceremonies. But the red candy stocking was still lying where it had fallen at my feet with bits of broken candy like splinters of glass. The shouted words still rang in my ears. They made me shiver and feel afraid.

"What was the matter with that man?" I asked Aunt Em when all the baskets had been given out and we were following Uncle Wallace into his office.

"Try not to think about it," she answered me. "He wasn't—well, he wasn't quite himself."

I was not satisfied.

"He didn't like us," I persisted. "Why didn't he? And why did he throw the things away?"

I heard Aunt Em put in a question and Mr. Parker answer her.

"Vancovitch is the name—good worker, but a crank. Never know when something'll set him off. Had to drop him a couple of months ago, but the wife was sick and there's a family. We thought, seeing it was Christmas, we'd let them in for the distribution. Well, we'll have to tighten up on rules next year. Too bad, but you see where sentiment gets us."

I was very quiet all the way home. The lights and the river and the Christmas wreaths had lost something of their wonder. My happy confidence in gifts and carols and the spirit of good will had been shaken.

"What's a crank, Aunt Em?" I broke silence at last.

We had taken our places at the supper table, and I saw her lay down her spoon and hesitate before she answered.

"Oh"—her eyes met Uncle Wallace's across the table—"It's—well—bad feelings about things that get the better of people sometimes. Go on with your soup, dear."

"That man over at the mill," I persisted, "someone said that's what he is."

"I know, but never mind."

"Now, Em," Uncle Wallace unexpectedly took my part in the discussion, "you can't put the child off like that. She was there and she heard it all, so you'd better answer her questions."

Aunt Em frowned and sighed before she spoke.

"Well then, if you have to remember what happened at the mill party this afternoon, just say to yourself that sometimes people get all twisted up in their minds about other people—"

"About us? He acted as if he hated us, and he meant me too."

A hurt look came into her eyes, but she went on quietly.

"We can't expect to be praised and liked all the time, no matter if we try to do what seems right to us. You'll find that out, Emily, the older you grow. Sometimes people can't see our side, and sometimes, I suppose they think we can't see theirs."

Long after I had hung up my stocking beside Janice's by the fireplace, I lay awake in bed remembering another stocking of flimsy red mesh, seeing the shadow of waving arms, hearing a voice that shouted accusing words, the more frightening because they had been half understood. I have heard others like them since then, but I have never learned to be indifferent to hatred and bitterness, on whichever side of the river they may have been spoken.

A DAY OF PLEASANT BREAD

from *Adventures in Friendship*

BY DAVID GRAYSON (RAY STANNARD BAKER)

Under his own name, Ray Stannard Baker wrote serious essays, short stories, several volumes of autobiography, and the Pulitzer-Prize-winning authorized biography of Woodrow Wilson. As "David Grayson," however, he discovered a secret literary life. Grayson's essays, later identified as Baker's work, were assembled from magazines into various books essentially American in their pattern of thought and commingling of philosophy, observation, and quiet humor. From Adventures in Friendship *comes "A Day of Pleasant Bread."*

They have all gone now, and the house is very still. For the first time this evening I can hear the familiar sound of the December wind blustering about the house, complaining at closed doorways, asking questions at the shutters; but here in my room, under the green reading lamp, it is warm and still. Although Harriet has closed the doors, covered the coals in the fireplace, and said good-night, the atmosphere still seems to tingle with the electricity of genial humanity.

The parting voice of the Scotch Preacher still booms in my ears:

"This," said he, as he was going out of our door, wrapped like an arctic highlander in cloaks and tippets, "has been a day of pleasant bread."

One of the very pleasantest I can remember!

I sometimes think we expect too much of Christmast Day. We try to crowd into it the long arrears of kindliness and humanity of the whole year. As for me, I like to take my Christmas a little at a time, all through the year. And thus I drift along into the holidays—let them overtake me unexpectedly—waking up some fine morning and suddenly saying to myself:

"Why, this is Christmas Day!"

How the discovery makes one bound out of his bed! What a new sense of life and adventure it imparts! Almost anything may happen on a day like this—one thinks. I may meet friends I have not seen before in years. Who knows? I may discover that this is a far better and kindlier world than I had ever dreamed it could be.

So I sing out to Harriet as I go down:

"Merry Christmas, Harriet"—and not waiting for her sleepy reply, I go down and build the biggest, warmest, friendliest fire of the year. Then I get into my thick coat and mittens and open the back door. All around the sill, deep on the step, and all about the yard lies the drifted snow: it has transformed my wood pile into a grotesque Indian mound, and it frosts the roof of my barn like a wedding cake. I go at it lustily with my wooden shovel, clearing out a pathway to the gate. . . .

All the morning as I went about my chores I had a peculiar sense of expected pleasure. It seemed certain to me that something unusual and adventurous was about to happen—and if it did not happen offhand, why, I was there to make it happen! When I went in to breakfast (do you know the fragrance of broiling bacon when you have worked for an hour before breakfast on a morning of zero weather? If you do not, consider that heaven still has gifts in store for you!)—when I went in to breakfast, I fancied that Harriet looked preoccupied, but I was too busy just then (hot corn muffins) to make an inquiry, and I knew by experience that the best solvent of secrecy is patience.

"David," said Harriet presently, "the cousins can't come!"

"Can't come!" I exclaimed.

"Why, you act as if you were delighted."

"No—well, yes," I said, "I knew that some extraordinary adventure was about to happen!"

"Adventure! It's a cruel disappointment—I was all ready for them."

"Harriet," I said, "adventure is just what we make it. And aren't we to have the Scotch Preacher and his wife?"

"But I've got such a *good* dinner."

"Well," I said, "there are no two ways about it: it must be eaten! You may depend upon me to do my duty."

"We'll have to send out into the highways and compel them to come in," said Harriet ruefully.

I had several choice observations I should have liked to make upon this problem, but Harriet was plainly not listening; she sat with her eyes fixed reflectively on the coffeepot. I watched her for a moment, then I remarked:

"There aren't any."

"David," she exclaimed, "how did you know what I was thinking about?"

"I merely wanted to show you," I said, "that my genius is not properly appreciated in my own household. You thought of highways, didn't you? Then you thought of the poor; especially the poor on Christmas Day; then of Mrs. Heney, who isn't poor any more, having married John Daniels; and then I said 'There aren't any.'"

Harriet laughed.

"It has come to a pretty pass," she said, "when there are no poor people to invite to dinner on Christmas Day."

"It's a tragedy, I'll admit," I said, "but let's be logical about it."

"I am willing," said Harriet, "to be as logical as you like."

"Then," I said, "having no poor to invite to dinner, we must necessarily try the rich. That's logical, isn't it?"

"Who?" asked Harriet, which is just like a woman. Whenever you get a good healthy argument started with her, she will suddenly short-circuit it, and want to know if you mean Mr. Smith, or Joe Perkins's boys, which I maintain is *not* logical.

"Well, there are the Starkweathers," I said.

"David!"

"They're rich, aren't they?"

"Yes, but you know how they live—what dinners they have—and besides, they probably have a houseful of company."

"Weren't you telling me the other day how many people who were really suffering were too proud to let anyone know about it? Weren't you advising the necessity of getting acquainted with people and finding out—tactfully, of course—you made a point of fact—what the trouble was?"

"But I was talking of *poor* people."

"Why shouldn't a rule that is good for poor people be equally as good for rich people? Aren't they proud?"

"Oh, you can argue," observed Harriet.

"And I can act, too," I said. "I am now going over to invite the Starkweathers. I heard a rumour that their cook has left them and I expect to find them starving in their parlour. Of course they'll be very haughty and proud, but I'll be tactful, and when I go away I'll casually leave a diamond tiara in the front hall."

"What *is* the matter with you this morning?"

"Christmas," I said.

I can't tell how pleased I was with the enterprise I had in mind: it suggested all sorts of amusing and surprising developments. Moreover, I left Harriet, finally, in the breeziest of spirits, having quite forgotten her disappointment over the non-arrival of the cousins.

"If you *should* get the Starkweathers—"

" 'In the bright lexicon of youth,' " I observed, " 'there is no such word as fail.' "

So I set off up the town road. A team or two had already been that way and had broken a track through the snow. The sun was now fully up, but the air still tingled with the electricity of zero weather. And the fields! I have seen the fields of June and the fields of October, but I think I never saw our countryside, hills and valleys, tree spaces and brook bottoms, more enchantingly beautiful than it was this morning. Snow everywhere—the fences half hidden, the bridges clogged, the trees laden: where the road was hard it squeaked under my feet, and where it was soft I strode through the drifts. And the air went to one's head like wine!

So I tramped past the Pattersons'. The old man, a grumpy old fellow, was going to the barn with a pail on his arm.

"Merry Christmas," I shouted.

He looked around at me wonderingly and did not reply. At the corners I met the Newton boys so wrapped in tippets that I could see only their eyes and the red ends of their small noses. I passed the Williams's house, where there was a cheerful smoke in the chimney and in the window a green wreath with a lively red bow. And I thought how happy everyone must be on a Christmas morning like this! At the hill bridge who should I meet but the Scotch Preacher himself, God bless him!

"Well, well, David," he exclaimed heartily, "Merry Christmas."

I drew my face down and said solemnly:

"Dr. McAlway, I am on a most serious errand."

"Why, now, what's the matter?" He was all sympathy at once.

"I am out in the highways trying to compel the poor of this neighborhood to come to our feast."

The Scotch Preacher observed me with a twinkle in his eye.

"David," he said, putting his hand to his mouth as if to speak in my ear, "there is a poor man you will na' have to compel."

"Oh, you don't count," I said. "You're coming anyhow."

Then I told him of the errand with our millionaire friends, into the spirit of which he entered with the greatest zest. He was full of advice and much excited lest I fail to do a thoroughly competent job. For a moment I think he wanted to take the whole thing out of my hands.

"Man, man, it's a lovely thing to do," he exclaimed, "but I ha' me doots—I ha' me doots."

At parting he hesitated a moment, and with a serious face inquired:

"Is it by any chance a goose?"

"It is," I said, "a goose—a big one."

He heaved a sigh of complete satisfaction. "You have comforted my mind," he said, "with the joys of anticipation—a goose, a big goose."

So I left him and went onward toward the Starkweathers'. Presently I saw the great house standing among its wintry trees. There was smoke in the chimney but no other evidence of life. At the gate my spirits, which had been of the best all the morning, began to fail me. Though Harriet and I were well enough acquainted with the Starkweathers, yet at this late moment on Christmas morning it did seem rather a hare-brained scheme to think of inviting them to dinner.

"Never mind," I said, "they'll not be displeased to see me anyway."

I waited in the reception room, which was cold and felt damp. In the parlour beyond I could see the innumerable things of beauty—furniture, pictures, books, so very, very much of everything—with which the room was filled. I saw it now, as I had often seen it before, with a peculiar sense of weariness. How all these things, though beautiful enough in themselves, must clutter up a man's life!

Do you know, the more I look into life, the more things it seems to me I can successfully lack—and continue to grow happier. How many kinds of food I do not need, nor cooks to cook them, how much curious clothing nor tailors to make it, how many books that I never read, and pictures that are not worth while! The farther I run, the more I feel like casting aside all such impedimenta—lest I fail to arrive at the far goal of my endeavour.

I like to think of an old Japanese nobleman I once read about, who ornamented his house with a single vase at a time, living with it, absorbing its message of beauty, and when he tired of it, replacing it with another. I wonder if he had the right way, and we, with so many objects to hang on our walls, place on our shelves, drape on our chairs, and spread on our floors, have mistaken our course and placed our hearts upon the multiplicity rather than the quality of our possessions!

Presently Mr. Starkweather appeared in the doorway. He wore a velvet smoking jacket and slippers; and somehow, for a bright morning like this, he seemed old, and worn, and cold.

"Well, well, friend," he said, "I'm glad to see you."

He said it as though he meant it.

"Come into the library; it's the only room in the whole house that is comfortably warm. You've no idea what a task it is to heat a place like this in really cold weather. No sooner do I find a man who can run my furnace than he goes off and leaves me."

"I can sympathize with you," I said, "we often have trouble at our house with the man who builds the fires."

He looked around at me quizzically.

"He lies too long in bed in the morning," I said.

By this time we had arrived at the library, where a bright fire was burning in the grate. It was a fine big room, with dark oak furnishings and books in cases along one wall, but this morning it had a dishevelled and untidy look. On a little table at one side of the fireplace were the remains of a breakfast; at the other a number of wraps were thrown carelessly upon a chair. As I came in Mrs. Starkweather rose from her place, drawing a silk scarf around her shoulders. She is a robust, rather handsome woman, with many rings on her fingers, and a pair of glasses hanging to a little gold hook on her ample bosom; but this morning she, too, looked worried and old.

"Oh, yes," she said with a rueful laugh, "we're beginning a merry Christmas, as you see. Think of Christmas with no cook in the house!"

I felt as if I had discovered a gold mine. Poor starving millionaires!

But Mrs. Starkweather had not told the whole of her sorrowful story.

"We had a company of friends invited for dinner to-day," she said, "and our cook was ill—or said she was—and had to go. One of the maids went with her. The man who looks after the furnace disappeared on Friday, and the stableman has been drinking. We can't very well leave the place without someone who is responsible in charge of it—and so here we are. Merry Christmas!"

I couldn't help laughing. Poor people!

"You might," I said, "apply for Mrs. Heney's place."

"Who is Mrs. Heney?" asked Mrs. Starkweather.

"You don't mean to say that you never heard of Mrs. Heney!" I exclaimed. "Mrs. Heney, who is now Mrs. 'Penny' Daniels? You've missed one of our greatest celebrities."

With that, of course, I had to tell them about Mrs. Heney, who has for years performed a most important function in this community. Alone and unaided, she has been the poor whom we are supposed to have always with us. If it had not been for the devoted faithfulness of Mrs. Heney at Thanksgiving, Christmas and other times of the year, I suppose our Woman's Aid Society and the King's Daughters would have perished miserably of undistributed turkeys and tufted comforters. For years Mrs. Heney filled the place most acceptably. Curbing the natural outpourings of a rather jovial soul, she could upon occasion look as deserving of charity as any person that ever I met. But I pitied the little Heneys: it always comes hard on the children. For weeks after every Thanksgiving and Christmas they always wore a painfully stuffed and suffocated look. I only came to appreciate fully what a self-sacrificing public servant Mrs. Heney really was when I learned that she had taken the desperate alternative of marrying "Penny" Daniels.

"So you think we might possibly aspire to the position?" laughed Mrs. Starkweather.

Upon this I told them of the trouble in our household and asked them to come down and help us enjoy Dr. McAlway and the goose.

When I left, after much more pleasant talk, they both came with me to the door seeming greatly improved in spirits.

"You've given us something to live for, Mr. Grayson," said Mrs. Starkweather.

So I walked homeward in the highest spirits, and an hour or more later who should we see in the top of our upper field but Mr. Starkweather and his wife floundering in the snow. They reached the lane literally covered from top to toe with snow and both of them ruddy with the cold.

"We walked over," said Mrs. Starkweather breathlessly, "and I haven't had so much fun in years."

Mr. Starkweather helped her over the fence. The Scotch Preacher stood on the steps to receive them, and we all went in together.

I can't pretend to describe Harriet's dinner: the gorgeous brown goose, and the apple sauce, and all the other things that best go with it, and the pumpkin pie at the end—the finest, thickest, most delicious pumpkin pie I ever ate in all my life. It melted in one's mouth and brought visions of celestial bliss. And I wish I could have a picture of Harriet presiding. I have never seen her happier, or more in her element. Every time she brought in a new dish or took off a cover it was a sort of miracle. And her coffee—but I must not and dare not elaborate.

And what great talk we had afterward!

I've known the Scotch Preacher for a long time, but I never saw him in quite such a mood of hilarity. He and Mr. Starkweather told stories of their boyhood—and we laughed, and laughed—Mrs. Starkweather the most of all. Seeing her so often in her carriage, or in the dignity of her home, I didn't think she had so much jollity in her. Finally she discovered Harriet's cabinet organ, and nothing would do but she must sing for us.

"None of the newfangled ones, Clara," cried her husband: "some of the old ones we used to know."

So she sat herself down at the organ and threw her head back and began to sing:

> "Believe me, if all those endearing young charms,
> Which I gaze on so fondly to-day—"

Mr. Starkweather jumped up and ran over to the organ and joined in with his deep voice. Harriet and I followed. The Scotch Preacher's wife nodded in time with the music, and presently I saw the tears in her eyes. As for Dr. McAlway, he sat on the edge of his chair with his hands on his knees and wagged his shaggy head, and before we got through he, too, joined in with his big sonorous voice:

"Thou wouldst still be adored as this moment thou art—"

Oh, I can't tell you here—it grows late and there's work tomorrow—all the things we did and said. They stayed until it was dark, and when Mrs. Starkweather was ready to go, she took both of Harriet's hands in hers and said with great earnestness:

"I haven't had such a good time at Christmas since I was a little girl. I shall never forget it."

And the dear old Scotch Preacher, when Harriet and I had wrapped him up, went out, saying:

"This has been a day of pleasant bread."

It has; it has. I shall not soon forget it. What a lot of kindness and common human nature—childlike simplicity, if you will—there is in people once you get them down together and persuade them that the things they think serious are not serious at all.

CHRISTMAS CLOSES A GULF

from *Act I*

BY MOSS HART

At the time of his death, 1961, Moss Hart was one of the most famous and fascinating figures of the American theater. But success did not come easily. In his autobiography, Act I, a best seller of 1960, he points out that he grew up in an atmosphere of bitter poverty, often of actual want. His family did little to relieve the situation, and memories of an unhappy childhood haunted Moss Hart throughout his life. Only when he was ten years old, did he feel close to his father, and then he was unable to express either sympathy or understanding.

It was the Christmas after my aunt had left the house, and since it was she who always supplied the tree and the presents for my brother and myself, this first Christmas without her was a bleak and empty one. I remember that I was more or less reconciled to it, because my father had worked only spasmodically throughout the year. Two of our rooms were vacant of boarders and my mother was doing her marketing farther and farther away from our neighborhood. This was always a sign that we were dangerously close to rock bottom, and each time it occurred I came to dread it more. It was one of the vicious landmarks of poverty that I had come to know well and the one I hated most. . . .

Obviously Christmas was out of the question—we were barely staying alive. On Christmas Eve my father was very silent during the evening meal. Then he surprised and startled me by turning to me and saying, "Let's take a walk." He had never suggested such a thing before, and moreover, it was a very cold winter's night. I was even more surprised when he said as we left the house, "Let's go down to a Hundred Forty-ninth Street and Westchester Avenue." My heart leaped within me. That was the section where all the big stores were, where at Christmastime open pushcarts full of toys stood packed end-to-end for blocks at a stretch. On other Christmas Eves I had often gone there with my aunt, and from our tour of the carts she had gathered what I wanted the most. My father had known of this, of course, and I joyously concluded that his walk could mean only one thing—he was going to buy me a Christmas present.

On the walk down I was beside myself with delight and an inner relief. It had been a bad year for me, that year of my aunt's going, and I wanted a Christmas present terribly—not a present merely, but a symbol, a token of some sort. I needed some sign from my father or mother that they knew what I was going through and cared for me as much as my aunt and my grandfather did. I am sure they were giving me what mute signs they could, but I did not see them. The idea that my father had managed a Christmas present for me in spite of everything filled me with a sudden peace and lightness of heart I had not known in months.

We hurried on, our heads bent against the wind, to the cluster of lights ahead that was 149th Street and Westchester Avenue, and those lights seemed to me the brightest lights I had ever seen. Tugging at my father's coat, I started down the line of pushcarts.

There were all kinds of things I wanted, but since nothing had been said by my father about buying a present, I would merely pause before a pushcart to say, with as much control as I could muster, "Look at that chemistry set!" or, "There's a stamp album!" or, "Look at the printing press!" Each time my father would pause and ask the pushcart man the price. Then without a word we would move on to the next pushcart. Once or twice he would pick up a toy of some kind and look at it and then at me, as if to suggest this might be something I might like, but I was ten years old and a good deal beyond just a toy; my heart was set on a chemistry set or a printing press. There they were on every pushcart we stopped at, but the price was always the same and soon I looked up and saw we were nearing the end of the line. Only two or three pushcarts remained. My father looked up, too, and I heard him jingle some coins in his pocket. In a flash I knew it all. He'd gotten together about seventy-five cents to buy me a Christmas present, and he hadn't dared to say so in case there was nothing to be had for so small a sum.

As I looked up at him I saw a look of despair and disappointment in his eyes that brought me closer to him than I had ever been in my life. I wanted to throw my arms around him and say, "It doesn't matter . . . I understand . . . this is better than a chemistry set or a printing press. . . . I love you." But instead we stood shivering beside each other for a moment—then turned away from the last two pushcarts and started silently back home. I don't know why the words remained choked up within me. I didn't even take his hand on the way home nor did he take mine. We were not on that basis. Nor did I ever tell him how close to him I felt that night—that for a little while the concrete wall between father and son had crumbled away and I knew that we were two lonely people struggling to reach each other.

I came close to telling him many years later, but again the moment passed. Again it was Christmas and I was on my way to visit him in Florida. My father was a bright and blooming ninety-one years of age now and I arrived in Florida with my wife to spend Christmas and New Year's with him. On Christmas Eve we sat in his living room, and while my wife chatted with his nurse and companion, I sat on a sofa across the room with my father, showing him the pictures of his two grandchildren. Suddenly I felt his hand slip into mine. It was the first time in our lives that either of us had ever touched the other. No words were spoken and I went right on turning the pages of the picture album, but my hand remained over his. A few years before I might have withdrawn mine after a moment or two, but now my hand remained; nor did I tell him what I was thinking and feeling. The moment was enough. It had taken forty years for the gulf that separated us to close.

DOWN PENS

from *The Short Stories of Saki*

BY SAKI (H. H. MUNRO)

Saki has an undisputed niche as one of England's greatest humorists of the early twentieth century. His Short Stories have been constantly praised by a discriminating body of readers for their urbane lightness and sparkling malice. "Down Pens" is an example of the wit with which he treats the familiar challenge of Christmas correspondence.

"Have you written to thank the Froplinsons for what they sent us?" asked Egbert.

"No," said Janetta, with a note of tired defiance in her voice; "I've written eleven letters today expressing surprise and gratitude for sundry unmerited gifts, but I haven't written to the Froplinsons."

"Someone will have to write to them," said Egbert.

"I don't dispute the necessity, but I don't think the someone should be me," said Janetta. "I wouldn't mind writing a letter of angry recrimination or heartless satire to some suitable recipient; in fact, I should rather enjoy it, but I've come to the end of my capacity for expressing servile amiability. Eleven letters today and nine yesterday, all couched in the same strain of ecstatic thankfulness: really, you can't expect me to sit down to another. There is such a thing as writing oneself out."

"I've written nearly as many," said Egbert, "and I've had my usual business correspondence to get through too. Besides, I don't know what it was that the Froplinsons sent us."

"A William the Conqueror calendar," said Janetta, "with a quotation of one of his great thoughts for every day in the year."

"Impossible," said Egbert; "he didn't have three hundred and sixty-five thoughts in the whole of his life, or, if he did, he kept them to himself. He was a man of action, not of introspection."

"Well, it was William Wordsworth, then," said Janetta; "I know William came into it somewhere."

"That sounds more probable," said Egbert; "well, let's collaborate on this letter of thanks and get it done. I'll dictate, and you can scribble it down. 'Dear Mrs. Froplinson—thank you and your husband so much for the very pretty calendar you sent us. It was very good of you to think of us.' "

"You can't possibly say that," said Janetta, laying down her pen.

"It's what I always do say, and what everyone says to me," protested Egbert.

"We sent them something on the twenty-second," said Janetta, "so they simply had to think of us. There was no getting away from it."

"What did we send them?" asked Egbert gloomily.

"Bridge-markers," said Janetta, "in a cardboard case, with some inanity about 'digging for fortune with a royal spade' emblazoned on the cover. The moment I saw it in the shop I said to myself 'Froplinsons' and to the attendent 'How much?' When he said 'Ninepence!' I gave him their address, jabbed our card in, paid tenpence or elevenpence to cover the postage, and thanked heaven. With less sincerity and infinitely more trouble they eventually thanked me."

"The Froplinsons don't play bridge," said Egbert.

"One is not supposed to notice social deformities of that sort," said Janetta; "it wouldn't be polite. Besides, what trouble did they take to find out whether we read Wordsworth with gladness? For all they knew or cared we might be frantically embedded in the belief that all poetry begins and ends with John Masefield, and it might infuriate or depress us to have a daily sample of Wordsworthian products flung at us."

"Well, let's get on with the letter of thanks," said Egbert.

"Proceed," said Janetta.

" 'How clever of you to guess that Wordsworth is our favourite poet,' " dictated Egbert.

Again Janetta laid down her pen.

"Do you realize what that means?" she asked; "a Wordsworth booklet next Christmas, and another calendar the Christmas after, with the same problem of having to write suitable letters of thankfulness. No, the best thing to do is to drop all further allusion to the calendar and switch off on to some other topic."

"But what other topic?"

"Oh, something like this: 'What do you think of the New Year Honours List? A friend of ours made such a clever remark when he read it.' Then you can stick in any remark that comes into your head; it needn't be clever. The Froplinsons won't know whether it is or isn't."

"We don't even know on which side they are in politics," objected Egbert; "and anyhow you can't suddenly dismiss the subject of the calendar. Surely there must be some intelligent remark that can be made about it."

"Well, we can't think of one," said Janetta wearily; "the fact is, we've both written ourselves out. Heavens! I've just remembered Mrs. Stephen Ludberry. I haven't thanked her for what she sent."

"What did she send?"

"I forget; I think it was a calendar."

There was a long silence, the forlorn silence of those who are bereft of hope and have almost ceased to care.

Presently Egbert started from his seat with an air of resolution. The light of battle was in his eyes.

"Let me come to the writing table," he exclaimed.

"Gladly," said Janetta. "Are you going to write to Mrs. Ludberry or the Froplinsons?"

"To neither," said Egbert, drawing a stack of notepaper towards him; "I'm going to write to the editor of every enlightened and influential newspaper in the Kingdom. I'm going to suggest that there should be a sort of epistolary Truce of God during the festivities of Christmas and New Year. From the twenty-fourth of December to the third or fourth of January it shall be considered an offence against good sense and good feeling to write or expect any letter or communication that does not deal with the necessary events of the moment. Answers to invitations, arrangements about trains, renewal of club subscriptions, and, of course, all the ordinary everyday affairs of business, sickness, engaging new cooks, and so forth, these will be dealt with in the usual manner as something inevitable, a legitimate part of our daily life. But all the devastating accretions of correspondence, incident to the festive season, these should be swept away to give the season a chance of being really festive, a time of untroubled, unpunctuated peace and good will."

"But you would have to make some acknowledgment of presents received," objected Janetta; "otherwise people would never know whether they had arrived safely."

"Of course, I have thought of that," said Egbert; "every present that was sent off would be accompanied by a ticket bearing the date of dispatch and the signature of the sender, and some conventional hieroglyphic to show that it was intended to be a Christmas or New Year gift; there would be a counterfoil with space for the recipient's name and the date of arrival, and all you would have to do would be to sign and date the counterfoil, add a conventional hieroglyphic indicating heartfelt thanks and gratified surprise, put the thing into an envelope and post it."

"It sounds delightfully simple," said Janetta wistfully, "but people would consider it too cut-and-dried, too perfunctory."

"It is not a bit more perfunctory than the present system," said Egbert; "I have only the same conventional language of gratitude at my disposal with which to thank dear old Colonel Chuttle for his perfectly delicious Stilton, which we shall devour to the last morsel, and the Froplinsons know that we are bored with their calendar, whatever we may say to the contrary, just as we know that they are bored with the bridge-markers in spite of their written assurance that they thanked us for our charming little gift. What is more, the Colonel knows that even if we had taken a sudden aversion to Stilton or been forbidden it by the doctor, we should still have written a letter of hearty thanks around it. So you see the present system of acknowledgment is just as perfunctory as the counterfoil business would be, only ten times more tiresome and brain-racking."

"Your plan would certainly bring the ideal of a Happy Christmas a step nearer realization," said Janetta.

"There are exceptions, of course," said Egbert, "people who really try to infuse a breath of reality into their letters of acknowledgment. Aunt Susan, for instance, who writes: 'Thank you very much for the ham; not such a good flavor as the one you sent last year, which itself was not a particularly good one. Hams are not what they used to be.' It would be a pity to be deprived of her Christmas comments, but that loss would be swallowed up in the general gain."

"Meanwhile," said Janetta, "what *am* I to say to the Froplinsons?"

THE CHANUKAH BUSH

BY GERTRUDE BERG

Gertrude Berg is beloved by millions as one of America's favorite stars of radio, television, and stage. The pages of her autobiography, Molly and Me, *portray with gaiety and deep affection a large, lively, affectionate, and delightfully funny family. In "The Chanukah Bush" Gertrude Berg relates an incident that reflects her unique sprightliness, humanity, and charm.*

Once upon a time when the children were young—which was yesterday if you ask me and pre-history if you ask them—we had a problem, not that we didn't always have problems but this was a problem that we had never had before. Now we had it only because the children were growing up, which all by itself is a problem. Out of the clear blue sky of a cold December they asked for a Christmas tree.

In the manner of adults we didn't answer, not because we didn't want to, but only because we didn't know what to say. Usually we celebrated Chanukah, the Jewish version or variation of Christmas, and we wanted the children to grow up in a tradition and a religion that happened to call the mid-winter celebration not Christmas but Chanukah.

After long talks we decided to tell both children that some people celebrated Christmas and some celebrated Chanukah and some people wouldn't know what the meaning of either holiday was if you painted them a picture. The effect of the explanation was that the children called us the two Scrooges and asked, repeatedly, why couldn't they have a Christmas tree? Why?

My father, who was called Grandpa even by me because he seemed to belong to the kids and to no one else, tried to explain about religion. He told them that religions are personal expressions of belief and that everyone had a religion—some more, some less, and some absolutely. A Christmas tree belonged to another religion of which we just happened not to be subscribers.

Why not? We weren't, that's all.

Well, the children complained, couldn't we be just for Christmas?

Grandpa tried to explain that things just didn't work that way. We weren't going to have a tree. We were going to celebrate Chanukah and that was that.

As the twenty-fifth of December came closer and closer, the children grew more insistent. Their father took refuge in history and philosophy and tried to explain the whys and wherefores through H. G. Wells, Lewis Browne, Descartes, and Bulfinch. These eminent men, however, who had made their impressions on a world of thinkers could not explain why two children shouldn't have a Christmas tree.

The night before Christmas was a night of low spirit. I wanted to give in. My husband wanted to give in. Grandpa couldn't stand it, put on his greatcoat, and stomped out of the house.

We tried getting smiles with songs and stories, funny faces, and silly costumes but nothing made an impression. I would have liked some sort of miracle right then and there but my husband, a scientist, wouldn't allow it. Besides, we had made our decision and, even if it was wrong, it *was* a decision, and we were stuck with it.

Just as we were about to put the children to bed, Grandpa came home. He walked through the door carrying a big green pine tree and a little red stand.

The kids yelled, ran to him, kissed him, and thanked him for their Christmas tree.

Grandpa looked down at the kids, straightened a few bent branches on the tree and, with a Talmudic gesture that called for silence, gravely announced that this was not a Christmas tree. It was, he pronounced with a special glare at the adults, a Chanukah bush.

A GIFT FOR MOLLY

from *Wide Meadows*

BY JEAN BELL MOSLEY

Wide Meadows *by Jean Bell Mosley is a treasury of true stories, homelike, vivacious, and inspiring. The action takes place shortly after the turn of the century. The scene is located at the St. Francois River Valley in southeastern Missouri with the Ozark Mountains as a background. The main characters include three generations of the Bell family who live in harmony and happiness under one farmhouse roof, each member helping to mold the lives of the others, who in turn influence their neighbors in the small community. In "A Gift for Molly" Jean Bell Mosley demonstrates the Christmas message that "truth exists for the wise, beauty for the feeling heart."*

Winter comes down from the mountains in a white fury and locks the valley tight in its icy grip. The river slows and comes to a frozen stop. Icicles fringe the eaves of the buildings and a tiny one hangs from Grandpa's moustache when he comes in from the barn. The pumps freeze. The wood box is in constant need of refilling and we stamp and sputter and blow and allow, in heavy understatement, as how it is right smart cold outside.

Old Nell and Maude make velvet whinnies in their stalls and the cows, their shaggy winter hair portentous of bleak days ahead, munch tunnels far back into the haystacks.

The cold north wind, rebuffed by battened windows, shakes the old house till it creaks and groans, and blows cold breath down the chimney ways. Then softly in the night comes the eider-downy blanket of snow to mute the sounds and put soft white tam-o-shanters atop the fence posts and old field stumps.

By their comings and goings, furry animals, with softly padded feet, stitch together, in the night, the fields and roads and frozen streams as though the valley were in danger of ripping apart.

The word "Christmas" creeps into our conversation and we begin, early, wrapping glasses of jelly, buckets of maple syrup, and boxes of nuts, for some of the city folks may make just one more trip to the farm before Christmas (the roads are well nigh impassable afterwards), and we will have their presents ready, however early. Lou and I begin to cast calculating eyes at cedar trees, choosing this one, discarding that one. There is a wealth to choose from. But we do not go after the tree until the last present is wrapped and tied. For Mama and Grandma we have embroidered dresser scarves. For sister Lillian we have made blue and pink satin-covered garters, lace-trimmed. For Grandpa and Dad we pool our pennies and purchase a fat pouch of tobacco. For each other we may have Crayolas, a powder puff, or a can of violet-scented talcum powder.

Grandma has been working long hours on her Passage-of-Time quilt, and at last it is in the frames ready to be quilted. But, I remember, all was not well with Grandma at this particular Christmas. She was worried. Molly Layton was coming to the Christmas quilting party and·Grandma had no gift for her. For all the other ladies she had made little presents—lacey-edged handkerchiefs, quilted pot holders, needlecases, patchwork pillow tops, but for Molly she had made nothing because she hadn't known Molly was coming.

It was more than a year now since Molly had worked for us and the other neighbor ladies, helping with the house cleaning, canning, and cooking. She had left as suddenly as she had come and no one had heard from her since, not until now, when Mrs. Stacey had called up on the day of the quilting party to ask if we remembered Molly Layton and to say that she was there at her house and wanted to come along to help with Grandma's Passage-of-Time quilt.

We remembered Molly, all right. One summer day she had

walked in off the road—run-over shoes, skimpy, faded dress, a large mole on her nose, straight, sun-faded hair hooked behind her ears—and announced that she had come to do our sewing. When she spoke, we saw that one of her front teeth was missing.

"But I do my own sewing," Mama had told her. "You must have the wrong place."

"No, ma'am," she said, putting her hand over her mouth to hide the defect. "I'll do your cookin', then."

"We-ll," Mama faltered, puzzled at this strange girl. "We got plenty of cooks." She motioned to us girls and Grandma.

"Cleanin'?" Molly asked.

Mama shook her head and said nothing.

"Milkin', then. What about milkin'?" Molly asked.

"Good land! We all milk," Mama replied.

Molly turned then and walked forlornly back to the gate. Her thin shoulders under the faded dress seemed to droop even lower, and we saw her wipe her arm across her eyes as she hooked her fallen hair back over her ear.

"Wait a minute," Mama called as Molly fumbled with the latch. "Come back and have a bit of gingerbread and a glass of milk, anyway."

Molly blew her nose noisily and came back. "Excuse me, ma'am," she said apologetically, for the tears, "But I sure do need a job."

"Well, just sit and rest a while and have a bite to eat. You look all tuckered," Mama said.

"I guess I ought to be. I started out day before yesterday morning, and I've stopped at every house I've seen, and nobody wants any work done, and now I'm way out in the country, where the houses are far apart." The tears started again.

"Where's your folks?" Mama inquired.

"Just me left. That's all." Molly gave a long shivering sigh.

"Well, we're canning beans tomorrow. Maybe you could help us," Mama said.

So Molly stayed for the canning, and then the threshers came and she stayed on to help cook, and then it was time to put up the peaches. We couldn't pay her much, but she carefully hoarded her money. She was going to have the mole taken off, a new tooth put in, and get some water-wave combs for her hair. "Of course I could get the combs right away, but they wouldn't help much with this face. Ain't I the ugliest thing you ever saw?"

Molly would deride herself, trying to be gay about it and acting as if it didn't matter. But it hurt. You could tell that by the way she'd look at herself in the mirror, fluff her hair out speculatively, and then turn away.

And she appreciated beautiful things. On Sundays, when we used Grandma's rose-sprigged china, she would hold a dish up to the light and say, "Aren't they the most beautiful things you ever saw?" She'd wipe the plates lovingly and stack them with tissue paper in between. She loved the silver spoon and the old clock with its jewel-like pendulum, and she would fondle the rose-in-glass paperweight as a child would a doll. Over Grandma's Passage-of-Time quilts, Molly went into ecstasies.

These quilts were Grandma's way of keeping a history of the family and friends. There were twenty-four blocks to a quilt, each one depicting in appliqué and embroidery the most interesting events that happened in our lives as time went by. She drafted her own designs, for she was good at drawing, and sometimes the completed block would be intricate beyond all reason and as complicated as a mosaic tile. Take the time the bull butted Grandpa into the river and jumped in after him. There were three scenes in this one block—Grandpa standing on the riverbank innocently fishing; Grandpa halfway across the river, the bull in hot pursuit; and Grandpa climbing a tree on the other side, water dripping from his clothing in the form of blue French knots and a satin-stitch blue jay perched in a tree watching.

Sometimes we chided Grandma about her drawings. The barn didn't sway in the middle the way ours really did, and in the block where she had me in the swing, the tree was generously foliaged and well proportioned instead of a spindly old walnut.

"Well, I draw them like they look to me," Grandma would say, and that seemed excuse enough.

When relatives gathered, we put these quilts on the beds for spreads, for they provided no end of fun when the incidents pictured were recalled. "Where's that block of Dad getting the skunks out from under the floor?" Uncle Hayden would ask and go around from bed to bed until he found it. He'd stand and laugh until the tears rolled down his cheeks and tell the story all over again to anyone near. Grandma always had as many funny blocks as she could.

Molly would feast her eyes for hours at a time on these

quilts. "Just seems like if you'd look at pretty things long enough, and handle them often enough, you'd be bound to soak up a little of their beauty, doesn't it?" she would ask pathetically, fingering the mole on her nose.

When work got slack at our house, Molly went on to Staceys', MacFarlands', and Ritters'. "You folks have been awful kind," she said when she left. "You don't know how it makes me feel. Almost like it didn't matter so much." We knew she meant her face.

"I guess being kind is the most beautiful thing in the world, and you can't even see it." Molly thought about that for a while and looked sad because you couldn't see such a beautiful thing as kindness. "Maybe that's the kind that you soak up," she added, "the kind you can't see."

After staying a while with all the neighbors, Molly left, and we assumed she had at last saved enough money to have her face "corrected," as she always called it.

She had made sufficient impression, though, to warrant a block in Grandma's quilt. And, as we all liked the funny blocks, we urged Grandma to make one of Molly taking Communion at church with the forgotten pillow pinned over her hips. Molly admired the wasp waists and generous hips of the other ladies, but she was waspy all the way down. Other thin women used discreet padding and crinoline ruffling to make their skirts stand out; but Molly had no time to fix up such trappings for herself and on this particular Sunday she used the simple expedient of a patchwork cushion to correct her figure faults.

"If only she hadn't taken her coat off," deplored the women, who had to listen to much chiding from their menfolk after that. But the old stove in the church had acted up, and Molly, along with many others, took off her coat and marched up the aisle to take Communion, completely oblivious of her "figure correction."

Grandma demurred at making such a block. "Poor, dear girl. I wouldn't poke fun at her for anything," she said. But we continued to insist, assuring Grandma that we'd never hear from Molly Layton again.

But here we had! "Same old Molly," Mrs. Stacey had reported to Grandma over the telephone.

"You mean she didn't get the mole off or the tooth in, as hard as she worked and saved?" Grandma asked.

"No. It seems like a distant cousin of Molly's turned up without any money and needing medicine of some kind. And Molly spent all she had on the cousin getting her straightened out, and didn't have enough left over for herself," Mrs. Stacey said. "Coming back out to go to work again."

And so Grandma was worried. No gift for Molly! Besides, the picture in the quilt!

"I could run her up a little needlecase, I guess," Grandma said, looking at her quilt already stretched in the quilting frame.

We all went out to the kitchen to get the refreshments ready and left Grandma alone while she worked fast on Molly's present.

The house smelled real Christmasy, for we had put the tree up early for the quilting party. Bayberry candles were burning on the mantel, and cinnamon rolls were in the oven. It was snowing softly outside, and the ladies were in a holiday mood as they began arriving.

Molly was the same old Molly, hiding her mouth with her hand when she laughed and hooking her hair behind her ear. If anything, she was even thinner. "When I heard you had another one of those pretty quilts ready," she said to Grandma, "I sure wanted to come along and help work on it."

"Well, we'll start before long," Grandma said, "but first you ladies warm up with a spot of tea." She passed the tea and let me pass the cinnamon rolls and spoons. I saw to it that Molly got the silver spoon. Then Grandma distributed the presents.

There wasn't anything for Molly but an old thimble of Grandma's that had become too large for her. I felt so sorry for Molly, and even sorrier for Grandma, who hadn't had time after all to make anything suitable for Molly.

But Grandma didn't look at all worried. "Molly," she said, "I've put you in the quilt."

A slow blush of pleasure crept up over Molly's face. She threw back her shoulders and took her hand away from her mouth. I followed her to the quilt to see the picture. Wasn't Grandma doing this all wrong? I wondered. Maybe Molly wouldn't have recognized herself. I watched Molly's face closely. She looked a long time at the block. A softness came into her face and then a glow. Why, Molly looked radiant! I peered down at the block. It wasn't the one of Molly with the cushion at all. It was one of Molly putting flowers into a vase. You could tell it was her by the little maid's ruffle she always wore on her head. Grandma had ripped out the other block and substituted this one while we thought she was making the needlecase. I looked at Molly's face again.

Tears were spilling down her cheeks as she lifted her eyes to Grandma's. "But you've made me pretty," she said very softly.

It was true. Grandma had added little lines here and there, and the girl pictured was pretty, but still Molly, all right.

"Well, I just draw them like they look to me," Grandma said.

Somehow, the little thimble Molly had received didn't matter at all. For here, tied in the brightest, shimmering, invisible package, was Grandma's gift to Molly—the kind you couldn't see at all.

CHRISTMAS PROBLEMS WITH RASCAL

from Rascal

BY STERLING NORTH

Sterling North is one of the most versatile, influential, and appealing authors of our time. Rascal, an authentic memoir of his own boyhood in a small Midwest town at the close of World War I, is a heart-warming story in the delightfully nostalgic vein of his earlier best seller, So Dear to My Heart. The animal hero is a captivating little raccoon, brought into a motherless household where eleven-year-old Sterling lived with his kindly but absent-minded father, a pet crow, four skunks, a drooling Saint Bernard dog, woodchucks, and several cats. A half-completed canoe adorned a large part of the living room. The boy's self-reliance and independence, his love of the outdoors, and strong family ties are highlighted at vacation time, country fairs, and school days. We give you the Christmas celebration at the North household and the problems of Sterling with his fascinating family, including all the animals, especially Rascal.

The first flurry of snow came early in December, whirling a few flakes into Rascal's hollow in the tree. I feared that a real blizzard might make that den quite uncomfortable. From a piece of sheet copper I fashioned a hood over the entrance, and I lined the hole itself with old blankets and an outgrown sweater of mine so that my raccoon would have a snug winter nest. Rascal took an immediate fancy to the sweater, perhaps associating it with me.

As cold weather set in, Rascal grew sleepy. Raccoons do not actually hibernate, but they do sleep for many days at a time, emerging only occasionally to pad around in the snow seeking a full meal. Every morning before I left for school I would go into the cage and reach into the hole. I wanted to make sure that Rascal was safe and comfortable. It was a great satisfaction to feel his warm, furry body breathing slowly and rhythmically, and to know that he was sleeping soundly in his pleasant home.

Sometimes he stirred when I petted him, and murmured in his sleep. Now and then he awoke sufficiently to poke his little black-masked face out of the hole to look at me. I always rewarded him with a handful of pecans.

My financial problems increased as we approached Christmas. In recent autumns I had earned as much as seventy-five dollars trapping muskrats. This allowed me to purchase thoughtful gifts for the family. But since signing my peace treaty with the musk-rats and other wild animals, I was finding that peace does not always bring prosperity.

I solicited nearby neighbors and shoveled many walks, earning a top price of fifty cents for moving a couple of tons of snow. I also increased my efforts to sell more *Saturday Evening Posts*. But the silver accumulated very slowly, and prices were frightfully high in the stores.

One Saturday, after a discouraging tour of the stores, I stopped at the Post Office to find two cheerful letters in our box. One was the first from Herschel since the Armistice. The other was from my beloved sister Jessica, still taking postgraduate work at the University of Chicago. Both letters relieved my mind in a number of ways.

Herschel had survived the war and influenza. He said the Paris garters I had sent were better than a rabbit's foot. No metal *had* touched him.

Then came the disappointing news that he had been ordered to march to the Rhine to help establish a bridgehead near Coblenz, Germany, and that he would not be demobilized for six months at the earliest. He asked us not to send gifts, saying he would bring his presents with him when he came home.

Letters from Jessica were always a joy. Bright, salty, and affectionate, they told so much concerning her unselfish character. Flashes of temper were to be expected. But these were outweighed by the gaiety and Spartan good humor of this sister who had cared for my father and myself for so many months after my mother died.

Jessica was coming home for Christmas. She enclosed a ten-dollar check, made out in my name, to help me with my Christmas shopping.

With my financial crisis eased, I turned to the pleasant tasks of buying a tree and sweeping and decorating the house. My father paid little attention to such matters, and furthermore he was again away on business.

Almost immediately I realized that Rascal presented a new and difficult problem. It had always been our custom to invite some of the animals to be with us on Christmas Eve when we distributed the gifts. In the past we usually had limited the four-footed delegation to Wowser and the best behaved of the cats. But it was unthinkable to exclude Rascal, who, however, could never discipline his hands when shining objects were within his reach.

How could we have both Rascal and a Christmas tree? And yet we must have both. The answer to this dilemma struck me as a real inspiration.

There was a large semicircular bay extending from the living room, with six windows that overlooked the flower garden. This was where we always mounted our Christmas tree. I bought and decorated a thick spruce, which tapered gracefully to the star at its tip and nearly filled the bay with its fragrant greenery. This took me most of one Saturday. Then I made careful measurements of the rectangular opening leading to the bay and hastened to my work bench in the barn. I had sufficient chicken wire to cover a a frame, designed carefully and precisely to fit the opening I had just measured. In less than an hour I was maneuvering this construction through the big, double front door into the living room.

Another few minutes and the job was complete. And there, safe behind the wire was the decorated tree, every bauble secure from my raccoon.

I put a Christmas wreath above the fireplace, laced Christmas ribbons through the ribs of my canoe frame, hung a few sprigs of holly from archways and chandeliers, and stood back to admire the total effect. I was immoderately pleased with my work and could scarcely wait to show it to my father and to Jessica.

When my father returned from his trip, I led him happily into the living room and pointed to the Christmas tree, wired off from the rest of the world as though it might try to escape to its native forest.

"My word," my father said mildly. "What are you building, Sterling, another cage for Rascal?"

"You're warm," I said. "It's so that Rascal can't climb the tree and spoil the ornaments."

"Well," my father hesitated, "at least it's unusual."

"Do you think Jessica will hit the ceiling?"

"She might," my father said. "You never can tell what Jessica might do."

There was one train a day from Chicago, an old ten-wheeler pulling a baggage car, a passenger coach, and sometimes a freight car and a caboose. We loved that train and listened for it to rumble across the river bridge, blow four times for the lower crossing, and come huffing and puffing up the slight grade to the station.

Train time was exciting even if the passenger coach did not carry someone as much loved as my sister Jessica.

The conductor helped her down the steps and my father and I took her suitcase and her many packages. She was wearing a wide-brimmed velvet hat which looked very fashionable, a new coat with a fur collar, and high-laced shoes that came to the hem of her dress. She had recently sold several groups of poems and a short story, and she seemed quite affluent.

"Merry Christmas, Jessica. Welcome home," we cried.

She kissed us, and then held me off and looked at me critically. "You've outgrown your Mackinaw, Sterling. And you'll catch your death of cold not wearing a cap."

"He never wears a cap," my father explained.

Obviously I was clean, and had combed my stubborn curls into some semblance of order, so Jessica wasn't altogether disapproving.

We went homeward through the iron-cold air and bright

sunlight, up Fulton Street, past all the stores, still laughing and chattering and asking a hundred questions in the manner of most families gathering for Christmas.

Perhaps we were extra gay to cover an underlying sadness. Mother would not be at the gracious double door to greet us. Herschel was still in France, but "alive and unwounded" as we kept repeating. Theo and her kind husband Norman would be spending Christmas in their own home far to the north. Already our closely knit family was dwindling and dispersing as all families eventually must. But the three of us would do the best we could to bring cheer to the old house.

As we entered the living room, I wasn't sure whether Jessica wanted to laugh or cry. I had done my best in decorating the tree and the canoe, which was supposed to hold our cargo of gifts. But suddenly I saw it through my sister's eyes—an unfinished boat, chicken wire, and dust on the furniture.

"You simply *can't* go on living like this!" she said. "You *must* hire a full-time housekeeper."

"But, Dottie," I pleaded, using her pet name, "I worked so hard on the tree and decorations, and the cage to keep Rascal out."

Then Jessica was laughing and hugging me in the crazy way she often acted. She was, and is, the most spontaneous affectionate, thoughtful, brilliant, and unreasonable sister one could wish for. A very attractive combination, I have always maintained.

"At least we can take the canoe to the barn," Jessica said (not wishing to lose her advantage).

"But, Dottie, I can't take it to the barn. It's cold as blazes out there. I have to put on the canvas first."

"Well, put on the canvas, and we'll still have time to clean this room for Christmas."

"That sounds sensible," my father agreed.

"But you don't understand," I explained. "I had to spend all my money to build the cage, and then all the other money I could scrape together to buy Christmas presents, and . . ."

"Sterling, get to the point," Jessica said.

"So I haven't any money left for canvas, and it will cost about fifteen dollars, I think."

Jessica looked at my father severely, and he said, "Now be reasonable, Jessica. I'm a busy man. I can't know everything that's going on in Sterling's head and I didn't know he needed money for canvas."

Jessica sighed, realizing that we were both quite hopeless and greatly in need of her care. "Well, at least I can cook you some decent meals and clean up this house."

"It's perfectly clean," I protested. "I swept every single room and shook out the throw rugs and scoured the bathrooms. You don't know how hard I worked getting this place beautiful for you. And, besides, we like our own cooking, and we don't want a housekeeper. You sound like Theo."

"We're happy," my father said. "As happy as we can be since your mother died."

"Don't be sentimental," Jessica said fiercely, wiping tears from her own eyes. "You just wait until I get on an apron! And another thing, you're going to have a housekeeper whether you like it or not."

On the day before Christmas we wrapped our gifts in secrecy in various rooms of the house, camouflaging some in odd-size packages. We arranged them according to the recipient: those for my father in the prow of the canoe, those for Jessica in the stern, and those for me amidships.

After an early dinner we brought in the animals—Rascal first, to allow him to wake up for the festivities, then Wowser, and finally the selected cats. Jessica immediately fell in love with my raccoon. And when she saw how he struggled to reach through the wire to touch the Christmas-tree baubles, she forgave me for building the barricade.

The Yule log was blazing in the fireplace, shedding light on the tree and its ornaments and making the chicken wire gleam like a dew-drenched cobweb. The argosy of brightly wrapped gifts greatly intrigued my raccoon.

Animals, like children, find it difficult to wait for a gift which is almost within reach. So we always gave them their presents first. Each cat received a catnip mouse, making the old toms and tabbies as playful as kittens, and causing a certain amount of possessive growling. For Wowser, confined to his bath towel on the hearth, I had a new collar. But for my pampered pet, Rascal, I had only Christmas candies and pecans, being unable to think of a single other thing he might need.

In opening the family packages we proceeded in rotation. This gave us a chance to admire each object and to express gratitude. There were many thoughtfully chosen books, ties, socks, warm gloves, scarves—all appreciated.

The best gifts came last. Theo and Norman had been quite extravagant. They had sent Jessica a fur muff and my father a sheared beaver cap. To me they had given shoe ice skates, very rare in our region in those days. I eagerly awaited our next game of hockey.

My father brought forth from his pocket a small buck-skin pouch and poured into his hand seven beautifully cut and polished agates. They were ringed like Rascal's tail, from golden yellow through oak-leaf brown to deep maroon. With unexpected forethought he had sent our best rough stones from Lake Superior to a gem-cutting firm in Chicago, insisting that they be returned in time for Christmas.

My father was pleased by our response. He chose three agates for Jessica and three for me. Then he did a most surprising thing. Calling for Rascal, he handed him the handsome little stone that the raccoon himself had found.

Always fascinated by shining objects, Rascal felt it carefully, sat up, holding it between his hands to examine it and smell it, then carried it to the corner where he kept his pennies and unceremoniously dropped it among his other treasures. He came back chirring cheerfully.

This might well have topped the gift-giving. But one more large package still lay amidships, "To Sterling, from Jessica." I was very curious but could not imagine what it might be. Upon removing the wrappings I found an unbelievable present—enough heavy, strong white canvas to cover my entire canoe. I was near to unwanted tears, but Jessica saved the day.

"Now perhaps we can get this canoe out of the living room," she said.

Wowser, Rascal, and the cats were soon asleep around us. My father asked Jessica to read from the second chapter of St. Luke, as Mother had done on so many Christmas Eves.

"And it came to pass in those days, that there went out a decree from Caesar Augustus . . .

"And she brought forth her firstborn son, and wrapped him in swaddling clothes, and laid him in a manger; because there was no room for them in the inn. . . .

"And there were in the same country, shepherds, abiding in the field, keeping watch over their flock by night.

"And, lo, the angel of the Lord came upon them . . . and they were sore afraid."

Faintly through the drifting snow came the strains of the church organ playing "Silent Night, Holy Night."

THE HOUSE OF CHRISTMAS

from *The Collected Poems of G. K. Chesterton*

BY G. K. CHESTERTON

There fared a mother driven forth
Out of an inn to roam;
In the place where she was homeless
All men are at home.
The crazy stable close at hand,
With shaking timber and shifting sand,
Grew a stronger thing to abide and stand
Than the square stones of Rome.

For men are homesick in their homes,
And strangers under the sun,
And they lay their heads in a foreign land
Whenever the day is done.
Here we have battle and blazing eyes,
And chance and honour and high surprise,
But our homes are under miraculous skies
Where the yule tale was begun.

A Child in a foul stable,
Where the beasts feed and foam;
Only where He was homeless
Are you and I at home;
We have hands that fashion and heads that know,
But our hearts we lost—how long ago!

In a place no chart nor ship can show
Under the sky's dome.

This world is wild as an old wives' tale,
And strange the plain things are,
The earth is enough and the air is enough
For our wonder and our war;
But our rest is as far as the fire-drake swings
And our peace is put in impossible things
Where clashed and thundered unthinkable wings
Round an incredible star.

To an open house in the evening
Home shall men come,
To an older place than Eden
And a taller town than Rome.
To the end of the way of the wandering star,
To the things that cannot be and that are,
To the place where God was homeless
And all men are at home.

V   The Spirit of Christmas

It is the spirit that quickeneth. (John 6:63)

Throughout the world Christmas is a holiday of deep and moving significance, a religious observance with heart and mind, a festival of rejoicing with Light and Spirit in their conquest of darkness. From its beginning in the calendar of the centuries, it has remained in the soul, always coming, always growing. Months in advance of the Christmas anniversary, its great and good gifts, its rich blessings lie hidden under a heavy burden of material substitutes. But gradually kind thoughts and generous deeds replace all mundane elements. They seem to vanish at lighting-up time, the time when the Child returns to earth in celestial splendor to remind us of His birth and message. There comes to everyone a sense of inner vision, of peace and brotherhood, of gratitude for faith and love and life. Ever since the coming of the Child, Christmas has been sent to illuminate "the vision splendid" and to reaffirm the shining glory known in Bethlehem almost two thousand years ago.

❋　　❋　　❋

AND THE WORD WAS MADE FLESH

from *Brother Sun in Little Plays of St. Francis*

BY LAURENCE HOUSMAN

Brother Sun (St. Francis) leaves the camp of the Christians at Damietta on a mission to convert the Soldan of the Saracens. Taken prisoner and brought before the monarch in his tent, Francis proclaims the wonder and glory of Christ in this dramatic treatment of the story of faith.

Light looked down and beheld Darkness.
    "Thither will I go," said Light.
Peace looked down and beheld War.
"Thither will I go," said Peace.
Love looked down and beheld Hatred.
    "Thither will I go," said Love.
So came Light, and shone.
So came Peace, and gave rest.
So came Love, and brought Life.
And the Word was made Flesh, and dwelt among us.

CHRISTMAS DAY IN THE MORNING

BY PEARL BUCK

While to myriad readers Pearl (Sydenstricker) Buck (Mrs. Richard Walsh) will always be the author of The Good Earth *and many cogent Eastern novels, she has won renown in various other literary fields which have broadened our vistas on the contemporary American scene. "Christmas Day in the Morning" reminds us that this is a blessed time for giving, that love alone can awaken the spirit of Christmas.*

He woke suddenly and completely. It was four o'clock, the hour at which his father had always called him to get up and help with the milking. Strange how the habits of his youth clung to him still! Fifty years ago, and his father had been dead for thirty years, and yet he waked at four o'clock in the morning. He had trained himself to turn over and go to sleep, but this morning, because it was Christmas, he did not try to sleep.

Yet what was the magic of Christmas now? His childhood and youth were long past, and his own children had grown up and gone. Some of them lived only a few miles away but they had their own families, and though they would come in as usual toward the end of the day, they had explained with infinite gentleness that they wanted their children to build Christmas memories about *their* houses, not his. He was left alone with his wife.

Yesterday she had said, "It isn't worth while, perhaps—"

And he had said, "Oh, yes, Alice, even if there are only the two of us, let's have a Christmas of our own."

Then she had said, "Let's not trim the tree until tomorrow, Robert—just so it's ready when the children come. I'm tired."

He had agreed, and the tree was still out in the back entry.

He lay in his big bed in his room. The door to her room was shut because she was a light sleeper, and sometimes he had restless nights. Years ago they had decided to use separate rooms. It meant nothing, they said, except that neither of them slept as well as they once had. They had been married so long that nothing could separate them, actually.

Why did he feel so awake tonight? For it was still night, a clear and starry night. No moon, of course, but the stars were extraordinary! Now that he thought of it, the stars seemed always large and clear before the dawn of Christmas Day. There was one star now that was certainly larger and brighter than any of the others. He could even imagine it moving, as it had seemed to him to move one night long ago.

He slipped back in time, as he did so easily nowadays. He was fifteen years old and still on his father's farm. He loved his father. He had not known it until one day a few days before Christmas, when he overheard what his father was saying to his mother.

"Mary, I hate to call Rob in the mornings. He's growing so fast and he needs his sleep. If you could see how he sleeps when I go in to wake him up! I wish I could manage alone."

"Well, you can't, Adam." His mother's voice was brisk. "Besides, he isn't a child any more. It's time he took his turn."

"Yes," his father said slowly. "But I sure do hate to wake him."

When he heard these words, something in him woke: his father loved him! He had never thought of it before, taking for granted the tie of their blood. Neither his father nor his mother talked about loving their children—they had no time for such things. There was always so much to do on a farm.

Now that he knew his father loved him, there would be no more loitering in the mornings and having to be called again. He got up after that, stumbling blind with sleep, and pulled on his clothes, his eyes tight shut, but he got up.

And then on the night before Christmas, that year when he was fifteen, he lay for a few minutes thinking about the next day. They were poor, and most of the excitement was in the turkey they had raised themselves and in the mince pies his mother made. His sisters sewed presents and his mother and father always bought something he needed, not only a warm jacket, maybe, but something more, such as a book. And he saved and bought them each something, too.

He wished, that Christmas he was fifteen, he had a better present for his father. As usual he had gone to the ten-cent store and bought a tie. It had seemed nice enough until he lay thinking the night before Christmas, and then he wished that he had heard his father and mother talking in time for him to save for something better.

He lay on his side, his head supported by his elbow, and looked out of his attic window. The stars were bright, much brighter than he ever remembered seeing them, and one star in particular was so bright that he wondered if it were really the Star of Bethlehem.

"Dad," he had once asked when he was a little boy, "what is a stable?"

"It's just a barn," his father had replied, "like ours."

Then Jesus had been born in a barn, and to a barn the shepherds and the Wise Men had come, bringing their Christmas gifts!

The thought struck him like a silver dagger. Why should he not give his father a special gift too, out there in the barn? He could get up early, earlier than four o'clock, and he could creep into the barn and get all the milking done. He'd do it alone, milk and clean up, and then when his father went in to start milking, he'd see it all done. And he would know who had done it.

He laughed to himself as he gazed at the stars. It was what he would do, and he mustn't sleep too sound.

He must have waked twenty times, scratching a match each time to look at his old watch—midnight, and half past one, and then two o'clock.

At a quarter to three he got up and put on his clothes. He crept downstairs, careful of the creaky boards, and let himself out. The big star hung lower over the barn roof, a reddish gold. The cows looked at him, sleepy and surprised. It was early for them too.

"So, boss," he whispered. They accepted him placidly and he fetched some hay for each cow and then got the milking pail and the big milk cans.

He had never milked all alone before, but it seemed almost easy. He kept thinking about his father's surprise. His father would come in and call him, saying that he would get things started while Rob was getting dressed. He'd go to the barn, open the door, and then he'd go to get the two big empty milk cans. But they wouldn't be waiting or empty; they'd be standing in the milkhouse, filled.

"What the—" he could hear his father exclaiming.

He smiled and milked steadily, two strong streams rushing into the pail, frothing and fragrant. The cows were still surprised but acquiescent. For once they were behaving well, as though they knew it was Christmas.

The task went more easily than he had ever known it to before. Milking for once was not a chore. It was something else, a gift to his father who loved him. He finished, the two milk cans were full, and he covered them and closed the milkhouse door carefully, making sure of the latch. He put the stool in its place by the door and hung up the clean milk pail. Then he went out of the barn and barred the door behind him.

Back in his room he had only a minute to pull off his clothes in the darkness and jump into bed, for he heard his father up. He put the covers over his head to silence his quick breathing. The door opened.

"Rob!" his father called. "We have to get up, son, even if it is Christmas."

"Aw-right," he said sleepily.

"I'll go on out," his father said. "I'll get things started."

The door closed and he lay still, laughing to himself. In just a few minutes his father would know. His dancing heart was ready to jump from his body.

The minutes were endless—ten, fifteen, he did not know how many—and he heard his father's footsteps again. The door opened and he lay still.

"Rob!"

"Yes, Dad—"

"You son of a—" His father was laughing, a queer sobbing sort of a laugh. "Thought you'd fool me, did you?" His father was standing beside his bed, feeling for him, pulling away the cover.

"It's for Christmas, Dad!"

He found his father and clutched him in a great hug. He felt his father's arms go around him. It was dark and they could not see each other's faces.

"Son, I thank you. Nobody ever did a nicer thing—"

"Oh, Dad, I want you to know—I do want to be good!" The words broke from him of their own will. He did not know what to say. His heart was bursting with love.

"Well, I reckon I can go back to bed and sleep," his father said after a moment. "No, hark—the little ones are waked up. Come to think of it, son, I've never seen you children when you first saw the Christmas tree. I was always in the barn. Come on!"

He got up and pulled on his clothes again and they went down to the Christmas tree, and soon the sun was creeping up to where the star had been. Oh, what a Christmas, and how his heart had nearly burst again with shyness and pride as his father told his mother and made the younger children listen about how he, Rob, had got up all by himself.

"The best Christmas gift I ever had, and I'll remember it, son, every year on Christmas morning, so long as I live."

They had both remembered it, and now that his father was dead he remembered it alone: that blessed Christmas dawn when, alone with the cows in the barn, he had made his first gift of true love.

Outside the window now the great star slowly sank. He got up out of bed and put on his slippers and bathrobe and went softly upstairs to the attic and found the box of Christmas-tree decorations. He took them downstairs into the living room. Then he brought in the tree. It was a little one—they had not had a big tree since the children went away—but he set it in the holder and put it in the middle of the long table under the window. Then carefully he began to trim it.

It was done very soon, the time passing as quickly as it had that morning long ago in the barn. He went to his library and fetched the little box that contained his special gift to his wife, a star of diamonds, not large but dainty in design. He had written the card for it the day before. He tied the gift on the tree and then stood back. It was pretty, very pretty, and she would be surprised.

But he was not satisfied. He wanted to tell her—to tell her how much he loved her. It had been a long time since he had really told her, although he loved her in a very special way, much more than he ever had when they were young.

He had been fortunate that she had loved him—and how fortunate that he had been able to love! Ah, that was the true joy of life, the ability to love! For he was quite sure that some people were genuinely unable to love anyone. But love was alive in him, it still was.

It occurred to him suddenly that it was alive because long ago it had been born in him when he knew his father loved him. That was it: love alone could waken love.

And he could give the gift again and again. This morning, this blessed Christmas morning, he would give it to his beloved wife. He could write it down in a letter for her to read and keep forever. He went to his desk and began his love letter to his wife: *My dearest love . . .*

THE SPIRIT OF CHRISTMAS   221

When it was finished he sealed it and tied it on the tree where she could see it the first thing when she came into the room. She would read it, surprised and then moved, and realize how very much he loved her.

He put out the light and went tiptoeing up the stairs. The star in the sky was gone, and the first rays of the sun were gleaming the sky. Such a happy, happy Christmas!

A PARTRIDGE IN A PEAR TREE

from *Like a Mighty Army*

BY HALFORD E. LUCCOCK

Dr. Halford E. Luccock, formerly Professor of Homiletics at Yale Divinity School, wrote at least a book a year for his more than quarter-century of teaching and preaching. He was a friendly wit, a wag, a critic, and a warmhearted philosopher—one of the essentially great and beloved clergymen who could combine all these with a high seriousness and a sense of commitment to God and humanity. From Christian Century's Simeon Stylites column comes "A Partridge in a Pear Tree." In this representative letter, Dr. Luccock pinpoints some of his thoughts on the familiar old Christmas carol.

Sir: With Christmas coming up, may I remind you that there is no carol that offers more fun for a few people singing together, whether they can sing or not, than the old stand-by "The Twelve Days of Christmas." There is a fine lilt to it, and the fascination that children of all ages find in a cumulative song on the model of "The House That Jack Built," where the list of things to be remembered and repeated gets longer with each stanza and you get all out of breath and have a grand time.

It is an old and universal carol, in celebration of the twelve days from Christmas to Epiphany. You know it—

> On the first day of Christmas
> My true love gave to me
> A partridge in a pear tree.

Then it goes on with a list of the most riotously inappropriate and ludicrous gifts—two turtle doves, three French hens, six geese laying, seven swans singing, eight maids milking, ending with twelve drummers drumming.

Nonsense? Not by a jugful of wassail. It is a profound philosophy of giving. It celebrates the high wisdom of completely inappropriate and largely useless gifts. And a good thing to remember just before Christmas. A partridge in a pear tree— what on earth could one do with that? That's the beauty of it! That makes it something to sing about! And folks have been singing about it for several hundred years. Would they have sung about a floor mop (highly appropriate for house-cleaning) or a teakettle or a foot warmer? Not much!

So take a suggestion for your shopping list. Give your true love an inappropriate gift. Don't get grandma another lace cap or pair of woolen mittens. She has plenty already, and besides she hates the things. Get her a little bottle of Chanel No. 5 or a set of lipsticks or a pair of dancing slippers. That will boost her morale, make her feel she is still alive. As you reach for that fine book for your beloved pastor, the learned tome *Archaeology and the Bible*, stay your hand. Reach over to the next counter and get him the *New Yorker Book of Cartoons*. There will be several cartoons by Peter Arno, highly inappropriate for the clergy. That's the idea. There are few joys greater than that of stepping out of character for a time. And I'll bet it will do a lot more for his sermons too. And father—lay off the neckties and the conservative scarf. Get him a Lionel electric train, appropriate for age nine. (All his own; Junior keep away!) Dad has always had a yen for one. And for your wife—well, that has me stumped, as usual. How about a—er—ah—Oh, well, how about a partridge in a pear tree? It would be a surprise.

The best gifts of love are those which show a lovely lack of common sense. Flowers (they fade, don't they?), a bracelet (invariably a nuisance). It is usually on the twenty-fifth anniversary that a husband gives a vacuum cleaner or a Mix Master.

There is high precedent for all this. The first Christmas gift was highly inappropriate—a Baby in a barn. Who wanted that? No one clapped his hands and said, "Goody, goody, just what I wanted!" That is, no one except a few souls who could really see— Simeon and Anna in the Temple, some shepherds, His mother.

They were all looking for a king
To slay their foes and lift them high.
Thou cam'st a little baby thing
To make a woman cry.

Yours with a sprig of holly,
SIMEON STYLITES.

LET NOTHING YOU DISMAY

BY RUTH P. HARNDEN

Ruth Peabody Harnden is a Radcliffe graduate, and studied in 1936 at Trinity College, Dublin, Ireland. She has written two novels and various short stories, several of which have won awards. In "Let Nothing You Dismay," Miss Harnden praises the gifts that express the Christmas spirit.

She had spent the afternoon trimming the tree. She had trimmed it after the fashion of her native land, with bright red polished apples hanging, for balance and for beauty, under each pure-white candle. The old customs, her distant youth, were sharp to her memory. Sometimes they were sharper than the events of her present life in this New England village where she had come so many years ago and raised her American family. Sometimes, and more often of late, she would find herself forgetting things that had happened only the week before. She would make confusing mistakes, answer letters she had answered already, or else forget to answer them at all. It surprised her very much. She could remember so brilliantly every tree in her mother's garden, every street in the small Swedish town where she had grown up, every face and name of her early playmates and neighbors. It was very puzzling.

She sat now in the dark room, in the fragrance from the balsam tree, and watched the year's first snow falling beyond the window. She would not light the candles yet. She was saving them for the children. If the snow kept up, she knew, it would make the walking bad. But she hoped that it would keep up. She found it beautiful—and more than that. She had never lost, or perhaps she had found again, a childlike sense of magic in the presence of the first snowfall.

How strange it must be, she thought, to live where there is always snow. There was Hilda in the mountains of Oregon— Hilda who had cooked for her so faithfully until she married that crazy miner and went to live in some shack in the wilds. So *cold*, she would write in her letters. *Always so cold it is, I think I never be warm again.*

Rocking gently in the warm room, smelling the Christmas tree, watching the quick, feathered air outside, she thought with satisfaction of the socks she had knit for Hilda. Six pairs, extra heavy. Hilda's feet, at least, would be warm.

She had mailed them in plenty of time. Last week, wasn't it? And there was still a week to go before Christmas. But then, she asked herself abruptly, what was it that she had mailed this morning? Something to Hilda, she was sure. She remembered thinking of her at the post office this morning, and she had written on the wide, flat box—But that was impossible! That was the box from Martins. That was the nightie for Janie who was getting married right after Christmas.

Her granddaughter getting married! Only think. It was hard to realize. And it was the loveliest nightie she could find, the color of honeysuckle and trimmed with real lace. "Extravagant," she told herself dutifully now, but it didn't prevent her from smiling. It was so beautiful, and so was Janie—and she was getting married. Nineteen. Janie was nineteen. It didn't seem possible. And she had sent the nightie this morning to . . .

She stopped the gently rocking chair and sat straighter, trying to stop her thoughts until she could straighten them.

She had stood at the table in the post office, under the placard listing the states and their mailing dates—For Florida, For Oregon —and she had thought of Hilda. "Oh, dear!" she said aloud, because now she could remember very clearly writing Mrs. Hilda Borge, writing the Oregon address. "And the socks?" she asked herself. Had she sent the socks to Janie in Florida? But she could write to Janie. She could explain. It was of Hilda that she needed to think.

For a moment she was seeing the plain and practical Hilda with an awful clarity, because she was seeing her in relation to the bridal nightie, the gleaming satin, the cobweb lace. It was a picture so incongruous as to be almost indecent. And no one would be quicker to know that than Hilda herself. How she scorned all softness, all luxury and beauty, out of the protective shell she had built around her own poverty and plainness. "Such nonsense!" she could hear Hilda saying. "When so many are hungry, and cold." But it was really the beauty that Hilda feared, as though she had to deny its existence or she would have to admit her own deprivation—her small, middle-aged, shapeless body, her homely work-scarred hands, the hopeless plainness of her face. She was unredeemed by a single beauty, and the only wonder was that even the thickheaded, bowlegged miner had wanted to marry her.

Would Hilda ever understand that it was only an old woman's fumbling mistake and not an insult, not a mockery to send that exquisite gossamer nightie into her poor stark shack where, in all likelihood, she slept in her long woolen underwear? Or would it break her heart with its terrible contrast to her own ugliness, its terrible reminder of all the luxury and loveliness that had no place in her own life? "How could I?" she asked herself. "And for Christmas, too?" The happiest time of the year, the time for remembering old friends with love and with loving gifts. Even now in the distance, but still distinctly, she could hear the carol singers lifting their voices on the sharp and snow-filled air. "God rest you merry, gentlemen, let nothing you dismay . . ." How ironic the words seemed to her now, like a rebuke to her shameful stupidity, her cruel blunder.

It was only the day after Christmas that she had Janie's wire from Miami—Janie who was so young and impatient, and too busy with her wedding plans to sit down and write a letter. *Marvelous ski socks*, the wire read. *How did you guess where we were spending our honeymoon?* So that, at least, was all right, even though she had forgotten, after all, to write an explanation to Janie. Now she was glad that she hadn't written. Ski socks, indeed! It made her think of her own youth in Sweden, and it was a number of minutes before her mind returned to the present. But then she *had* sent the nightie to Hilda! For a little while, for a few happy Christmas days she had forgotten.

It was another week before Hilda's letter came. *Old Hilda*, it began (in the middle of her own thought, after the habit of her simplicity). For a second she thought her worst fears had been realized and her heart shook. But her eyes moved rapidly on. *Old Hilda, they think, there is only to keep her warm. So they send the sweaters, the mittens, the socks. What could make her pretty, such a one, eh? But you, my lovely friend, you have the other heart, the other eyes, and I am beautiful now! I open up the tight-air stove so the room is full of heat, and I put on my beautiful dress made for dancing, and what you think? I dance! Old Hilda dance, can you think of it? And my Tim he come and dance with me. Ha, I think my Tim he fall in love with me all over again.*

SOMETHING NEW IS BORN

from *Beloved Bondage*

BY ELIZABETH YATES

Elizabeth Yates, widely known for her beautiful stories for children and young people, is also recognized as a novelist of insight, compassion, and originality. Beloved Bondage, her third full-length book, presents the distinctive problem of John Bennet and his wife, Althea, who has fled from the hard realities of life and taken refuge in a dream world of her own. In "Something New Is Born," Louisa Frazer, the town librarian, teaches us a new approach to Christmas sharing.

Christmas was the one day of the year when Louisa Frazer allowed herself absolute leisure. She slept late, dressed only partially, then donned the ancient but comfortable house coat and slid her feet into the worn but cozy pair of bedroom slippers. She made herself a generous pot of coffee and heated some specially purchased sugar buns, then she seated herself in the sitting room with her presents and cards beside her and gave herself to a long series of single and separate joys. Opening her gifts, she marveled at the children's acumen as they gave her what they thought she could use or what they wanted to see her wear. It was like Rhoda to give her a bottle of toilet water with a pronounced and expressive scent; it was like Grace to give her a pot of spring bulbs that would extend delight over a long period.

The presents evidenced her immediate environment; but the cards went back over many years. They came from fellow workers in other libraries, old friends, relatives in different parts of the world, for though the Frazers were a far-flung family they never forgot each other at Christmas. It was a slender link, this one of loving messages, but it sufficed; and through the relaying of a year's news in a single letter the bond was maintained.

Roland's letter she saved till the last; she always did. His small careful writing was restful to her eyes after the various calligraphies she had been reading or struggling to read. His news, tersely put and neatly expressed as became a writer, was always worth reading slowly; and when she put his letter down, she could not say how long a time might elapse before she would want to take up the strands of the day again. For twenty years— it had been all of that since they last met—she had felt that Christmas Day belonged to them. They spent it together. During the year she gave little thought to Roland, unless a book of his came out or some item about him appeared in the press, but on this day she roamed far back into memory with him. It was her Christmas present to herself.

Late in the afternoon, when darkness was already coming, through the streets and causing lights to be lit in houses, Louisa Frazer with Pourri on his lead went out for a walk. There was an emptiness to the town, a loneliness to the streets, for cheer dwelt within houses and merrymakers were all on the warm side of lighted windows. It must be a hard day for those who were alone, she thought, but it was not for her: she was companioned by memory and Pourri was a good friend. Her heart went out to people who, for one reason or another, might be friendless or homeless. For them, the tinsel and gilt, the gaiety and joy must be hollow indeed. She hoped there were not many. She went to the library, as she wanted to get some papers that were in her office.

"Now, Pourri," she said, "you've had quite enough presents and even if the library does possess a mouse it's not yours today. Understand?"

He mewed. He understood exactly as far as it pleased him to understand, and no farther. Miss Frazer ought to know that.

A half hour later, she left her office by the basement door and walked around to the front of the building to give Pourri a little extra airing before starting for home. It was dark, except for the street lights, and as she came around the building she thought she saw a man turn up the walk and approach the front door. She walked more quickly, Pourri objecting but having little attention paid to him. Miss Frazer saw the man try the door, then turn away when he found that it was locked.

"The library isn't open today," she called out. "Is there anything I can do for you?"

The man turned toward her. She thought he looked familiar, but at that distance she could not be sure.

"No, thanks, Miss Frazer."

It was someone that knew her. She picked Pourri up and hurried across the grass.

"Why, John Bennet," she said, in her surprise calling him by his full name. She stood beside him. And then, without any words of his, she knew—knew why he had come to the library to read on the afternoon of Christmas Day.

His hat was turned down over his eyes, and his collar was turned up to keep out the cold. His face looked gray and tired, as if he had not slept at all the night before; but it was more than sleeplessness that etched the deep lines down his cheeks and under his eyes. It was hopelessness. Loneliness hung over him like a cloud heavy with portent, and it was not just the temporary sense of abandon when a loved one is distant for a while, but the soul-destroying sensation of being utterly and terribly alone in the world.

Louisa Frazer put her hand on his arm, "Come home and have some tea with me."

He drew back from her touch. "No, thank you."

"Come along, John," she pleaded.

Her use of his Christian name arrested him more than the touch of her hand on his arm or the tone of her voice. "Haven't you got company or—or something?" he asked.

"No," she laughed. "I'm all alone too. Pourri and I always keep Christmas Day for ourselves. Abominably selfish, but we like it that way."

Unwilling to believe her yet drawn more by his need than her invitation, he walked beside her.

She opened the door and turned on a light. The room was tidy; Miss Frazer had seen to that before she went out. Christmas cards had been ranged in neat arrays on mantel and window sills, presents were together in a basket. There was a pot of white cyclamen sent by the Highlands Library staff, and a single sprig of holly bearing a mass of berries. The room had a look of holiday enjoyment without too conscious an air of festivity; but all John saw was a room that was warm with the life that flowed through it, two deep comfortable chairs, plenty of books, and friendly faces smiling out of photographs. It was a small room that might hold one happily in, buttressed by comeliness of living. Pourri had gone quickly off to a corner, where he was working methodically on paws and coat. He suffered a walk in winter weather only because for some unaccountable human reason his mistress seemed to wish it, and he always made immediate haste to repair its ravages to his well-being and appearance.

"Let me have your coat and hat," Miss Frazer was saying. "I'll hang them up for you."

John gave her his hat and coat; his rubbers he had already taken off and left by the door. Miss Frazer, putting his things away, could not help but notice that his coat lining should have been repaired long ago. It would take a whole new lining now to make it presentable.

John stood awkwardly in the room, conscious of the fact that his suit needed pressing and that he should have put on a clean shirt that morning. While Miss Frazer was taking off her hat and coat he straightened his tie and ran his hands over his hair.

"Do sit down and make yourself comfortable," she called to him. "It will take me a few minutes to get the tea. There's a new book on the table. Isn't that love," she laughed heartily, "to send a librarian a book to read? But it's one I never get a chance at, for it's been out ever since it first came in."

"Are you sure I'm not causing you any trouble? Perhaps you were going out or—or—"

"Trouble? You're the event of the day! Pourri and I would be feeling very lonely just about now if you hadn't come along. Sit down and make yourself at home."

John sighed deeply. The feeling of awkwardness was sliding off him. He began to feel that he was doing Miss Frazer a favor by spending an hour or so with her. He took up the book she had spoken of and sat down with it in his hands, but he did not care whether he read or not. It was enough to be in a room that was warm and gay and comfortable, a room that was lived in, where people talked and perhaps even spun ideas.

Pourri landed in John Bennet's lap with a light clump and a long "Prrrr—prrrrr—prrrrp" that sounded like an elongated question mark.

John had never had a cat in his lap before and he drew back instinctively from the dubious visitation, but Pourri's agate glance and continuous purring were unmistakable in intent. Slowly John relaxed. He put out his hand and tentatively stroked the glossy black coat. Pourri arched himself and pushed up against the hand, showing how he liked to be stroked. John, in a mild daze, went on caressing the cat. He still was amazed that Pourri had come to him, that anything had come to him, and for the first time in what seemed to be an endless twenty-four hours the ache of loneliness within him eased a little. The pain was still there, reminding him that it would be back again in full force, but temporarily it was less demanding.

Twenty minutes later Miss Frazer came in with the tea tray. Pourri was by then curled up into a ball on John's lap. John started to rise.

"Oh, please don't," Miss Frazer implored as she set the tray down, "I've never seen Pourri take to someone he hasn't met at least six times previously. It's most unusual, really, and I know he shouldn't be disturbed."

John smiled. His right hand slid easily over Pourri's back, rounding the curve by the long tail and following it to its end among four soft pink paws.

How much younger he looks when he smiles, Miss Frazer thought, realizing sharply that she had seen him smile but rarely. She poured his tea, adding the cream and sugar he asked for; she put it on the table beside him and poured her own, then they both gave themselves to enjoyment—he hesitantly, as if he did not quite dare to let himself, as if he might wake from a dream if he spoke too loud or summoned too much vigor; and she with the gusto and relish that she had for anything good—a cup of tea, a book, a friend. She had toasted muffins and buttered them generously and there were two pots of newly opened jam—both Christmas presents—to go on the muffins; there were small round Christmas cookies brought by one of the children and slices of rich dark fruitcake that had been sent to her by a friend.

John's shyness melted away after a sip or two of tea, a bite of muffin, and he began to relish the occasion. Miss Frazer knew that much was pressing on his mind but she wanted to see him well fed and at ease before she asked him about himself. She never had believed in mixing food and confidences. Enjoy your meal, was her motto, and then turn to the business in hand; and, she had often added, like as not it won't seem so urgent.

Pourri left John's lap only when a saucer of cream with a dash of tea in it was put down on the floor before him.

"Look at that!" Miss Frazer exclaimed. "Isn't it all bribery and corruption! I give the best years of my life to that cat and in the twinkling of an eye he tosses me in the dust heap of forgotten friends and devotes himself to you. And the only way I can get him back is with a saucer of cream!"

John laughed. He stood up to smooth his trousers and then help Miss Frazer gather the dishes on the tray. His effect on the cat delighted him.

Miss Frazer took the tray out to her kitchen, resisting all John's offers of doing the dishes, and came back to the sitting room. Pourri, having had his fill of people, retired to a corner of the room and laid himself out flat, looking long and sleek and relaxed.

"I'm not going to ask you if you had a nice Christmas," Miss Frazer began.

"Thanks. It's better not."

"I'm sorry," Miss Frazer said quietly, "but I doubt if it's worth feeling too disturbed about it. After all, it's only one of three hundred and sixty-five days. It has the same number of hours and it goes as soon. It's just been dressed up and made very fancy. Tomorrow will come—quite as easily as the tenth of April or the first of August."

He winced.

"Don't you like that day either?" she asked, as one might an overparticular child.

He shook his head. "It was my wedding day."

"Oh—and you'd like to cut it out of the calendar too! You are hard on all the festive occasions."

He was silent for a moment, then he leaned forward, looking not at her but the pattern on the carpet. "My life is an awful mess," he said dismally.

"And that gives you leave to behave as you do—going around with an air of grievance as if the world owed you something! My, my, the way we humans put the cart before the horse is certainly ridiculous."

It was her sharp pungent tone that drew him. Had she been soft and sympathetic with him, as some people had been, he would have gone further into his shell; but this slightly acid attitude of hers captivated him. He lifted his gaze from the carpet and looked at her.

"That's better!" she exclaimed. "I'd like to think I'm a little more compelling than my carpet—at least, I'm in slightly better repair."

He laughed. She was challenging him to some sort of battle. He wanted to flex his muscles and test his strength.

"I suppose you know all about me?" he began.

Her dismissal surprised and jolted him. "I scarcely know a thing about you—and I'm not particularly more interested in you than I am in any user of the library."

"My wife isn't well," he said, and then it seemed a very lame utterance to him. Compared with Miss Frazer's stocky attitude to life he was a weakling taking refuge behind a feeble screen.

"I'm sorry, but isn't that more her affair than yours?"

John looked thoughtful. "Probably it is. I never thought of it that way before."

"Was it all right for you to leave her?" Miss Frazer's concern for another came through her voice, making it warm and tender.

John nodded. "I couldn't do anything more for her and I had

to get out for a while. An old lady lives below us and she looks in on Althea whenever I'm out. I knew I'd be back a little after nine."

John felt as if he could and would tell Miss Frazer anything, but oddly enough she did not seem to want to know anything about the nature of Althea's illness. She was not at all interested in what had happened to her. She was not even curious. She seemed to want to know only about himself. John was baffled at first by the thought that anyone could possibly be interested in him, but when he admitted to himself that Miss Frazer was, the effect on him was like Pourri's jumping into his lap. He felt eased and reinstated. As he had gingerly smoothed Pourri's fur and then more confidently, so the thoughts he had such need to release came, first cautiously, and then in good spate.

He told Miss Frazer of the plans he and Althea had had for Christmas. They had bought a little tree and trimmed it, got presents for each other and done them up gaily, decorated the apartment—then suddenly, during the afternoon of Christmas Eve, in the midst of their festive preparations, the old weakness had come over Althea. She had become bewildered and soon collapsed. Perhaps it had been his fault, he admitted, he might have said or done something. He couldn't remember. Perhaps it was because he had put a doll under the tree. He didn't know what had made her go off. Anyway, he had cared for her through the night, and in the morning, just when they might have been opening their presents, she had gone into one of those strange exhausted states of slumber from which she would rouse herself to eat and that would be all.

"It may last days, it has lasted for months," he said, and the edge of his tone was one of weary bitterness while behind the dull sound of his voice was an anguished railing at fate.

"What did you mean," Louisa Frazer asked quietly, "when you said you put a doll under the tree?"

"I was in a toyshop a few days before Christmas," John explained, "and I bought a doll for my little daughter. I put it under the tree. I—I didn't think Althea would see it."

"Oh, John, John, you can't do things like that."

"Why?" he asked stubbornly, and his voice was hard and sullen. "It wasn't any crime to do that, was it? I bought it with my money.

I wasn't going to tell Althea who it was for but when she saw it I had to."

"And then?"

"That was the end of Christmas for us," he laughed harshly. "I still don't see what I did that was wrong. She plays with imaginary people at times, and just because I had one—"

"A child can have an imaginary playmate, John, but a man can't." Miss Frazer's voice was very low. "It's just one of the prices we have to pay for growing up. What have you done with yourself today?"

He told her how he could not stand the sight of the Christmas baubles, the greens they had filled the house with, the trinkets they had hung on the tree. He had taken delight in smashing the ornaments on the tree and dragging the tree down to the ash can; he had pulled down the decorations and put all the presents in in an empty drawer, and he had not felt like himself until the rooms were bare and plain again. He hated the thought of Christmas. When he went out on the street he was reminded of it wherever he went, wherever he looked. In desperation he had turned to the library.

"When I found it closed I—I—" He twisted his hands together. "I'm frightened now to think what I might have done if you hadn't called to me."

Miss Frazer thought to herself that she was frightened too.

He looked around the room. "I'm glad you haven't got any reminders of Christmas. I couldn't stand it if you had."

"I think you could, John. I think you would find that the pervading spirit of Christmas is deeper and richer than all the baubles that surround it. You do wrong when you try to rule it out. It's simply an expression of the overflow of man's heart— that's the tide for you to be on, not vandalism, iconoclasm."

And then he told her more about Althea.

"Perhaps you knew her family when you lived in Highlands. The name was Trainer."

Louisa Frazer thought for a moment. "It rings a very faint bell —a big old house and a tragedy some years ago."

"Yes," John nodded, "Mrs. Trainer died under peculiar circumstances. It happened while we were on our wedding trip. Sometimes I think that Althea has never forgiven me or herself that it did happen."

"She was devoted to her mother?"

"Not exactly, but she was her mother's little pet. She came and went, wore things, did things—all to please her mother, just like a little Pekinese. But I didn't know all that when I married her."

"The Trainers were not library users," Miss Frazer said shortly, for that was always the beginning and end with her of knowing people.

"No—they bought books or went without. Things that had been used by others were not fit for the Trainers. When we couldn't afford to buy books during the first years of our marriage we didn't have any."

"That must have been hard on your wife."

"Perhaps it was."

"If your life has been so difficult you've done well to endure it this long."

He moved his shoulders in a gesture of hopelessness. "Along with a good many others, I'm a prisoner to the marriage bond."

"Sometimes a sentence can be commuted."

"Mine won't be until I die."

"Why haven't you left your wife?"

John started at the directness of the question from someone he felt he scarcely knew, but its directness conditioned his answer.

"There wasn't anyone else to take care of her—and she needs care, very much at times."

"And you think you don't love her?"

John shook his head. "I know I don't—haven't for a long time. I've just done things—well, because I got into the way of doing them."

"But you did love her once?"

"Yes," John said, honestly, but slowly, as if he were trying to recall his early emotion, "and I wanted to be true to her all my life, but I lost those feelings a long time ago."

"Do you ever talk to anyone, John?"

He shook his head. "Just to my daughter, but that's in letters."

"Don't you have any close friends?"

"There was a fellow I used to know, but he was killed in an accident a couple of years ago. I haven't wanted to talk to anyone since then. I had to invent someone or go crazy."

Miss Frazer longed to put her arms around the lonely man

who sat in the chair opposite her, but her voice that was rich and warm with love circled him in sympathy. "Death for the young is tragedy," she said, "for the old it is part of life's completion. Yet I have known those that I have loved to be nearer me after they have gone. Memory is a present place and affection is a kindly keeper."

He made no reply.

"Have you had anything to eat today?" she asked him suddenly.

He nodded. "The old lady who lives below us brought up a plate of dinner. I didn't want it but I ate it."

"Who is she?"

"Just an old deaf person who hooks rugs for a living. She's got an impediment in her speech and no one but Althea can ever understand what she says."

"Does your wife see her often?"

"She's about the only person Althea does see, but the old lady is getting all crippled with arthritis. She won't be able to do her rugs much longer and then I suppose they'll take her off to some kind of home."

The tone of John Bennet's voice made Louisa Frazer shudder inwardly. His own years of suffering had calloused him to that of others.

"Poor prisoner," she said.

"Who?"

"That old lady."

"Oh, she seems to be quite happy. I wouldn't call her a prisoner."

"No? Then she's found her freedom, in spite of walls of deafness and stiffness?"

John felt a wave of shame sweep over him. There was something embracing about Miss Frazer. She took in so many but she always seemed to have room for one more.

"Freedom is a curious thing," she was saying. "We don't think much about it until we've lost it—and then the more we think about it the more we find we have it within us. In fact, I'm not sure that we ever really know freedom until we've known some form of limitation; for freedom, in its real sense, is not external, spatial, it's in the heart and the mind. Physically man can be bound by almost any kind of material, but nothing can fetter him mentally except his own despair."

"What does freedom have to do with Althea?"

Miss Frazer smiled quickly, widely, as she had that first time in her office when John had felt that he was being taken into her heart. She shook her head. "It hasn't only to do with her, bless her heart, it has still more to do with you."

"With me?"

"We've all been prisoners of some kind or other, John, and those of us who find our release find with it the way to help others. All that matters is that we get our release, become free men instead of enduring as slaves. You did not put up Althea's barriers, but because you stand in the closest human relation to her your own freedom will help take them down. I don't know her at all and I know you very little, but I'm quite sure that you hold the key to her heart and that you are the only one who does. I don't think you've lost the key but I think you've forgotten how to use it."

"I have," John said slowly, and the bitter ache in his heart came through his voice. "I can't do anything right any more and everything I do seems to be the wrong thing. I haven't got the things I thought life held. I wanted a loving wife, a nice home, a child that would bear my name. It wasn't wrong to want those things, was it?"

"No, John, they are the dear deep desires of all the human race. But I think you went wrong somewhere. Haven't people always wanted Althea for something? Her mother wanted her to be her own private indulgence, and you wanted her for her child. When someone wants her wholly for herself it may be the turning point in her life."

"A doctor told me some years ago that there was a delicate balance within Althea that easily became upset." John sighed. "I've weighed too much for her."

"You can't ask her for what she cannot give you, John, but you can go back to when you married her and love her for herself."

There was a long pause, then John said huskily, "And you don't think I'll ever have my little girl?"

Louisa Frazer leaned forward and touched John's hand, more

to arrest his attention than as a gesture of affection though it served for both. "John, I did not say that, I said, don't seek Althea for what she can give you but for what she is in herself."

So much divided them, but in that moment of time Louisa Frazer felt nearer John Bennet than she had felt to anyone in her life. Her longing was great to help him since the time to do it in seemed shorter than ever; for how could his Althea ever be identified with reality if he was fast losing his hold on reality himself? The pressure of her hand on his arm increased.

"John, the world is full of children. Perhaps Althea is the little girl you long for. A child is loved into the world. It's up to you to love Althea into active participation in the world."

John put his head in his hands and rocked it back and forth. "But why, why," he mumbled through his hands, "have I had this come to me? Why couldn't I have had the plain sort of life I longed for? I wasn't asking for more than most people do."

"There isn't any accepted answer to that why, John. It has been wailed countless times since the world began and it will be wailed again and again as time goes on, for each one of us has to find his own peculiar answer. I don't know why such a task came to you when some apparently get by in life so easily, but something in you must have made you worthy of it. There must be a prince for every sleeping beauty. I cannot answer your why except by saying that I think you are the prince."

The little Swiss clock on the mantel struck nine and John got up from his chair.

"You don't have to go, do you?"

"She knows the library closes at nine. She'll expect me soon after."

"Will she be awake then?"

"Yes and no, a sort of half state. She'd know if I were not in and yet once I am in it won't make any difference."

"Perhaps it will tonight."

He shook his head. "I've fooled myself with hoping for so long that I don't do it any more. I just accept. If she's awake, all right; if not—"

"That was before you knew you were the prince." Louisa Frazer smiled provocatively. "Coming to the library tomorrow night?"

He nodded. "It's the only life I have—books."

"It's a good life."

He put on his hat and coat, then reached down to stroke Pourri, who was winding in and out between his legs. At the door he turned to Miss Frazer and thanked her. They shook hands and John thought how strong her clasp was. Louisa Frazer, looking into his eyes, was aware of their color for the first time that day, as if they had been darkened by anguish but now that was allayed their own true brown shone forth. Some subtle look of fear had worn off his face during their visit and she was glad to see it gone. A frightened man could never be a free one.

She went to the window and pushed the curtain aside so she could watch him until a turn in the street took him from sight. He was walking as one would for whom life still held something; not as he had been that afternoon when she first caught sight of him. She crossed the room to her desk, opened the drawer, and took out a small leather portrait case. She gazed for a long time at the portrait of the man within.

"It's still our day, Roland. It's still Christmas."

She thought back in her mind over the many Christmases that she had spent alone. Such a drear thought it was to some to spend the day alone, and yet always something had happened to her because she had been alone: today, it was meeting John Bennet and bringing him back to tea; last year, in Highlands, it was spending the evening with the janitor's wife when her husband was in the hospital. A few years ago she had taken her dinner in a restaurant, sitting at a table with a stranger. A tale of lonely grief had been poured out to her and with it the decision to end an unbearable life. They had talked together. Gradually a change had taken place and something new had been born. It was not hard to find the sad or weary people at this time, they stood out like shadows in a season of light. One by one she recalled them as her thoughts traveled back through the years, things that never could have happened if she had accepted any of the many invitations that came to her. And they had happened because she had kept the day for Roland.

"It's almost as if these people were our children, Roland," she said, looking at the face in the leather frame. "Yet, when I write them to you, you say you can never put them in your stories, for they are not complicated enough. But it is all so very simple, really, a key turning and something changing in a single human life—and all of life thereafter somehow very different."

She folded the leather case and put it away in the drawer of her desk. She might not look at it again for a long time.

THE OLD LADIES

from *The Old Ladies*

BY HUGH WALPOLE

Hugh Walpole will long be remembered as an effective teller of tales and a masterly delineator of characters. The scene of his novel The Old Ladies *is a small picturesque English cathedral town, where three old ladies are linked together by destiny on the same floor of a shabby, antiquated house. The following abridged account of "Christmas Eve— Polchester Winter Piece" reveals the importance of faith, courage, and beauty in the heart.*

Polchester of the old days was an enclosed town. The Riviera was unknown to it and the Garden of Allah a dream with Omar. Though London might call to the richer citizens on one occasion or another, at Christmas time every one stayed at home and, more wonderful yet to our modern disillusion, enjoyed family parties with Christmas trees, plum puddings, stockings, and the waits invited into the hall. Glebeshire, warmer than any other part of the British Isles, has never had an intimate acquaintance with crisp and shining snow. About once in twenty years there are snowfalls, frosts, and blue skies, and how happy then every one is and how eagerly every one hands down the year to an envious posterity!

This was such a year, and ten days before Christmas the frost came and held, the powdered snow remained jewelled and resplendent, the sun looked down from a sky as delicately blue as an egg-shell and laughed to see the fun. And fun there was!

Magnet's toy-shop in the Market Cloisters had a Father Christmas, a true and veritable Father Christmas to be seen with two crimson cheeks and long snow-white beard any afternoon between two and four. Every one did their best. In the Market-place there was a Punch and Judy with a thick-set jolly-faced man in charge. Half-way up the High Street, Gummridge's the stationers had a whole Christmas tree in their window. Here was a stumbling-block to the whole High Street traffic. It was a tree frosted, coloured, and shining, hung about with every glittering bauble, shaped to a perfect pinnacle of exquisite symmetry. But best of all was the window of Hunt & Griffin, the General Store, for here, for the first time in Polchester history, was a whole front window given over to pageantry, to none other than the scene in the life of Cinderella when, despondent beside the fire, she is amazed by the sudden apparition of her peaked-hatted Godmother. So great was the confusion outside the window that had this occurred in these traffic-haunted times the show must have been forbidden, but in those lucky days nobody minded, nobody cared. Let the children have a good time, Christmas comes but once a year.

The town rang with laughter and the ringing of bells. The Cathedral let itself go and burst into perpetual peals of merriment. There was fun everywhere, apples and oranges in the Market-place, and carols up and down the streets after dark. It was the best Christmas that Polchester had known for many a day past or would know for many a day to come.

Mrs. Amorest was one who had always enjoyed a seasonable Christmas. To her as to every old person Christmas was filled with sad memories, but she had a wonderful gift of enjoying fun at the moment of its occurrence, and very small occurrences amused and excited her.

This was the happiest Christmas known to her for many a day. Struggle as she might not to think of the money coming to her, she could not keep it out of her consciousness. She told herself again and again that she must not place too strong a reliance on her cousin's promise. "He may have altered his mind the next moment. It's silly to believe him." Nevertheless the solemnity of his words, the caress of his hand as it rested on her head—these things were difficult to dismiss. She *could* not keep down her spirits as, being a penniless, lonely old widow of over seventy, she should.

And this Christmas she lost completely her self-control. She adored above everything else in the world the spending of money, perhaps for the very reason that she never had very much to spend. She liked greatly to be given things, but still better was it herself to make presents. The excitement of giving some one something he or she wanted was intense, to watch the opening of the parcel, to see the stare of pleasure and surprise, to hear the exclamation, to feel the affection flowing out—was there any luxury in life like it?

And it was a luxury that, of late, she had been compelled to deny herself. Last Christmas she had given Agatha Payne half a dozen pocket-handkerchiefs, and her cousin a pocket-book. Worst sorrow of all, it was impossible to send Brand anything. No use to throw parcels out into the void. The best she could do was to write two letters, one a month in advance, and this she sent to the only address she had, something in California, and then one on Christmas Eve, such as she had always written to him at Christmas time. This she also sent out to California, but she wrote it because for a moment it brought him closer to her —she felt, with his photograph up there in front of her, as though she had him with her in the room. These were all but poor substitutes for reality, and, cheat ourselves as we may, our subconscious selves refuse to be deceived. Mrs. Amorest knew nothing about her subconscious self, but she did know that after last Christmas she had a miserable sense of inadequacy and frustrated purpose. She had made nobody happy. This year she would fling her cap over the mill. She had prospects.

The plan came to her in the middle of the night, or rather in one of those early morning hours when the first cock crows and the hidden despair raises its abominable head. Lying there in the early morning she drove her despairs away and considered Miss Beringer. Poor Miss Beringer! What a frightened, nervous, trembling creature she was! She would like to do something for her! She would like to give her a happy Christmas! And Agatha Payne, too. It was then that the idea came to her.

At first she was frightened of it. It would demand energy and persistence. And *had* she money enough? She examined her purse and found that she had sufficient did she use part of next quarter's rent. She trembled at that, but she was sure that kind Mr. Agnew, when he knew of the promise that her cousin had made to her, would not hesitate to advance her. . . .

She trembled. Her heart warned her. Her cheeks were flushed and she had a guilty air. But she held to her purpose, and once she had begun she did not look back, she *could* not look back. She moved, during those frosty coloured days, about the town, the very spirit of adventure. She found that she must go quietly. The excitement tired her, and sometimes she would, in a moment, feel so weary that she *could* not get to the top of the High Street, and on one occasion when she was at the top she could not go down again and had to take refuge in the shop of Mr. Bennett, the grand bookseller. There she sat, greatly alarmed, on a chair in the very middle of the shop. . . .

She tried to keep her head about her purchases. She found, as many another has found before and after her, that the best things were always the most expensive. And then when it came to the central purchase of all, to the core, the heart, the pinnacle, she found that *here* expense was inevitable. Try as you would, it must cost more than you had supposed. Of course she only wanted a small one, but even the small ones . . . And then at the last, two days before Christmas, she found in the Market-place, in a corner behind the old woman under the green umbrella, the very thing, a perfect specimen, a miracle, and, when she enquired of the nice round-faced man whose possession it was, she found that it was only . . . well, less than the experience of the last two days had led her to believe possible, although more, a good deal more, than she had originally intended. She bought it, and ordered that it should be sent to her room, blushing a little as she named the address. She gave her name very carefully, begging him to be watchful that it should not be sent to any other room by mistake, and he promised her, saying that he would himself bring it.

He did in fact arrive with it when she was there, and she liked him very much, holding him in conversation for quite a while, and then giving him an orange for the baby. After that she guarded her room like a dragoness and would not allow May Beringer, who was already forming a too constant habit of "dropping in," to cross her threshold.

Christmas Eve arrived, and Mrs. Amorest was delighted when

she discovered how fine and clear it was; no wind, the smoke rising from the chimneys elephant grey against the blue, the thin rind of frost, the sparrows already chattering at her window for their crumbs.

After her little mid-day meal she sat down to the table, found her paper and envelopes, and wrote to Brand. Her letter was as follows:

My dearest, darling Boy—I must write to you as I always do, although I sadly fear that it will be a long time before you get this letter. The one that I wrote to you a month ago may reach you before Christmas, and I hope it will. This I am writing because it seems as though I am talking to you, and I don't wish to allow Christmas to pass by without having a word with my dear boy.

Perhaps you have been writing to me and still to the old address. I told them in Cheltenham to forward anything on, but they are so stupid at the post-office, although I daresay they are good men.

Well, dearest boy, I try to imagine to myself the kind of Christmas you are having, but it is really difficult for me, because you told me in the last letter I had from you that it was quite hot at Christmas time. That seems to me very strange and not very nice, I think.

I am very well in health. If only I could hear that you are quite well and will come home soon for a visit I would be quite happy. You know, dear boy, I am an old woman now and can't expect to live for ever, so that I do hope you'll be able to come home soon. It's very nice here and I'm very comfortable. There's something else I'd like to tell you about, but I suppose that I must not just yet because it isn't quite settled. I think of you so much and pray for you night and morning. At this time of the year when God came down to earth and took upon Him our flesh and was a little baby in a manger, I think we should all make Him feel how thankful we are. I know that He is looking after you and so I don't worry about you.

My dearest boy, you are always in my thoughts.—

Your loving
MOTHER.

She sat for a long time after she had written the letter with his photograph in front of her. She thought of him in all the ways that she had known him—as a baby at her breast, as a small boy in his first trousers, as a boy going to his first day-school and forgetting her so quickly in the new excitements of other boys and games and masters, as all right and proper boys must do, of course. And then, as he grew, her interest in the strange new personality that developed, as flower from the bud—a personality that was so strange because it was like neither herself nor his father, somebody quite new. And then his growing independence, his chafing at the literary and artistic interests of his father, his desire for the open-air life and complete independence. Then her own strange sympathy with him; and although she loved him so dearly she understood that he should want to get away and be free. He left her and at intervals returned to her. She had been a woman of forty when she had borne him, and he had been only twenty-seven when she had last seen him, still a boy although so strong and independent! She looked at the photograph until she seemed to draw him out of the frame and he came to her and put his arms round her and teased her in the old laughing way that he had always had. But she was not simply a sentimental woman; she was in fact scornful of emotion that led to nothing, and so she put on her bonnet and her coat, and, because it was already three o'clock and would soon be dusk, hurried off to take her present to her cousin.

This year she was giving him a picture, a photogravure in a nice black frame of Holman Hunt's "Carpenter's Shop." She had not been quite lately to visit him lest she should seem to be reminding him of his promise. She had not heard how his health was, but she hoped that this bright weather had helped him, and that he would perhaps see her. Nevertheless as she crossed the bridge and climbed the hill a little chilling wind, whence she knew not, breathed upon her heart. Rising out of the dark purple-hued river appeared the figure of Agatha Payne.

She saw, quite unexpectedly, reasons for May Beringer's terrors. There *was* something alarming about Agatha, something not quite normal and healthy, something odd and twisted. It came, perhaps, because the poor old thing lived so much alone, but Mrs. Amorest gave a little shiver and thought to herself that she would move from that house in the spring to somewhere brighter and more companionable. She could not drive the company of Agatha from her mind. All up the hill it kept pace with her.

And then, pausing for breath before she entered her cousin's gate, she smiled at her folly. Her practical mind drove her fancies like mist into the frosty air.

The house, always ugly and forbidding, seemed simply not to belong to the fresh and wonderful day. To Mrs. Amorest, as she approached it, it seemed to say: "You aren't truly so sentimental as to believe that the human race is loving and kind. Rid yourself of your illusions. You should be ashamed of yourself at your age that you have any."

As she rang the bell and heard it clang defiantly through the house she felt again a dim and unhappy foreboding. She always disliked her meeting with the housekeeper. She felt that that woman despised and patronised her. But one could only pass to her cousin over the housekeeper's body. There was no other way for it.

The woman herself opened the door and was more forbidding than she had ever been. Mrs. Amorest suspected that in some way she had learnt about her cousin's promise. To-day she blocked the doorway with her peevish ill-natured body and showed no sign at all of moving. Mrs. Amorest felt a sudden, almost affectionate, pity for her gift. It had cost, as it seemed to her, a large sum, but in the eyes of this woman it would be simply another wheedling attempt on her part to extort more money from her cousin. She summoned her courage and smiled her friendliest smile.

"Good afternoon. How is my cousin to-day?"

"Not at all well, I'm afraid."

"Oh dear, I am sorry to hear that. I thought that this fine weather might have done him some good."

There was no answer to this, so after a little pause Mrs. Amorest, feeling the chill of the afternoon air, said:

"Of course, it *is* cold, isn't it, but I thought that, being in bed, he might not notice it. Has the doctor been to-day?"

"Yes, the doctor has been."

Well, she might ask me into the hall, thought Mrs. Amorest. "Could I see him for a moment, do you think? Just to wish him a happy Christmas."

"I'm afraid not, Mrs. Amorest. It was the doctor's orders that he is not to be disturbed by anybody."

There was a pause, and then Mrs. Amorest said cheerfully:

"Oh, well, I'm sure that's quite right if the doctor says so. I only wanted to wish him a happy Christmas. I have a little gift." She produced it from under her arm. "I have written a little note in case I should not be able to see him. Would you kindly give it to him?"

"Certainly."

She took the parcel, looking neither at it nor at Mrs. Amorest, but forward into the brown and naked garden with a frown of determination as though she was not going to stand any of that sort of nonsense.

There was another little pause, then Mrs. Amorest said: "Would you most kindly wish him a very happy Christmas for me? Of course I know that it can't be a *very* happy Christmas for him as ill as he is, but I always think it makes a difference if one knows that people are thinking of one, don't you?"

"I will certainly tell him."

"And I hope you'll have a happy Christmas too," said Mrs. Amorest, trembling with the cold.

"Thank you very much, Mrs. Amorest. I wish you the same, I'm sure."

That was all. There was nothing more to be done. The door closed with a horrible final clang, and in some strange flash of vision she knew that she was never to enter that house again.

She walked down the hill, and in spite of all her courage, forebodings now crowded upon her. . . . As she crossed the bridge over the Pol it seemed to her that in another moment her courage would desert her. Because if that money did not come to her!

She summoned all her pluck, standing for a moment on the bridge and watching the river take on its evening colour, softly purple under the dark shadow of the rising hills.

Then, thinking of the evening that was coming and the fun that it would be, she smiled. Things always turned out better than you expected. The stars that were now breaking into the sky above her head were the eyes of God. She was watched over and cared for and protected. She had no need to fear.

The town as she passed up through the High Street was bubbling with merriment and gaiety. The shops blazed with lights; the street was crowded; every one was laughing and happy, hurrying along loaded with parcels, stopping to speak, it seemed, to any one who was near that they might wish them good luck. This was the world that Mrs. Amorest loved. Why might it not always be like this? She stopped at the Cinderella window. How pretty and touching! She turned round to a stout man beside her and said, "Isn't it pretty?"

"Indeed it is, mum," he answered her, smiling. "My little girl wants to take it home. Don't you, Pansy?" and a diminutive child squeaked out "Yes."

"What a pretty little girl!" said Mrs. Amorest.

"Thank you, mum," answered the fat man. "A merry Christmas, I'm sure."

"And the same to you," said Mrs. Amorest.

The rest of the way home seemed easy.

Arrived in her room, she set about the development of her plan. She had asked Agatha Payne and May Beringer to come and visit her at eight o'clock. She had two hours for her preparations. The time flashed by and in a moment it was a quarter to eight. She hurriedly put on her silk dress, hung around her neck her thin gold chain with the locket that held Brand's portrait, brushed her lovely white hair, put on her lace cap fresh and crisp from the laundry, then her stiff white cuffs. Finished. Completed. She sat down to survey her work. A smile played about her lips. It was the most beautiful thing that she had ever seen in her life.

At five minutes past eight there was a knock on her door, and then another knock. Agatha Payne and May Beringer entered. They stood bewildered on the threshold.

It was indeed a pretty sight. The curtains were drawn and the far end of the room was duskily shadowed, but at the fireplace end stood—THE TREE!

And what a tree! Of just the right size for the room, it had a shape and symmetry that surely no other tree in all Christmasdom could equal. It tapered gradually with exquisite shape and form to a point that quivered and flickered like a green flame. On the flame sturdily triumphed Father Christmas, diminutive in body, but alive in his smile, his stolidity, his gallant colour. It was the colour that entranced the eye. Mrs. Amorest had worked with the soul of an artist. She had not over-burdened the slender branches. The thin chains of frosted silver that hung from bough to bough seemed of themselves to dance in patterned rhythm.

Balls of fire, emerald and ruby, amethyst and crystal, shone in the light of the candles. And at every place colour blended with colour. The tree was always the tree. The light that flashed from its boughs was not foreign to it, but seemed to be, integrally, part *of* its life and history. It had been placed on a long and broad looking-glass, into which it looked down as though into a lake of crystal water. The candles seemed to be the voices of the tree; it was vocal in its pleasure, its sense of fun at its own splendour, its grand surprise that after all it had come off so well.

In proportion, in blending of colour, in grandeur of spirit, it was the finest tree in England that night. On either side of the tree were two tables spread with white cloths. On one table were some parcels beautifully tied with coloured ribbons, and on the other sandwiches, a plum-cake with white icing, some saffron buns, and a dish of sweets and chocolates.

The two ladies stood amazed. So pretty was the room with its soft pink colours, its light dim save for the aureole of golden splendour shed by the tree, so utterly unexpected the display, that words would not come; only at last May Beringer cried, "Oh dear! Dear me! Dear me!"

Both ladies had dressed in their party best; May in her orange silk, that suited her not too well, and Agatha in her dark purple, a dress of a fashion now forgotten, too small for her, but that nevertheless with her black hair finely brushed, her dark eyes flashing gave her the air of older days, the air that had made Mr. Payne, thirty-five years ago, call her his "Gipsy Queen."

"Oh, I do hope you won't both think me too silly," said Mrs. Amorest, coming forward, "but I simply had to do something this Christmas. We've just done nothing the last two Christmases and it did seem too bad. Don't you think so? I do hope you don't mind?"

"Mind?" said May Beringer, coming towards the tree and gazing at it with her mouth open like a school-girl. "Why, Mrs. Amorest, it's lovely! It's the loveliest thing! Why, I can't speak. I can't, indeed. Words won't come. I can't say anything at all."

Agatha Payne was moved more deeply still. The colour possessed her as colour always possessed her, coming towards her like a living breathing person, holding out its arms to her, whispering to her, "You and I! We are the only ones here who understand. I have been waiting for you, and you alone."

Indeed it seemed to her that the tree belonged to her and was hers absolutely. The two other women vanished from her consciousness; she could see only the pale golden flame of the candles, so steady, so pure, so dignified, the balls of amethyst and ruby and crystal as they swung and turned and gleamed so slightly and yet always with a secret life and purpose of their own.

And the deep green of the tree, richly velvet under the light of the candles! She stood absorbed, entranced, waves of sensuous pleasure running through her body.

So silent were they both that after a minute had passed Mrs. Amorest was alarmed.

"I'm so glad you like it," she said almost timidly. "Shan't we sit down and look at it? I like to think of all the other trees there are tonight in everybody's homes and the children dancing round them and the presents—"

She broke off because a longing for Brand came to her so urgently that it was all she could do not to call out his name. For a moment it seemed to her foolish humbug, sham, and ridiculous sentiment, that the three of them, old, forgotten, not wanted by anybody, should indulge in this display. But looking up at the tree she was comforted. Anything so beautiful had its own purpose. She had made a beautiful thing. She felt the joy of the creator in her handiwork.

MRS. BARBER'S CHRISTMAS

from *The Bazaar and Other Stories*

BY MARTIN ARMSTRONG

Martin Armstrong has scattered his writing efforts over numerous unrelated fields. A delightful collection of his many-faceted stories has been drawn together for The Bazaar. *There he displays his fascination*

with the essence of human life as it is distilled moment by moment,
and interest permeates "Mrs. Barber's Christmas" as faith guides her
through the twilight zone between living and eternity.

Old Mrs. Barber sat alone in her wooden chair whose arms,
gripped by the hands of three generations of grandmothers and
grandfathers, were smoothed and worn till they looked like
polished bones. The blinds were drawn, the lamp lighted, and a
merry fire crackled in the grate where the kettle was just beginning to sing. At first its songs were far-off and sad—thin ghosts
of songs forgotten, but soon they settled to a warm homeliness
like the comfortable purred song of a cat. And the two together—
the sadness and the homeliness—soothed old Mrs. Barber till she
really felt quite well again. That uncomfortable, dazed feeling in
her head had gone and she settled down into a blurred, peaceful
mood in which, like a spool unwinding itself, her mind effort-
lessly reproduced the doings of the day. Yes, on the whole she
had enjoyed herself, and anyhow she was glad she had gone:
Lizzy would have been hurt if she had not turned up for dinner
on Christmas Day. Four miles each way was a long walk but—
well—she was glad she had gone, even though the walk back
had almost been the death of her. Yes indeed, and if it hadn't
been for Mr. Robson, the Lord knows what would have become
of her. Directly she left Lizzy's to walk home again, she had
felt it was going to be too much for her, and by the time she
had done two miles she was feeling really bad. What a mercy
that Mr. Robson in the cart had overtaken her and given her
a lift for the rest of the way. And even then how ill she had
felt: at one moment she really believed she was going to die
in the cart, and when they stopped at her cottage Mr. Robson
had to lift her down just as if she were a child again. Then
she couldn't find her key, in fact she was feeling too ill to bother
about it. All she wanted was to lie down, and if Mr. Robson had
not held her up she actually would have lain down—just where
she was, in the road. "Let me lie down. Let me lie down," she
had whispered, and it was only after Mr. Robson had pretended
to be angry with her that she had managed to pull herself
together enough to remember where she had put the key. Then
Mr. Robson had propped her against her door and forbidden

her to lie down while he fastened his horse's reins to the railings, and after that he had unlocked her door and put her into her chair, and not only that but he had even made a fire for her and filled the kettle. Yes, he was a good fellow, was Robson, to bother so much about an old woman.

Once in her chair, she felt all right, she said, and so he had left her, promising to send his girl in an hour or two to see if she wanted anything.

And now she really did feel all right. The warmth of the fire seemed to be going right through her as though she were a pane of glass. It was grand. Mr. Robson certainly knew how to make a fire. . . . Yes, he was a good fellow, was Robson, to bother so much about an old woman. Sometimes a little shiver ran down her spine and the fire went blurred for a moment and seemed to recede from her, but that was rather nice, for it seemed to increase the sensation of tired well-being which had taken possession of her and rose sometimes on a little wave of ecstasy to a delicious feeling of numbness in her legs. As soon as the kettle boiled she would make herself a good strong cup of tea: and with a fire like that the kettle wouldn't be long . . . no . . . certainly Mr. Robson knew how to make a fire . . . Yes . . . he was a good fellow, was Robson, to bother so much about! . . .

The kettle suddenly began spluttering and she roused herself to take it off the fire and fill the teapot.

"After all," said Mrs. Barber to Janie Robson, who had looked in when she was at her second cup, "after all, there's nothing like a good strong cup of tea for putting you right, no matter what's wrong. How anyone could get along without it, beats me. And yet there's the Bible. You won't find a word about tea from beginning to end. Wine, water, and milk, you'll find—'He asked for water and she gave him milk': that was Jael, you know; and then there's 'Wine to gladden man's heart'—but seemingly they didn't go in for tea in those times. Well, there's no accounting for tastes." And then Mrs. Barber remembered again that it was Christmas Day and insisted on Janie running home. "You don't want to be bothered with an old woman on Christmas night, my dear," she said. "And tell your father from me that I'm doing nicely now."

At six o'clock the bells began to ring for the evening service:

first one, clear and high in the darkness; then another, a deeper, warmer one; and soon all eight fell into their places in the scale. Over and over they tumbled down the length of the scale until there was no beginning and no ending to it, but just a continuous flow like water down a long waterfall. And then the bells suddenly changed places and wove in and out of one another on a new tune.

Mrs. Barber liked the bells. They produced in her a warm, mysterious, slightly ecstatic feeling, faintly recalling a long line of buried memories. "Dear me," she said to herself, shaking her head wonderingly. "Deary, deary me!" And suddenly she decided that she would go to church. Why not? It was just exactly what she was feeling inclined for. Besides, the distance was nothing, not a quarter of a mile. Well, if she was going she would have to get ready at once, and she got up—dear me, how stiff she was, to be sure!—and put on her bonnet and coat and a warm woollen muffler. Then she placed the matches on the edge of the table where she would be able to lay her hand on them in the dark, extinguished the lamp, and went out.

As she locked the door behind her, she felt as pleased and excited as a child on the brink of a secret escapade. It was a bitter night. She could feel the cold go right down her throat, and she pulled the muffler up over her mouth and nose. The road was like iron: her steps knocked on it as though she were wearing clogs, and in the clear flinty darkness the grass in the ditches sparkled as if with a new-fallen shower of crystals. Her legs were still a little weak, but then the distance was nothing, not a quarter of a mile, and she would have a long rest in the church . . . an hour and ten minutes at least . . . and coming back would be all downhill . . . besides, the distance was nothing, not at . . . The porch looked like a cold yellow cave at the end of the path between the tombstones, but when she passed through it and down the step into the church, it was very far from being cold: it was deliciously warm, with a comfortable smell of hot-pipes and paraffin-oil. The crowd that flowed past her up the nave made her feel suddenly nervous and irritable and she took her seat far back among the empty pews where there would be no one to bother her or to notice if she did not stand up during the psalms.

From where she sat, the church looked like a huge softly-shining cavern upon whose floor the congregation was spread in a black, restless mass, out of which the pillars grew up, gradually more and more luminous, into the warm, misty light like the stems of giant lilies. Lamps hung from the arches and, far off in the distant chancel, which appeared as a glowing core of radiance beyond the paler light of the nave, the tall altar-candles shone like a row of stars.

For Mrs. Barber's old eyes the many lamps and candles filled the church with a golden fog, and sometimes the lights receded from her, just as it had happened at home when she was gazing into the fire, or became suddenly blurred and shed clusters of divergent rays downwards to the floor and up into the darkness of the roof, so that the whole cavern seemed full of blazing comets. "Like the blessed stars of Heaven," Mrs. Barber murmured to herself, wondering where the phrase had come from.

Then the organ began, building up out of nothing just such a wonderful world for the ear as the lights and pillars and arches had made for the eyes: and soon there was a quiet stir of white shapes in the chancel and she knew that the choir had come in.

She listened delightedly to the intoning of prayers and the rich, clear chanting of psalms whose words were lost in the warm resonance of the chancel, till the church seemed to brim up with a shimmering lake of sound which washed and soothed her tired brain. Then came the hymn she had known all her life, and as she stood, steadying herself by holding with both hands on to the book-ledge, the lights and the tall pillars and the black, uneven mass of the congregation seemed to sway with the swaying of the music. "O come, let us adore Him! O come, let us adore Him!" said the music, climbing and climbing to the height ,from which at last it curved so satisfyingly down to the closing chord. The old words surged back into her memory with the music—"God of God, Light of Light . . . Very God, begotten not created"—it had never occurred to her to wonder what they meant: their emotional meaning for her was profound and sufficient and when she sat down again she felt exhausted, more from the intensity of her feelings than from the effort of standing.

Far away in the chancel the monotone of an unheard prayer rose again, but she did not kneel. She felt that she must sit quite still for a while, and then, as she raised her eyes, the lights swam

away from her again, hung aloft and remote, and swung back
large and blurred, scattering long beams on the cowering congregation. "Like the blessed stars of Heaven," she whispered to
herself again. Again the stars swam upwards, up and up and up:
it seemed, this time, as if they would never come back. They swam
into a circle, then into another, circle above circle—like a crown—
like a bride's cake, and Mrs. Barber could see now (so clearly
that she wondered that she had failed to notice it before) that
every star was a lighted taper held by an angel. There they stood,
a calm, stationary whirlpool of angels, ascending whirl above
whirl into infinite height.

Suddenly—so suddenly that Mrs. Barber jumped—they burst
into song, a great chord of music, basses, tenors, altos, trebles,
ringing and vibrating together till the sound of it drew her right
out of herself and she saw herself receding upwards. Up and up
and up she flew, till she was no more than a minute pin-point
of light. Then her light expanded and she became herself again,
as it were: and there she was, among the angels—a great crowd
of them all facing one way. Their wings towered up before her
and on each side of her: she could see every plume in minute
detail, soft golden feathers laid perfectly one on another. She
could not resist the impulse to put out her hand and stroke the
wing in front of her. The angel looked round and his eyes
smiled at her, but his mouth did not stop singing. It seemed that
they were all expecting someone—Mrs. Barber too felt the expectancy and suddenly their voices burst out again, but right in
her ear this time, loud and startling. "Hallelujah! Hallelujah!"
they sang, as though for the entrance of a king. And all at once
they broke apart in front of her and curved away to the right
and left, and she saw that some one was standing in the space
which they had made. It was Jesus. He stood like a large, simple
giant, twice as large as any of the angels, wrapped in a plain
blue cloak. And then, as Mrs. Barber stood gazing at him, Jesus
caught sight of her. She felt afraid just for a moment, but then he
smiled as though he recognized her—such an extremely pleasant
smile that at once she felt at ease. . . . It was nice of him to
bother so much about . . . But he was calling her. "Mrs. Barber!"
he was saying: and then, much louder, "Mrs. Barber!" and again,
alarmingly loud, "Mrs. Barber!" "Yes, sir, yes!" she said, trying
in vain to move forward. And then a sudden giddiness came over

her and everything was lost in a golden fog. "Come, Mrs. Barber," the voice went on. "Why, I declare: you've been asleep." "O no, sir," laughed Mrs. Barber, struggling to her feet. "Not asleep, sir!" But, all the same, she felt a little confused, a little dazed, because she was back in the church among "the blessed stars of Heaven" —that is, among the lamps and candles—but now, somehow, the church was quite empty and she was going towards the door with the Vicar. How stiff and useless her legs were! It was so much more difficult to walk than to fly. She tried to explain to the Vicar: "It's difficult, you know, sir . . ." she said. "It's difficult after being up there." But though her legs were so helpless she was still glowing with happiness, and as they walked back to her cottage—apparently the Vicar was going to her cottage too—she told him, as well as she could, of the wonderful things she had seen. She wouldn't have told everybody, of course; but the Vicar, being a clergyman, would understand. "And all the angels," she explained, "carried . . . carried . . . bells." Then she paused, perplexed. Surely that wasn't the word? Bells? No, how silly of her! It was tapers. "Yes, all the angels, sir, carried tapers. Wonderful! You've no idea." But the Vicar was asking about her key, and he unlocked her door for her and lit the lamp and would not leave her until she had assured him that she was really quite well and had promised that she would go straight to bed. "O perfectly well, thank you, sir: and very, very happy."

She was too tired to undress: besides, she had promised the Vicar that she would get into bed at once. Yes, he was a good gentleman, was the Vicar . . . or was it Jesus? or Mr. Robson? . . . to bother so much about an old woman. . . . But all the angels were ringing bells . . . and the distance was nothing . . . not a quarter of a mile.

CHRISTMAS COOKIES

from *The Chinese Ginger Jars*

BY MYRA SCOVEL

In 1930 Myra Scovel arrived at Peking with her husband, a medical missionary, and their infant son. Twenty-one years later, when Communists drove the foreigners out, hatred, hostility, and terror dogged their slowly retreating footsteps. During those fearful days, as well as in happier times, a deep love for all humanity, uncommonly good sense, practical intelligence, and a lively sense of humor carried charming Myra Scovel and her busy household through every change of fortune and blessed them with a happy family life. In "Christmas Cookies," from her autobiographical book The Chinese Ginger Jars, *we learn how, even in a time of savage Japanese tyranny, ingenuity and loving sacrifice can make a real festival.*

And now it was Christmas again. There was no money to buy gifts for the children; every cent of the five hundred dollars had to be used for food. But there was a precious evergreen in the front yard; we would cut it down and decorate it. There must be *some* evidence of Christmas in the house.

This was not the first time we had been faced with a presentless Christmas. Once the gifts we had ordered from a mail-order house failed to arrive, and the Russian fur-buyers came down from Tientsin in the nick of time, their arms full of bundles. One package contained a toy gun that worried me. The rule of our house had been no guns to play with. Guns were used to do harm. We were people who healed. But the boys wanted guns so badly. I finally rationalized myself into agreeing that, since the children knew how I felt about it and that I would never buy them a gun, it might be all right for them to accept this gift of the kind Russian uncles.

But this time there were no Russian uncles. I looked through the trunks and found a few books I had meant to save until the

257

children were older—*Huckleberry Finn, Pinocchio, The Stars for Sam.* There were some scraps of cloth with which I could make and dress rag dolls for the girls. Fred carved out a horse's head, painted it, and put it on a broom handle for the boys. A strip of fur from the bottom of my coat made a glorious black mane. Christmas cookies would have to be omitted. There was no sugar.

There was no sugar at all. I had hoarded half a cup of it, but a Japanese officer called one cold afternoon, bringing with him a little prostitute waif who looked so thin and so sad that I took out the sugar for their coffee. I put a meager teaspoonful into each cup, but after the coffee had been handed around, the poor little girl crossed the room, took the sugar bowl in her hands and emptied its entire contents into her coffee. If I tended to regret the loss of the sugar, I had only to think of those burning eyes as the girl gulped down her coffee. My children could do without cookies.

"Teacher-Mother." It was the gateman with a message. "The Catholic Sisters are here making their Christmas calls." (Each year they came to thank the doctor for what he had done for them.)

The Sisters had brought a package which they now gave to the children. "You must open it carefully," they cautioned.

"Oh, Mother, look! Little angels and stars, and oh . . . they are made out of sugar cookies!"

"Sugar cookies! Sisters, how on earth did you—" I stopped myself. "Really, you shouldn't have done it," I finished feebly.

They ventured a smile at each other and began at once to help the children hang the little angels on the Christmas tree, insisting that a few cookies must be eaten while working.

"And you must come over to the church and see the crèche," they urged. "The children of the school are giving a play."

"Perhaps we may be able to get permission from the Japanese this once," I replied. "It is such a special occasion."

The crèche with its exquisite figures, made by a brother of one of the nuns and brought out carefully from Germany, the old carols sung in stilted English, by the Chinese children of the school—this was Christmas.

And Mother Superior confessing to me, "I vowed that these

poor Sisters, who have gone without so much all year, would have sugar for Christmas, even if it cost every cent we had in our meager treasury. So I bought a few pounds though the price was unbelievable. The Sisters insisted on dividing the sugar in half and making cookies for your children. We all love them very much, you know. I remember so well when little Golden-Haired One was a baby. It was the first time I had ever called on you. Do you remember? I hadn't seen a white baby in fifteen years. She looked like a little cherub. And now look at her, chatting away in Chinese to our girls. The children are pleased with the cookies, then?"

This—*this* was truly Christmas.

THERE IS A BALM IN GILEAD

from *The Little Professor of Piney Woods*

BY BETH DAY

In The Little Professor of Piney Woods, *Beth Day pays an inspiring biographical tribute to Professor Laurence Jones, creator and founder of the Piney Woods Country Life School in southern Mississippi. Throughout more than a half-century of dedication, self-sacrifice, and iron will, this modern Booker T. Washington produced a miracle of hope, education, and progress for the depressed Negro communities of the surrounding backwoods. Beth Day engenders new understanding of racial problems in the unusual life of Laurence Jones, who fought his way over a morass of suspicion, prejudice, and poverty to spiritual and physical victory. "There Is a Balm in Gilead" illustrates an unforgettable triumph when he and his devoted associates brought the light of a real Christmas to the souls of a forgotten people.*

After leaving Arkansas, Laurence Jones went to the Delta region, the rich, flat northwestern part of Mississippi where wealthy plantation owners exploited both the black land and the black man. Here share croppers worked, in terms of seeing, from "can to can't" in cotton fields that came up to their cabin doors, bought their food and clothing from the owner's commissary at whatever profit his conscience dictated, and, not being able to read or "figger," accepted on faith anything due at the end of the year.

Laurence quickly found that "sublime" ignorance was what the plantation owners wanted. "Educate them? No! What we want from them is that cotton and no sass." Nor did he receive any more encouragement from the Negroes themselves. "If we ask questions we is cussed," explained one old farmer, "and if we raises up—we is beat up or shot!"

Laurence had sense enough to realize that he was outmatched. The Delta would have to wait. Dejected and broke, he headed South to the small farm area. With winter coming on he took a job teaching at a small school in Hinds County, Mississippi. At Christmas he went home with one of his students to spend the holidays in Rankin County and had his first taste of the piney woods.

This was a world apart from the Delta country. Here small farmers, both white and colored, were caught in a subsistence-level economy. Only a few inadequate schools existed for the whites and practically none for the colored. It was a land of ignorance and superstition, of a starvation-level existence. Here was a practicing belief in "voodooism" and the "conjuh" men; graves were decorated with broken bits of colored glass; crops were planted when the moon was right; and most of life was lived in accordance with primitive taboos. He remembered vividly the crowning experience of that Christmas which strengthened a growing desire to cast his lot among the people of the piney woods.

Through the great dark woods by the light of a pine torch he was taken to a frolic. In a close room, filled with tobacco smoke and reeking with the odor of whisky, a crowd of men, women, and children, laughing and joking, jostled and danced to the music of an old guitar until early morning. Occasionally a man would step outside and with a succession of shots satisfy himself as to how quickly he could pull the trigger of his pistol.

The children seemed to participate in the frolic quite as much as the older people. They swore just as wickedly, and even the boys and girls nine years of age used quantities of snuff and tobacco. Their parents thought that anything, even liquor, if used by themselves, was all right for the children; so it was only necessary to ask "Pa" for what was wanted. Around the corners of the room the babies were dumped in the laps of women too old to dance.

It was the pathetic gaiety of bitter poverty; it was the one time of the year when the people let go and literally "shot the works." The Christmas frolic lasted for a full month, moving from cabin to cabin, exhausting all that had been saved in provisions and in spending all available money for fireworks, cheap jewelry, perfume, whisky, tobacco, and for the "makings" of pies and cakes that weighed heavily on stomachs flattened by the corn-pone and cowpea diet of the previous eleven months.

Here, young Jones realized, was the beginning point for educa-tion. The nickels and dimes that went for this heart-sickening waste—the waste of desperation and ignorance—if saved would mean the difference between not having and having meat on the table during the year, whitewash for the cabin, books and educa-tion, and the beginnings toward a better life. To supply that missing hope seemed to him the mission that he had been looking for.

Laurence talked to many of them individually that night of his first frolic—passionately and eagerly—and they listened with native courtesy but kept their reaction hidden behind the veiled withdrawal of their eyes. He found that there were a couple of schools for Negroes in the county which, if a child could get in, did not go beyond the eighth grade. There was no high school, although a church association had been trying to build one for twenty-five years.

The next day, while the frolic continued its uninterrupted frenzy, Laurence borrowed a mule from his host and went to look at the two school buildings. They were one-room structures with no windows and no blackboards—the only available facilities for many thousands of colored children. The two teachers who had finished only the fifth grade themselves were paid $18 a month for a three- or four-months period. Their pupils came in from miles around when not needed for work on the farms, and were of all ages. The cold "tater" that they brought for lunch did their stomachs about as much good as what they learned did their minds.

Like Booker T. Washington before him, the young man realized that education for these impoverished people must begin with the simple problem of survival—of how to raise sufficient food to feed their families; how to do a more skilled job than chopping cotton.

Though his own college work had been in Liberal Arts, Laurence had always had a feeling for practical education. His childhood hero, Robinson Crusoe, had made a deep impression because he had "made things to suit his needs" and in imitation of him the boy had built many back-yard coops and shelters, raised chickens and pigeons, and made a garden. In Iowa he had been fascinated by the accent on thrifty farming and the many agricultural developments.

On the last night of the frolic Laurence rounded up the group of celebrants—men, women, and children—and as they sat outside the cabin, around a huge pine-knot fire, he told them about Christmas and how it was celebrated in Iowa and Missouri—a solemn festival to our Lord with simple homemade gifts of fruit or candy and an accent on the spirit of "Christmas and the Christly example of brotherhood and love." He spoke of the farms of Iowa, where thrifty farmers raised food crops for their families to eat during the long winter months, where they varied their crops, planted wisely, and made enough so that they could educate their children. He told them he would like to come back and help them with their farms and crops and the education of their children so that they could look forward to a life like that.

Perhaps some of the men may have wanted to laugh at this slim young man standing there before them with his earnest eyes and big dreams, but with the childlike perception of simple folk, they knew his heart was right. So with simple dignity they thanked him for his talk, prayed that he might be "spared," and when he departed, no doubt expected to see no more of him.

But the memory of those firelit faces had burned too bright in Laurence's mind and heart. As soon as he got back to Hinds County, he sent to Iowa for books on agriculture, pamphlets, from the Iowa Corn Growers' Association and the Wallace experimentations, as well as government brochures on rural sanitation and rural economy, and each night, after classes, he studied these basic lessons in farm life—in preparation for his new job.

And now he was back and ready to begin. . . .

In September 1910, the second year of the Piney Woods School opened with five teachers—all under thirty—and more than a hundred students. Besides its principal, Laurence, there was Louis Watson and Yancy who, in addition, had married a young teacher and brought her back to help, and another young woman, a former student of Laurence when he had taught in Hinds County, named Doschia Weathersby.

The addition of the two women teachers made it possible to add a "training kitchen" which offered to the girls advanced training in cooking as well as better food for everyone. A second check from Emily Howland, the woman who had been Piney Woods' first donor, came in with the request that a hand press be bought and a school paper be put out so that she could receive regular news about what was happening at the school.

The press was duly installed in the little cabin where Laurence still lived, and he personally used it to instruct students in the art of printing as well as for putting out school reports. One of the first things printed was a letter from an aunt of Georgia Lee Myers, describing her reaction to her niece's progress at Piney Woods:

"I am glad to write and tell you about the improvement you has made in Georgia, she is better in the washtub and in the fields and in the kitchen and in the house. She is better everywhere I puts her than she was. She has work so faithful sense she come home that I wants to send her back."

Some of the older men, satisfied with a smattering of "readin' an' writin'," had dropped out. But William Dixon was still there, as were Laurence's original trio of "log boys" who were now sophisticated second-year students. Uncle Tom still haunted the clearing, toting his musket, between classes, as self-appointed watchman of the school grounds.

"Is that gun loaded?" Laurence asked his "guard" one day in a teasing tone.

"J-j-jes' l-l-let s-s-s-some old varmint t-t-try to sneak up and t-t-t-tech s-s-s-somefin' b-b-b-belongs to dis s-s-s-school, an' we'll s-s-s-see ef it's l-l-l-loaded!" declared the old man, with a fierce grip on his treasured weapon.

Laurence's inner laughter vanished in the face of such touching loyalty. He thanked his old guard gently and went on his way.

On opening day, as he stood before the rows of eager young faces, many of them betraying the curiosity and half-fear of the new students for whom this was a strange and awesome experience, Laurence thought back to his own first day at school, and his heart warmed with sympathy for the timid brown children. His mother had taken him to the old Lincoln School in St. Joseph, introduced him to "Miss Sadie," and left. Small for his age, terrified at the crush of bigger, older children, Laurence had huddled down in his seat, tears stinging his eyes, so over all miserable that Miss Sadie had asked him what was wrong. "I'm tired and hungry and sleepy and my Mama needs me," he had blurted out in one hot, agonized breath. And the wise teacher had summoned an older boy to "carry him home," saying, "Any boy with that many things wrong with him ought to go home and come to school another day." He had arrived at home on the back of the other boy barely ten minutes after his mother had gotten there. The next day he had stuck it out, but he never looked out over the frightened, curious faces of "first students" without a warm and amused compassion.

He greeted the students, then spoke to them in simple words of what they might expect at Piney Woods.

"You will find that our course of study is planned with thoughts of teaching what will be the best for you. There are courses in agriculture, morals, and manners, the Bible, rural economics, arithmetic as it is used in everyday life, the chemistry of the farm and the home—these are what you will be trained in here.

"You have come here to seek freedom not from the kind of slavery your parents endured, but from a slavery of ignorance of mind and awkwardness of body. You have come for your soul's freedom. You have come to educate your head, your hands, and your heart. You want to know how to think clearly, how to live in the right way, and how to make some material progress in the world."

The children before him, warmed by the kindness of his smile, stirred by the promise of his words, began to relax and look forward to the days ahead.

As he acquired teachers to take over specific classes and trades, Laurence more and more confined his own work to the "morals and manners"—the spiritual growth of his students. He led the Bible classes, gave the Sunday chapel talks, was available at all hours, for advice or counsel. Young as he was, the children were drawn to him by far more than educational ties. He was their teacher, their guide, their friend; he was the common "father" who had come to bring them a chance for a life they had not known existed. His very presence seemed to provoke in the neglected children a desire to be "good," "honest," "thrifty," and "kind." As one student later described the feeling they all had for their 'fessor: "You could not look into eyes like that and lie."

For his share of work Louis Watson took over a section of classes in basic reading and writing and the role of bookkeeper for the school. Though money was too meager for much figuring, he kept a complete record of the grades and work time of all the students as they piled up hours which would pay for future classes.

Young Watson, as Laurence before him, was both fascinated and horrified, as the holiday season approached, with the Christmas plans of the woods folks for their traditional frolics. The extreme poverty which the past few years, with the aid of the boll weevil, had brought meant scarcely "fireworks" money this year, let alone "gifs" or delicacies.

"Let's give them a real Christmas," Louis suggested impulsively one night as he and Laurence sat up late at their desks in the cabin, Watson over his books, Laurence tinkering with the little press which he intended to use to save many hours of work in writing letters to the friends of the school.

"Maybe we can bring in a tree from the woods and decorate it," Laurence said, "and of course we will have chapel services. But we haven't any money for gifts. Any money we have must go for food."

"I'll figure something," Louis said, his eyes dreamy. "I'd like to show these poor little kids what Christmas can mean."

"Do what you wish," Laurence said, "just so it doesn't cost anything."

A few weeks later Laurence regretted that he had granted Watson the permission. The young man, his thin, sensitive face alight with a vision, was working on his project with feverish intensity. Each night, after a strenuous day of teaching and office work, he stayed up till nearly morning, working on his "Christmas boxes." He had written home to his mother in Iowa for tiny candles and what tree decorations she could stir up. The rest he was making by hand. A talented artist, he worked out hand-designed motto cards for each child which he laboriously lettered by hand, then decorated with painted borders of trailing holly and mistletoe. The "boxes," made of pasteboard and colored tissue, were also individually made with children's names in gleaming reds and greens and silver, the sides decorated with hand-painted Christmas scenes.

As Watson labored nightly over his designs the other teachers caught the spirit and began working on an *a capella* concert, selecting Christmas songs, and rehearsing them with the students.

As Christmas day approached and news spread through the community about the school party, Laurence wondered how it would appeal in comparison to the frolics of former years.

Drawn by either curiosity or "nothing at home," people of all ages began pouring into the school grounds on Christmas morning, although the program was not scheduled until afternoon. They all came—from graybearded oldsters to the smallest, newest babies no more than blanketed mounds in their mothers' arms. By noon the chapel of Taylor Hall was bursting with Christmas visitors and guests.

That day, for the first time, the Piney Woods folks traded their fireworks and whisky and smoke-filled rooms for a simple sermon and a concert of sacred music. As Laurence spoke to them, looking out over the hushed crowd, he saw eyes that feasted with heart-warming pleasure on the stage that was decked with pine and cedar boughs. If he had any doubts at all they were dispelled when he listened as they joined wholeheartedly in the religious music, lifting their voices in "Glory Hallelujah to de Newborn King," then crooning with a softer joy, "Mary Had a Baby." He knew that a genuine Christmas spirit had found a place in their lives and was thankful that Louis Watson had suggested the services.

And then the Christmas tree!

How all the little brown folks gasped and shrieked with pleasure when the curtains were parted and they saw their first Christmas tree—a tall, stately pine shimmering with the myriad lights of a hundred candles, bright with colored balls, and trailing "snow." At its base all of Watson's gaily-decorated Christmas boxes lay, filled with candy and nuts, each one bearing the name of a child.

For Laurence this was the happiest and the most miserable Christmas he had ever spent.

That Louis Watson had literally worked himself to death to create this joyful scene was a tragic aftermath of the holiday. Two weeks after Christmas—his frail constitution weakened by poor diet, the drafty cabin, and his own exhausting enthusiasm for bringing joy to these poor children—Louis died.

As Laurence wired Watson's mother, then shipped the body home, he realized that in his poverty and his dedication to the school he could not accompany his friend's body for its last rites. He knew also that Louis would have understood.

This was the first human life that went into the creation of Piney Woods.

To the four shocked fellow workers that Louis left behind his death meant a renewal of a dedication that must never be found lagging.

HOLY NIGHT

from *A Mountain Township*

BY WALTER HARD

As Doctor Stevens came into the village
He let his horse slow down to a walk.
The moon broke through the clouds.
There was not a track on the new-fallen snow.
He was thinking how nice it was
That the Judson baby had come on Christmas eve.
He smiled his pleasant smile
As he passed lighted houses with trimmed trees inside.
What could Ellen Hicks be doing up at this late hour?
She didn't have anyone to be filling stockings for.
Poor thing! She didn't have anything to fill a stocking with.
A shadow moved regularly across the drawn shade.
She was sitting there rocking—rocking.

The village clock struck eleven.
From the south came the faint tinkle of sleighbells.

The snow creaked as he went up the steps.
The rocking stopped.
The light moved through the door into the hall.
Ellen unlocked the door.
She held the light up to see who her late caller was.
She had a worn patchwork quilt around her shoulders.

The Doctor went over to the chunk stove to warm his hands.
It gave out no heat. He touched it. It was barely warm.
No, of course there wasn't anything the matter with her.

She always sat up until midnight on Christmas eve.
She'd got to thinking about that Stebbins family,
And sat there rocking and forgot her fire.
How they could get along with all those young ones,
And him all crippled, she couldn't see.
They didn't even have wood to keep them warm.

"Ellen, have you been giving wood to the Stebbinses?"
She admitted she had called the boy in and loaded his sled.
Well, maybe she had sent some food.

Little by little the truth came out.
Her nephew did look after her; he always had.
But he'd told her she'd got to stop this sharing.
She'd promised.
But she couldn't bear to think of those Stebbinses.
She could get along. She still had wood in the shed.
The Doctor's scolding stuck in his throat.
He went to the shed and brought in the last armful of wood.

He shut the stable door.
He stopped to look down on the sleeping village.
So Ellen had to share.
He recalled the look on her face.
Sharing. That was what Christmas meant.

The clock in the village struck twelve.
Down in the valley a rooster crowed.
Overhead the moon moved slowly across the winter sky.
Holy night. Peaceful night.

VI   Christmas Memories

This second epistle, beloved, I now write unto you; in both which I stir up your pure minds by way of remembrance. (II Peter 3:1)

Christmas is a time for memories, a time for recalling the scenes and happenings that are treasured always in our hearts. It is also a time for love and generosity of spirit, a time for renewing family ties and friendships, and for exchanging the thoughts, events, kind deeds, and observances that have added to the true meaning and happiness of life.

In remembering our best experiences at Christmas, we find a message of utmost significance and inspiration that kindles the spark of hope for a better world into "a burning and a shining light."

❋　　❋　　❋

CHRISTMAS BELLS

from *The Works of Henry Wadsworth Longfellow*

BY HENRY WADSWORTH LONGFELLOW

I heard the bells on Christmas Day
Their old, familiar carols play,
  And wild and sweet
  The words repeat
Of peace on earth, good-will to men!

And thought how, as the day had come
The belfries of all Christendom
  Had rolled along
  The unbroken song
Of peace on earth, good-will to men!

Till, ringing, swinging on its way,
The world revolved from night to day
  A voice, a chime
  A chant sublime
Of peace on earth, good-will to men!

And in despair I bowed my head;
"There is no peace on earth," I said;
  "For hate is strong
  And mocks the song
Of peace on earth, good-will to men!"

Then pealed the bells more loud and deep:
"God is not dead; nor doth He sleep!
  The Wrong shall fail,
  The Right prevail,
With peace on earth, good-will to men!"

CHRISTMAS ON THE FARM

from *Farmer Takes a Wife*

BY JOHN GOULD

John (Thomas) Gould is a star in the cluster of regional writers about New England, especially Maine. Farmer, editor, memoirist, and constant contributor to the best newspapers, he is regarded as the historian, par excellence, of the "New England Town Meeting." Later he originated a goodly list of humorous books, including Farmer Takes a Wife *which describes his marriage and adventures on his Maine farm. In "Christmas on the Farm," a chapter of that volume, Gould skillfully interlaces the past and the present, glorifying his forebears and his family.*

When my wife said, "What do you want me to get you for Christmas?" Uncle Timothy said, "Nothing. Christmas is for children and them that have them, and it's too late this year for you to make arrangements. You might pray that I'll live long enough to see a kid's sock on the chimney again."

My wife put her hands on the arms of the rocker and leaned down to whisper, "I promise you, Uncle, I'll bend every effort so that next Christmas there'll be a stocking."

"It's been a long time," Uncle Timothy said. "When my brother David's childers were little we used to have Christmases in this old house, with aunts and uncles from all around, and there was one old ripper of a blizzard struck one year and we figured wouldn't nobody come. But they did, and we sat twenty-eight people to the table. And fed them, too. As I recollect, all twenty-seven gave me suspenders. That's what you might get me for Christmas this year, if you want to. Suspenders. I'm about caught up again."

It was rather a curious Christmas we made that year, the three of us going through all the business of wreaths, a tree, colored lights, and all the rest. Having visited us on Thanksgiving, my wife's folks went to see their son for Christmas, so we made it alone. Uncle Timothy announced that he wasn't going to give anything, and didn't want anything, and we both knew he'd already been to town and come home with two big bundles he hid in the barn. My wife had broken into the bale of new yarn and had somehow figured out Aunt Sarah's double-sawtooth design, and had made him a pair of mittens about an inch thick. That may not sound like much of a present, but I knew Uncle Timothy would fill up and swallow when he saw them—he knew mittens from away back, and he hadn't seen double-knit ones like these since his wife died. In our family people got mittens when they needed them, and they were slapped together fast. Grandmother used to do her housework with a ball of yarn in one apron pocket and the needles in another—the connecting worsted across her front like a watch chain. When her hands had nothing to do, they began at once to knit.

But Aunt Sarah's special double-sawtooth design was less like fancy work and more like a problem in higher mathematics. When she was knitting them her lips kept counting, and nobody spoke to her until she came to a stopping place and could look up. Ordinary mittens she could knit in her sleep—but the special ones for special gifts were special, and while other women in the family sometimes tried them, they never finished off just the same. My wife did all right, although she had to rip thumbs out several times and start over. I thought Aunt Sarah would have been proud of her, and I knew Uncle Timothy would be overjoyed.

I picked a couple of ducks, and we had a pheasant in the freezer for a Christmas morning pie. Uncle Timothy insisted we go down to the special church service, but he wouldn't go—said we could tell him about it and it would do him as much good. The only time he ever went near the church was every spring, when he whetted up his ax and went down to split the wood for the church and the parsonage. He never started on our own pile until he had the church and the minister fitted.

So all in all we made out a good Christmas, and I guess my wife was satisfied. Uncle Timothy told her, "There's been two hundred and eighteen Christmases on the old farm, and I think we done all right by the traditions. Some was better, maybe, but maybe some wasn't. And I guess, now you're here, it won't be the last."

He sat in his chair with his mittens on, and didn't take them off until he went to bed.

Uncle was wrong about the number of Christmases—he was one too many. The first Christmas of all hadn't been held on the farm, and as I'd told my wife about that occasion it helped her to make the most of her first Christmas on the farm. I mean, Christmas on the farm is generally thought of as a congregation of some size, with carol singing around the organ in the parlor, and a half-dozen women all helping to make dinner, and sleigh rides over through the Borough, with skating and coasting, popcorn balls, and all that sort of thing. Instead, she made a farm Christmas without any of her own family, in a house where three were a mockery of the family reunions they used to have. As Uncle said, there was the fireplace roaring its heat up the chimney and not a stocking in sight. The spiritual aspects of the day can abide in the lonely heart as staunchly as in the multitude—but in an old farmhouse Christmas is best when many share it.

But because I'd told the story of the first Christmas, my wife didn't think so much about that. Great-grandfather brought a new wife home to this place once, too, and Christmas came for them in a way that makes all succeeding Christmases an improvement.

They came up here in the early spring, just too late to get the full run of the maple sap, and Great-grandfather hardly got his kettle set up when the run was over. They cleared a strip, and when the wind was right burned to it—prodding their seeds into the ember-warm loam with sharp sticks. They had brought all their belongings in an ox cart, slashing a road ahead of the steers through forests that had never felt an ax before. They slept under the cart the first night they got here, and the next day Great-grandfather made a brush lean-to until the gardens were in.

That summer he chopped at the old-growth pines that towered over the Ridge—and he told afterward how he jumped the yoke of oxen onto a stump and turned them around without stepping off. He rigged a chain so the oxen would gee and roll a log, and he laid up a cabin as the summer advanced. He laid poles around through the woods and so made a pasture for the cow and pig. The oxen and hens lived in brush shelters. Great-grandfather didn't have a bed to sleep in until late in July, and the chimney wasn't laid up until September. They had to dig a cellar to store the few vegetables they got from a poor season, and the prospects of a long winter were nothing to cheer their spirits. Aunt Deborah Lane walked up the river trail from Georgetown to be with them for a time, but she frugally decided it would be cheaper for everyone if she went back to the settlement for the winter, and she snowshoed down with a long list of things to be sent up if anyone should try the river trail again before spring. When Aunt Debbie waved back from the edge of the clearing, Great-grand-mother broke down and cried all day.

You see, she was only eighteen then, and Great-grandfather was only nineteen, and they would be alone in their wilderness cabin now until the alders budded again and some trader would paddle up after the freshet to see what skins he could buy. Six months—at least; and maybe the trader wouldn't come then, and Jacob would have to leave her alone for a few days while he took his skins down himself.

Somehow, this recital made my wife feel better about her first winter here, and she frequently compared herself with the pio-neering ancestor-in-law. But things weren't so bad that first winter. They made out.

Great-grandmother was moody by times, and Great-grand-father was sympathetic and understanding—but what could he do about it? A woman likes to have another woman to "set" with now and again, and a windowless cabin surrounded by towering white pines that moan in the wind isn't the best thing in the world to cure lonesomeness. Another year or so, and things would be different, but for the time being the whole world was whittled down to a half-acre of snow in an unbroken forest of pine.

Then one fine morning in early December Great-grandfather went out in the quiet frost of sunrise and shielded his eyes against the east. Over on the other rim of the intervale a thin column of smoke rose into the sun. Grandfather pointed out the spot to me many times—it was halfway up Hall's Hill, a good four miles from here, about where the Curtis driveway turns off today. Smoke in the woods is something to investigate, but he didn't say anything about it in the cabin. He milked, had breakfast, and picked up his ax as if to go on clearing away big trees. But he circled the clearing and headed down towards Little River, climbed up on the other side, and soon could hear an ax ringing against frozen timber.

It was ringing for fair. Great-grandfather came out into a clearing just as a mighty pine teetered, swayed, gathered momen-tum, and crashed to the ground with a torrent of thunder that echoed throughout the forest. A pint-sized man in deerskin thereupon leaped onto the stump, sunk his ax in the trunk of the tree, waved his hat and cheered at his own triumph. Great-grandfather smiled, because he knew how it felt to get one more tree out of the way. The cheering brought a woman out of a hut at the far end of the clearing, and she waved at the pint-sized man and cheered with him.

Great-grandfather practically frightened the two when he began cheering as well, for until that moment they had believed themselves alone in the great Bowdoin grant. They shook hands, and Great-grandfather was invited to stay and break bread, but he couldn't because Great-grandmother would be expecting him. But he did promise to come back on Christmas and bring his wife. The pint-sized man had a voice like a bull, and he shouted, "We'll stew some venison and make Christmas worth remembering!"

The pint-sized man was a trapper, and he'd brought in food for the winter, so he hadn't needed the summer growing season. He'd come late in October, and until that morning he and Great-grandfather had each thought himself the first settler north of New Meadows. Great-grandfather sat breathless by the fire when he got home, and told all about his discovery—particularly about the woman just Great-grandmother's age, and he imitated the little fellow with the big voice so Great-grandmother laughed aloud for the first time in weeks.

The news did wonders for her. She hummed and sang, and finished her housework in half the time so she could be out with an ax and Great-grandfather, helping him limb the trees and talking about Christmas. "What can we take them for a present?" she asked, well knowing the scarcity of her cabin.

"I know," she answered herself. "I'll make up a little sugar. We hain't much, but they hain't none, probably, and won't see none 'til spring." So Great-grandfather fashioned a tiny wooden pail, staved from split pine and bound with willow. He found some black-alder berries, and Great-grandmother made a fir spray that served as a cover. She pounded out a cake of sugar, and twice decided she had enough, and twice went up the ladder for a doit more.

Great-grandfather, pleased with the tiny wooden pail, immediately made several big ones for Great-grandmother's Christmas present, and then decided to take one as a gift to his hostess. But his real present to Great-grandmother was a swing-dingle—for he wanted her to go calling in style.

How America has disintegrated, when a swing-dingle must be explained! It was a white maple trunk, the right size, and properly curved in growing so the turned-up end made a runner. The top was split its length, with a tree-nail at the proper place to stop its splitting all the way. The split part fitted like fills to a steer, and over the runner was erected a bob-sled sort of seat on which Great-grandmother could, and did, ride to Christmas dinner. Great-grandfather walked on ahead, teaming the single steer around blowdowns. At Little River he walked out and tested the ice, and then he scooted Great-grandmother across so she nearly bounced off when the swing-dingle hit the opposite bank. Up the other hill they went, and the pint-sized man was sitting on a stump by his cabin watching for them.

"Here they come!" he called, and his wife rushed from the cabin as eager and expectant as Great-grandmother was. "Merry Christmas!" she called, and Great-grandfather waved his goad-stick and called back, "Merry Christmas!"

"Merry Christmas," yelled the pint-sized man in his bull's voice, and Great-grandmother waved from her perch on the swing-dingle and said, "Merry Christmas!"

Then she added, "Neighbor!"

RATHER LATE FOR CHRISTMAS

by Mary Ellen Chase

*Maine has produced an amazing array of writers who have rendered
great services to the mind and spirit by opening doors on other lives.
Among those doing the most to enlarge our experiences is Mary Ellen
Chase, distinguished as both teacher and author. "Rather Late for
Christmas" introduces us with subtlety, wit, and whimsy to her
grandmother who thought it more blessed to give than to receive.*

During those confusing days before Christmas, while I wrap
gifts for sisters and brothers, brothers-in-law and sisters-in-law,
nephews and nieces, aunts and great-aunts, neighbors and friends,
the milkman, the postman, the paper boy, the cook and the cook's
children, the cleaning-woman and the cleaning-woman's children,
I remember my grandmother who, in the twenty years I knew
her, wrapped Christmas gifts for no one at all. My grandmother
never stood half-submerged in a jungle of silver cord, gold cord,
red ribbon, tinsel ribbon, white tissue-paper, red tissue-paper,
paper marked with Aberdeens or angels. She viewed with fine
scorn all such pre-Christmas frenzy. I remember her again when
my January bills weigh down my desk and my disposition. My
grandmother in all those years never bought a Christmas gift for
anyone, although she gave many. Nor did she make her Christmas
gifts by the labour of her hands which were almost never idle.

To be sure, she spent most of her waking hours during twelve
months of the year in making gifts, but they were not for
Christmas. She made yards upon yards of tatting, fashioned
hundreds of tea-cosies, tidies, and table-mats, hemstitched innumerable handkerchiefs, crocheted fine filet for pillowcases
and sheets, knit countless scalloped bands of white lace for the
legs of white cotton drawers, and countless stockings, gloves,
mittens, scarfs, sacques, and shawls. These creations were all gifts,
yet they were never given at Christmas. Instead, they were
presented at odd moments to all sorts of odd and sundry persons
—to the gardener, the minister's wife, a surprised boy coasting
down the hill, the village school-mistresses, the stage-driver, a
chance Syrian pedlar, the fish-man, the paper-hangers, an unknown woman distributing religious literature at the back-door,

the sexton. Moreover, no one of my grandmother's many acquaintances ever called upon her without departing from her door richer, or at least more encumbered, than when she entered it; nor did my grandmother ever set out empty-handed to return those calls.

My grandmother's nature was essentially dramatic. She loved all sudden, surprising, unexpected things; but she loved them only if either she or God instigated them. Quite illogically she denied this privilege to others. She was distinctly irritated if anyone took her unawares either by a sudden gift or by an unexpected piece of news. She was so filled with life herself that she forever wanted to dispense rather than to receive, to initiate rather than to be initiated.

She loved sudden changes of weather, blizzards, line gales, the excitement of continuous winter cold, Northern lights, falling stars; and during many years of her long and abundant life she had had her fill of such abrupt and whimsical behavior on the part of God. For she had spent much of her life at sea where holidays were mere points in time, unprepared for, often even unnoticed, slipping upon one like all other days, recalled if wind and weather were kind, forgotten if God had other and more immediate means of attracting one's attention to His power and His might. She had spent Christmas in all kinds of strange places: off Cape Horn in a gale; running before the trades somewhere a thousand miles off Africa; in a typhoon off the Chinese coast; in the doldrums where the twenty-fifth of December was but twenty-four still hours in a succession of motionless days; in the bitter cold of a winter storm too near the treacherous cliffs of Southern Ireland for comfort or security. Small wonder that she would find it difficult, after her half-reluctant return to village life, to tie up Christmas in a neat parcel and to label it with a date.

As children we were forever asking our grandmother about those Christmases at sea.

"Didn't you give any presents at all, grandmother? Not to the sailors or even to grandfather?"

"The sailors," said my grandmother, "had a tot of rum all around in the dog-watch if the weather was fair. That was the sailors' present."

We always smiled over *tot*. This facetious, trifling word attached to one of such enormity as *rum* in those days of temperance agitation seemed impious to say the least. "What is a tot of rum, grandmother?"

"A tot," answered my grandmother, with great dignity, "is an indeterminate quantity."

"Did the sailors sing Christmas carols when they had the tot?"

"They did not. They sang songs which no child should ever know."

"Then did you and grandfather have no presents at all, grandmother?"

"Whenever we got to port, we had our presents, that is, if we did not forget that we had had no Christmas. We had Christmas in January or even March. Christmas, children, is not a date. It is a state of mind."

Christmas to my grandmother was always a state of mind. Once she had left the sea, once she was securely on land where the behavior of God was less exciting, she began to supplement Providence and Fate by engendering excitement in those about her. Her objection to Christmas lay in the fact that it was a day of expectation when no one could possibly be taken by surprise. She endured it with forbearance, but she disliked it heartily.

Unlike most women of her generation, she cared not a whit for tradition or convention; but she remained to the end of her days the unwilling prey of both. Unlike most women of any generation, she scorned possessions; and she saw to it that she suffered them briefly. We knew from the beginning the fate of the gifts we annually bestowed upon her; yet we followed the admonition and example of our parents in bestowing them. From our scanty Christmas allowance of two dollars each with which to purchase presents for a family of ten, we set aside a generous portion for grandmother's gift. She was always with us at the Christmas celebration and received our offerings without evident annoyance, knowing that what she must endure for a brief season she could triumph over in the days to come.

As we grew older and were allowed at length to select our gifts free from parental supervision, we began to face the situation precisely as it was. Instead of black silk gloves for grandmother, we chose for her our own favorite perfumery; we substituted plain white handkerchiefs for the black-edged ones which she normally carried; a box of chocolates took the place of one of peppermints; a book called *Daily Thoughts for Daily*

Needs was discarded in favor of a story by Anna Katharine Green.

My grandmother waited for a fortnight or longer after Christmas before she proffered her gifts to family, neighbors, and friends. By early January, she concluded, expectation would have vanished and satiety be forgotten; in other words, the first fine careless rapture of sudden surprise and pleasure might again be abroad in the world. She invariably chose a dull or dark day upon which to deliver her presents. Around three o'clock on some dreary afternoon was her time for setting forth. Over her coat she tied one of her stout aprons of black sateen, and in its capacious lap she cast all her own unwanted gifts—a black silk umbrella, odd bits of silver and jewelry, gloves, handkerchiefs, stockings, books, candies, Florida water, underwear, bedroom slippers, perfumeries, knick-knacks of every sort; even family photographs were not excluded! Thus she started upon her rounds, returning at supper-time, empty-handed and radiant.

I remember how once as children we met her thus burdened on our way home from school.

"You're rather late for Christmas, grandmother," we ventured together.

"So, my dears, were the Three Wise Men!" she said.

The many days foretold by the Preacher for the return of bread thus cast upon the waters have in the case of my grandmother not yet elapsed. For, although she has long since gone where possessions are of no account and where, for all we know, life is a succession of quick surprises, I receive from time to time the actual return of her Christmas gifts so freely and curiously dispensed. Only last Christmas a package revealed a silver pie-knife marked with her initials and presented to her, I remembered with a start, through the combined sacrificial resources of our entire family fully thirty years before. An accompanying note bore these words:

> Your grandmother brought this knife to my mother twenty-eight years ago as a Christmas gift. I remember how she came one rainy afternoon in January with the present in her apron. I found it recently among certain of my mother's things, and, knowing your grandmother's strange ways as to Christmas gifts, I feel that honesty demands its return to you. You may be interested in this card which accompanied it.

Tied to the silver pie-knife by a bit of red ribbon, obviously salvaged long ago from Christmas plenty, was a card inscribed on both sides. On one side was written: "To grandmother with Christmas love from her children and grandchildren," and on the other: "To my dear friend, Lizzie Osgood, with daily love from Eliza Ann Chase."

CHRISTMAS IN MAINE

from *Christmas in Maine*

by ROBERT P. TRISTRAM COFFIN

Robert P. Tristram Coffin, many-sided author, teacher, lecturer, artist, and farmer, described himself as "a New Englander by birth, by bringing up, by spirit." Even when abroad or traveling in America, Maine was his home place, the heart and inspiration of his entire life. He talked and wrote proudly of family roots among the rock-ribbed whalers, Quaker settlers of Nantucket and points north. To fresh and fascinating reminiscences of his boyhood, Coffin brought a tangy humor and a vibrnt enthusiasm that appealed to Americans at large. Here he describes a Christmas in Maine with words that glow in the joys of faith, feasting, and love of mankind.

If you want to have a Christmas like the one we had on Paradise Farm when I was a boy, you will have to hunt up a salt-water farm on the Maine coast, with bays on both sides of it, and a road that goes around all sorts of bays, up over Misery Hill and down, and through the fir trees so close together that they brush you and your horse on both cheeks. That is the only kind of place a Christmas like that grows. You must have a clear December night, with blue Maine stars snapping like sapphires with the cold, and the big moon flooding full over Misery, and lighting up the snowy spruce boughs like crushed diamonds. You ought to be wrapped in a buffalo robe to your nose and be sitting in a family pung, and have your breath trailing along with you as you slide over the dry, whistling snow. You will have to sing the songs we sang, "God Rest You Merry, Gentlemen" and "Joy to the World," and you will be able to see your songs around you in the air like blue smoke. That's the only way to come to a Paradise Christmas.

And you really should cross over at least one broad bay on the ice, and feel the tide rifts bounce you as the runners slide over them. And if the whole bay booms out, every now and then, and the sound echoes around the wooded islands for miles, you will be having the sort of ride we loved to take from town, the night before Christmas.

I won't insist on your having a father like ours to drive you home to your Christmas. One with a wide moustache full of icicles, and eyes like the stars of the morning. That would be impossible, anyway, for there has been only one of him in the world. But it is too bad, just the same. For you won't have the stories we had by the fireplace. You won't hear about Kitty Wells who died beautifully in song just as the sun came over the tops of the eastern mountains and just after her lover had named the wedding day, and you will not hear how Kitty's departure put an end to his mastering the banjo:

> "But death came in my cabin door
> And took from me my joy, my pride,
> And when they said she was no more,
> I laid my banjo down and cried."

But you will be able to have the rooms of the farmhouse banked with emerald jewels clustered on bayberry boughs, clumps of everlasting roses with gold spots in the middle of them, tree evergreens, and the evergreen that runs all over the Maine woods and every so often puts up a bunch of palm leaves. And there will be rose-hips stuck in pine boughs. And caraway seeds in every crust and cookie in the place.

An aunt should be on hand, an aunt who believes in yarrow tea and the Bible as the two things needed to keep children well. She will read the Nativity story aloud to the family, hurrying over the really exciting parts that happened at the stable, and bearing down hard on what the angels had to say and the more edifying points that might be supposed to improve small boys who like to lie too long abed in the mornings. She will put a moral even into Christmas greens, and she will serve well as a counterirritant to the over-eating of mince pies. She will insist on all boys washing behind their ears, and that will keep her days full to the brim.

The Christmas tree will be there, and it will have a top so high that it will have to be bent over and run along the ceiling of the sitting room. It will be the best fir tree of the Paradise forests, picked from ten thousand almost perfect ones, and every bough on it will be like old-fashioned fans wide open. You will have brought it home that very morning, on the sled, from Dragonfly Spring.

Dragonfly Spring was frozen solid to the bottom, and you could look down into it and see the rainbows where you dented it with your copper-toed boots, see whole ferns caught motionless in the crystal deeps, and a frog, too, down there, with hands just like a baby's on him. Your small sister—the one with hair like new honey laid open—in the middle of a honeycomb—had cried out, "Let's dig him up and take him home and warm his feet!" (She is the same sister who ate up all your more vivid pastel crayons when you were away at school, and then ate up all the things you had been pretty sure were toadstools in Bluejay Woods, when you were supposed to be keeping an eye on her, but were buried so deep in *Mosses from an Old Manse* that you couldn't have been dug up with horses and oxen.)

Your dog, Snoozer, who is a curious and intricate combination of many merry pugs and many mournful hound-dogs, was snuffling all the time, hot on the feather-stitching the mice had made from bush to bush while you were felling the Christmas tree. A red squirrel was taking a white-pine cone apart on a hemlock bough, and telling Snoozer what he thought of him and all other dogs, the hour or so you were there.

There will be a lot of aunts in the house besides the Biblical one. Aunts of every complexion and cut. Christmas is the one time that even the most dubious of aunts take on value. One of them can make up wreaths, another can make rock candy that puts a tremble on the heart, and still another can steer your twelve-seater bob-sled—and turn it over, bottom up, with you all in just the right place for a fine spill.

There will be uncles, too, to hold one end of the molasses taffy you will pull sooner or later, yanking it out till it flashes and turns into cornsilk that almost floats in the air, tossing your end of it back and probably lassoing your uncle around his neck as you do it, and pulling out a new rope of solid honey.

The uncles will smoke, too, and that will be a help to all the younger brothers who have been smoking their acorn-pipes out in the woodshed and who don't want their breaths to give them away. The uncles will make themselves useful in other ways. They will rig up schooners no bigger than your thumb, with shrouds like cob-webs; they will mend the bob-sled, tie up cut fingers, and sew on buttons after you shin up to the cupola in the barn; and—if you get on the good side of them—they will saw you up so much birch wood that you won't have to lay hand to a bucksaw till after New Year's.

There will be cousins by the cart load. He-ones and she-ones. The size you can sit on, and the size that can sit on you. Enough for two armies, on Little Round Top and on Big, up in the hay-mow. You will play Gettysburg there till your heads are full of hay chaff that will keep six aunts busy cleaning it out. And then you will come in to the house and down a whole crock of molasses cookies—the kind that go up in peaks in the middle—which some-body was foolish enough to leave the cover off.

Every holiday that came along, in my father's house, was the gathering of an Anglo-Saxon clan. My father was built for lots of people 'round him. But Christmas was a whole assembly of the West Saxons! My father wanted people in squads. There were men with wide moustaches and men with smooth places on top of their heads, women· wide and narrow. Cousins of the second and third water, even, were there. Hired men, too. They were special guests and had to be handled with kid gloves, as New England hired men must. They had to have the best of everything, and you could not find fault with them, as you could with uncles, if they smacked you for upsetting their coffee into their laps. Babies were underfoot in full cry. The older children hunted in packs. The table had to be pieced out with flour barrels and bread boards and ironing boards. It was a house's length from the head of the table, where your father sat and manufactured the roast up into slivers, to your mother dishing out the pork gravy. Whole geese disappeared on the way down. The Christmas cake, which had been left sweetly to itself for a month to age into a miracle, was a narrow isthmus when it got to Mother. But Mother always said that Christmas, to her, was watching other people eat. She was the kind of mother who claimed that the neck and the back of the chicken were the tastiest parts.

The prize goose, whom you had brought up by hand and called Oliver Cromwell, Old Ironsides, or some such distinguished title, was duly carved. And Father found his wishbone snow-white and you all applauded, for that meant lots of snow and two more months of coasting on your sleds. There were mince pies by the legion. And if Uncle Tom were there, a whole raccoon baked just for him and girt around with browned sweet potatoes. Mother's wild strawberry jam was there on deck, winking at you like rubies from the holes in tarts that melted away like bubbles in the mouth. That dinner was three hours in Beulah Land!

Of course, there will be an apple pudding at such a season. Steamed in a lard bucket, and cut open with a string. A sauce of oranges and lemons to make an ocean around each steaming volcano of suet and russet apples as it falls crumbling from the loop of twine. It will have to be steamed in the boiler, if your Christmas is to be the size of ours, and cooked in a ten-pound lard pail. Better use a cod line instead of the twine of other holidays, to parcel it out to the members of the clan.

The whole nation of you in the house will go from one thing to another. The secret of the best Christmases is everybody doing the same things all at the same time. You will all fall to and string cranberries and popcorn for the tree, and the bright lines each of you has a hold on will radiate from the tree like ribbons on a may-pole. Everybody will have needles and thread in the mouth, you will all get in each other's way, but that is the art of doing Christmas right. You will all bundle up together for a ride in the afternoon. You had better take the horse-sled, as the pung will not begin to hold you. And even then a dozen or so of assorted uncles and aunts and cousins will have to come troop-ing after through the deep snow, and wait for their turn on the straw in the sled. Smaller cousins will fall off over the sides in great knots and never be missed, and the hullabaloo will roar on and send the rabbits flying away through the woods, showing their bobbing scuts.

Everybody will hang presents on the tree at once, when the sun has dipped down into the spruces in the west and you are back home in the sitting-room. There will be no nonsense of tiptoeing up and edging a package on when nobody is looking. Everybody knows who is giving him what. There is no mystery about it. Aunt Ella has made rag dinahs for all hands and the cook—for all under fourteen years of age—and she does not care who knows it. The dinahs are all alike, except that those for the children whose lower garments are forked have forked red-flannel pants instead of red-flannel petticoats. They all have pearl button eyes and stocking toes for faces. There will be so many hands at work on the tree at once that the whole thing will probably go over two or three times, and it will be well to make it fast with a hawser or so.

And then you will turn right around and take the presents off again, the minute you have got them all on and have lighted the candles up. There will be no waiting, with small children sitting around with aching hearts. The real candles will be a problem, in all that mass of spills. Boughs will take fire here and there. But there will be plenty of uncles around to crush out the small bonfires in their big brown hands. All the same, it would be well to have an Uncle Thomas who can take up a live coal in his thumb and finger, and light his pipe from it, cool as a cucumber. Better turn the extinguishing of the tree over to him.

There will be boughten presents, to be sure—a turtle of cardboard in a glassed, dainty box, hung on springs and swimming for dear life with all four feet, and popguns with their barrels ringed and streaked with red and yellow lines. Why popguns should be painted like broomsticks is one of the mysteries, along with the blue paint you always find on Maine cartwheels. Somebody will probably get one of those Swiss music-boxes that will eke out a ghostly "Last Rose of Summer," if tenderly cranked. There should be those little bottles of transparent candies, with real syrup in them, which I used to live for through the years. And there must be a German doll for every last girl, with mountains of yellow hair and cheeks looking as if life were a continuous blowing of bubbles. Boughten things are all right.

But if it is going to be our kind of Christmas, most of the presents will be home-made. Socks knit by the aunt who swears only by useful gifts. You have seen those socks growing up from their white toes for the last two weeks. Wristers, always red.

A box of Aunt Louise's candied orange peel that she will never let on to anybody how she makes. Your father will have made a sled for every mother's son and daughter of you, with a bluebird, or robin redbreast, more real than life, painted on each one and your name underneath. You will never have another present to match that, though you grow up and become Midases. Popcorn balls, big as muskmelons, will be common ware. They will be dripping with molasses, and will stick your wristers and socks and other treasures together.

But the pith of the party is not reached until the whole nation of you sits down in rocking chairs, or lies down on their bellies in front of the six-foot gulf of the fireplace. The presents are all stowed, heaped and tucked away, stuck fast with cornballs. The last lamps are out. The fireplace dances on the ceiling. It lights up the steel engraving of Major McCullock leaping from Kentucky to Ohio, with ten thousand mounted redskins yelling and reining in their steeds behind him. It lights up Daniel Boone's daughters as they lean away towards their boat's end and scream their silent screams and drop their water lilies, while Indian head after Indian head grins up at them from the river of the Dark and Bloody Ground.

All the babies will be hushed and put away. All the younger fry will be more than half asleep. The toasted cheese and red herring will go 'round. The herring, by the way—if you are worthy to wear my shoes after me—which you yourself have smoked with green oak, and have gotten your own two eyes so that they looked like two burnt holes in a blanket while doing it, and have hugely enjoyed every hour of it all.

Then you had best find a fair substitute for my father. Give him the best chair in the house—and the way to find *that* is to push the cat out of it—and let him tear! He will begin by telling you about such people as the brilliant young ladies of Philadelphia who had a piano too big to fit their house, so they put it on the porch and played on it through the open window. Then he will sit back and work his way to the Caliph of Bagdad, who had a daughter so homely that she had to wear a sack on her head when her suitors came awooing, and how she fell down a well and made herself a great fortune, and won the handsomest husband that ever wore a turban. That story, by the way, you will not find in the "Arabian Nights" even though you look for it, as I have done, till you have gray hairs in your head.

The firelight will get into your father's eyes and on his hair. He will move on from Bagdad to Big Bethel, and tell you all how the Yankee campfires looked like the high Milky Way itself, all night long before the battle; how the dew silvered every sleeping soldier's face and the stacked rifles, as the dawn came up with the new day and death. And you will hug your knees and hear the wind outside going its rounds among the snowy pines, and you will listen on till the story you are hearing becomes a part of the old winds of the world and the motion of the bright stars. And probably it will take two uncles at least to carry you to bed.

ONCE ON CHRISTMAS

from *Once on Christmas*

BY DOROTHY THOMPSON

Dorothy Thompson was esteemed as one of America's outstanding journalists and commentators, for many years a specialist on foreign affairs. She also wrote a number of books of international and political importance. Once on Christmas, *however, unveils a surprising nostalgic tenderness, a profound regard for a childhood Christmas in a happy Methodist parsonage during the early twentieth century.*

It is Christmas Eve—the festival that belongs to mothers and fathers and children, all over the so-called Western world. It's not a time to talk about situations, or conditions, or reactions, or people who emerge briefly into the news. My seven-year-old son asked me this evening to tell him what Christmas was like when I was a little girl, before people came home for Christmas in airplanes, thirty-odd years ago. And so I told him this:

A long, long time ago, when your mother was your age, and not nearly as tall as you, she lived with her mother, and father, and younger brother, and little sister, in a Methodist parsonage, in Hamburg, New York. It was a tall wooden house, with a narrow verandah on the side, edged with curley-cues of wood-work at the top, and it looked across a lawn at the church where father preached every Sunday morning and evening. In the backyard there were old Baldwin and Greening apple trees, and a wonderful, wonderful barn. But that is another story. The village now has turned into a suburb of the neighboring city of Buffalo, and fathers who work there go in and out every day on the trains and buses, but then it was just a little country town, supported by the surrounding farms.

Father preached in his main church there on Sunday mornings but in the afternoons he had to drive out to the neighboring village of Armor where there was just a little box of church in the middle of the farming country. For serving both parishes, he received his house and one thousand dollars a year. But he didn't always get the thousand dollars. Sometimes the crops were bad, and the farmers had no money, and when the farmers had no money the village people didn't have any either. Then the farmers would come to us with quarters of beef, or halves of pigs, or baskets of potatoes, and make what they called a donation. My mother hated the word, and sometimes would protest, but my father would laugh, and say, "Let them pay in what they can! We are all in the same boat together."

For weeks before Christmas we were very, very busy. Mother was busy in the kitchen, cutting up citron and sorting out raisins and clarifying suet for the Christmas pudding—and shooing all of us out of the room, when we crept in to snatch a raisin, or a bit of kernel from the butter-nuts that my little brother was set to cracking on the woodshed floor, with an old-fashioned flat-iron.

I would lock myself into my little bed-room, to bend over a handkerchief that I was hemstitching for my mother. It is very hard to hemstitch when you are seven years old, and the thread would knot, and break, and then one would have to begin again, with a little rough place, where one had started over. I'm afraid the border of that handkerchief was just one succession of knots and starts.

The home-made presents were only a tiny part of the work! There was the Christmas tree! Mr. Heist, from my father's Armor parish, had brought it from his farm, a magnificent hemlock, that touched the ceiling. We were transported with admiration, but what a tree to trim! For there was no money to buy miles of tinsel and boxes of colored glass balls.

But in the pantry was a huge stone jar of popcorn. When school was over, in the afternoons, we all gathered in the back parlor, which was the family sitting room. The front parlor was a cold place, where portraits of John Wesley and Frances Willard hung on the walls, and their eyes, I remember, would follow a naughty child accusingly around the room. The sofas in that room were of walnut, with roses and grapes carved on their backs, just where they'd stick into your back, if you fidgeted in them, and were covered with horse-hair which was slippery when it was new, and tickly when it was old. But that room was given over to visits from the local tycoons who sometimes contributed to the church funds, and couples who came to be married.

The back parlor was quite, quite different. It had an ingrain carpet on the floor, with patterns of maple leaves, and white muslin curtains at the windows, and an assortment of chairs contributed by the Parsonage Committee. A Morris chair, I remember, and some rockers, and a fascinating cabinet which was a desk and a book-case, and a chest of drawers, and a mirror, all in one.

In this room there was a round iron stove, a very jolly stove, a cozy stove that winked at you with its red isin-glass eyes. On top of this stove was a round iron plate, it was flat, and a wonderful place to pop corn. There was a great copper kettle, used for making maple syrup, and we shook the popper on the top of the stove—first I shook, until my arm was tired, and then Willard shook, until he was tired, and even the baby shook. The corn popped, and we poured it into the kettle and emptied the kettle, and poured it full again, until there was a whole barrel-full of popcorn, as white and fluffy as the snow that carpeted the lawn between the parsonage and the church.

Then we each got a darning needle, a big one, and a ball of string. We strung the popcorn into long, long ropes, to hang upon the tree. But that was only half of it! There were stars to be cut out of kindergarten paper, red and green, and silver, and gold, and walnuts to be wrapped in gold paper, or painted with gold paint out of the paint-box that I had been given for my birthday. One got the paint into one's finger-nails, and it smelled like bananas. And red apples to be polished, because a shiny apple makes a brave show on a tree. And when it was all finished, it was Christmas Eve.

For Christmas Eve we all wore our best clothes. Baby in a little challis dress as blue as her eyes, and I had a new pinafore of Swiss lawn that my Aunt Margaret had sent me from England. We waited, breathless, in the front parlor while the candles were lit.

Then my mother sat at the upright piano in a rose-red cashmere dress and played, and my father sang, in his lovely, pure, gay, tenor voice:

> "It came upon the midnight clear
> That glorious song of old.
> From angels bending near the earth
> To touch their harps of gold."

And then we all marched in. It is true that we had decorated the tree ourselves, and knew intimately everything on it, but it shone in the dark room like an angel, and I could see the angels bending down, and it was so beautiful that one could hardly bear it. We all cried, "Merry Christmas!" and kissed each other.

There were bundles under the tree, most alluring bundles! But they didn't belong to Christmas Eve. They were for the morning. Before the morning came three little children would sit sleepily in the pews of their father's church and hear words drowsily, and shift impatiently, and want to go to sleep in order to wake up very, very early!

And wake up early we did! The windows were still gray, and, oh, how cold the room was! The church janitor had come over at dawn to stoke the hot air furnace in the parsonage, but at its best it only heated the rooms directly above it, and the upstairs depended on grates in the floor, and the theory that heat rises. We shuddered out of our beds, trembling with cold and excitement, and into our clothes, which, when I was a little girl, were very complicated affairs indeed. First, a long fleece-lined union suit, and then a ferris waist dripping with buttons, then the cambric drawers edged with embroidery, and a flannel petticoat handsome with scallops, and another petticoat of cambric and embroidery, just for show, and over that a gay plaid dress, and a dainty pinafore. What polishing of cheeks, and what brushing of hair and then a grand tumble down the stairs into the warm, cozy back parlor.

Presents! There was my beloved Miss Jam-up with a brand new head! Miss Jam-up was once a sweet little doll, dear, who had become badly battered about the face in the course of too affectionate ministrations, and here she was again, with a new head altogether and new clothes, and eyes that open and shut. Scarfs and mittens from my mother's lively fingers. A doll house made from a wooden cracker box and odds and ends of wall paper, with furniture cut from stiff cardboard—and that was mother's work, too. And a new woolen dress, and new pinafores!

Under the tree was a book: *The Water Babies*, by Charles Kingsley. *To my beloved daughter Dorothy.*

Books meant sheer magic. There were no automobiles—none for Methodist ministers, in those days. No moving pictures. No radio. But inside the covers of books was everything, everything, that exists outside in the world today. Lovely, lovely words of poetry, that slipped like colored beads along a string; tales of rose-red cities, half as old as time. All that men can imagine, and construct and make others imagine.

One couldn't read the book now. But there it lay, the promise of a perfect afternoon. Before one could get at it, one would go into the dining room. And what a dinner! This Christmas there was turkey—with best wishes from one of my father's parishioners. And the pudding, steaming, and with two kinds of sauce. And no one to say, "No, dear, I think one helping is enough."

We glutted ourselves, we distended ourselves, we ate ourselves into a coma, so that we all had to lie down and have a nap.

Then, lying before the stove, propped on my elbows, I opened the covers of my Christmas book.

"Once upon a time there was a little chimney sweep, and his name was Tom. He lived in a great town of the North Country . . . in England."

How well I knew that North Country, with its rows on rows of dark stone houses, its mine pits, its poor workmen. From such a town my father had come, across the ocean, to this village in upstate New York. I forgot Christmas, forgot everything, except the fate of little Tom. What a book! It wasn't just a story. There was poetry in it. The words of the poems sang in my head, so that after all these years I can remember them:

> When all the world is young, lad,
> And all the trees are green;

> And every goose, a swan, lad,
> And every lass a Queen;
> Then hey for boot and spur, lad,
> And round the world away;
> Young blood must have its course, lad,
> And every dog his day.

The little girl lay and dreamed that all the world was wide and beautiful, filled only with hearts as warm and hands as tender, and spirits as generous as the only ones she had ever known . . . when she was seven years old.

> I wish you all a Merry Christmas!
> I wish us all a world as kind as a
> child can imagine it!

YULETIDE FESTIVAL AT FORT DODGE

from *Get Thee Behind Me*

BY HARTZELL SPENCE

As the son of a vigorous, lovable Methodist minister, Hartzell Spence, born in Iowa, 1908, received a thorough grounding in religion, which has always been interwoven in the fabric of his life and writing. Co-founder and editor of the army weekly Yank, *author of religious books, novels, and biographies, his reminiscences sparkle with stories of his parents, especially the spiritual values implanted and nurtured by his father. In the autobiographical* Get Thee Behind Me, *Spence gaily and affectionately describes life in a small town. Christmas at Fort Dodge gives an account of one happy celebration, typical of his childhood home.*

Christmas always was an exciting holiday. The family was a unit as at no other time, and father, who throughout the year had been big brother and uncle to the entire community, was remembered by scores of parishioners as though he belonged to their own households.

One of our greatest Christmases occurred at Fort Dodge. It was the last of the old-fashioned yuletide festivals, for war had come before the winter of 1914, and after the war Christmas was not quite the same.

In 1913 the merchant had not yet become the beneficiary; Christ in the manger was still worshiped. Most of the people of Fort Dodge made their own gifts, supplementing them only by such items as sleds and skates, which they could not handily produce at home. The parsonage celebration began two weeks earlier than that of our neighbors because of the ceremony of packing a box for our Canadian relatives. A week's lull followed, until a box arrived from Canada, after which we turned our attention to preparations for the church Christmas; we were not permitted to forget that first place was reserved for the Christ child, whose birthday the holy day was. We children learned verses and attended rehearsals for the Christmas pageant. A few days before Christmas a committee appeared at the house with tubs of candy and nuts and packed sacks for Santa Claus to give every member of the Sunday School on Christmas Eve. We loved this, because any candy left over was ours.

Then downtown on the day before Christmas went the whole family to select the Christmas tree. Father examined it for durability, mother for size, we children for symmetry. We went to Woolworth's to augment the ornaments saved from year to year. Eileen, Fraser, and I would have run riot here had not father and mother patiently curbed our extravagance both in money and taste. If mother shook her head, we rejected a gaudy ornament in favor of one more conventional; if father frowned, we were overreaching the budget.

Home again with our booty, we shared the intoxicating excitement of dressing the tree, which father enjoyed to the extent of writing his sermon on a clip board in the living room instead of in his study. When the ornaments were in place, we opened the big bundle from the Canadian relatives and hefted, rattled, and sniffed the individual packets for possible identification, father as curious as the rest of us. At the same time we helped father and mother to sort packages from other towns where father had served as pastor, and we arranged the offerings from his parishioners in Fort Dodge.

In the evening we went to the church and after the Christmas Eve service hurried home to appear in the window when the choir came by to sing carols. We smiled and beamed our appreciation, and then Eileen and I went outside to join the carolers on their round of the hospitals, the jail, and the homes of shut-in church members. This lasted until ten o'clock, or later if falling snow enhanced the festivities.

Christmas morning we were up early. Church members began to call at seven o'clock and continued to drop in throughout the day, bringing gifts and messages. There were a few presents we could count on: The Mohnike girls' homemade candy, Tony Roffel's cut glass or Haviland, Mr. McCutcheon's barrel of apples. Father waited anxiously for the appearance of the Men's Brotherhood, hoping that their remembrance would be in cash, but it wasn't; they contributed a leather chair.

By noon the tables overflowed with presents; hand-made lace, wearing apparel, preserved fruits, cakes, candies, oranges, nine scarves, four pairs of mittens, and for father seven pairs of knitted socks with ties to match. The gifts were tokens of love from men and women who had no other way of expressing their gratitude and devotion to the pastor who counseled them, freed their children from escapades, solved their domestic problems, found employment for them, and lent them money when he had it.

The lace, for example, that Sister Hawkins had been tatting since August had a story in it. Joe Hawkins, a farmer, had been stricken with a ruptured appendix just as the oats ripened. Father had managed the farm, helped to harvest the crop, and put up hay that would have been ruined by imminent rain. Joe Hawkins' hired man said the parson should have been a farmer, and that was reward enough for father. Mrs. Hawkins had spent every spare moment since on the lace.

The story of the six jars of plum butter from Mrs. Aiken was ten months old. The previous March Mrs. Aiken had contracted diphtheria and had been taken to the County Hospital for Contagious Diseases. Father had sent the Ladies Aid to the rescue, and their volunteers had kept the Aiken house running and the three children and husband fed until the mother could return.

Daily father had called on her at the hospital, delivered letters to her from her family, and bolstered her spirits. One day when she said, "Oh, Mr. Spence, I'll never be able to thank you," he had laughed it off. "You just make me some plum butter next summer, and we'll be even." She had put up the butter, all right; it was her Christmas gift.

People who were that generous with their preacher did not forget his children. We received candy enough to last, with careful hoarding, for six weeks or more and many games, which father inspected carefully to be sure that they could not be utilized for gambling. When he carried one to the furnace, we didn't mind; what was one among a dozen?

BUT ONCE A YEAR

from *Life Was Simpler Then*

BY LOULA GRACE ERDMAN

Loula Grace Erdman, a Missourian by birth, a Texan by adoption, is an instructor in creative writing at West Texas State College. She has written many popular books, novels for young and old alike, short stories and novelettes for magazines of national importance. In Life Was Simpler Then *Miss Erdman turns to reminiscences of her childhood in western Missouri and revivifies the way of life in a small Western town. "But Once a Year," telling of Christmas as she and her lively family knew it, touches our hearts with that nostalgia, humor, and pathos which springs from precious memories of our own.*

I don't believe it used to start so early.

The Christmas season, I mean. It came in officially, at least in the minds of us children, when Mr. Brunkhorst set up the clock in his store window. On the top was a Santa Claus head which went wagging back and forth, marking off the seconds.

No notices reminded us of the number of shopping days left until Christmas. Gift buying was a matter which we took care of at a rather leisurely pace. I remember one year we waited until Christmas Eve Day, and then barely made it home before the Big Snow came. Papa put the car in the garage where it stayed for almost a week. This stands out as one of the nicest Christmases we ever had, shut in as we were, without even the mail carrier coming until two days after Christmas.

Logs burned brightly in the fireplace. We played the victrola until Mama said she was ready to lose her mind; we telephoned friends and relatives several times a day; we listened, without apology, to every ring that came in over the line. And of course, Mama cooked all our favorite dishes.

It was also a good time to read our new Christmas books and reread the old favorites. Our house had a spot ideal for winter reading—a couch in the upstairs hall under a window overlooking the front yard. A bookcase stood nearby. Here, fortified by a plate of apples and a bowl of popcorn, we could sprawl for hours, utterly comfortable, completely content, lost to time and space, our eyes glued to the printed page.

Not one of us considered this an unexciting way to spend Christmas.

In fact, Christmas, like life in general, was simpler then. Not better, not worse. Just simpler. And a great deal easier on the pocketbook, to say nothing of the blood pressure.

Even though we might delay a bit on the shopping, the other preparations had started well ahead of time. The fruit cakes were made early in December and put away to ripen. Mama used a cherished recipe which called for dried apples. These we had grown on our own trees, and then, in the heat of August, we peeled them, cut them into small sections, and put them on a slab in the sun to dry. They had to be covered with mosquito netting to keep away the flies and other insects; they had to be turned every day; they had to be kept in the direct rays of the sun; they had to be brought in every evening before the dew fell. They were in short, treated with much the same tender loving care accorded a newborn babe.

But, like a well-brought-up child, they paid dividends. When we were ready to make the fruit cake, we soaked them over night and then the next morning candied them, using plenty of sugar, cooking them over a slow fire. When they were finished they were chewy, moist, a bright amber in color, and utterly delectable. It was a wonder they could bring themselves to blend with the ordinary raisins and spices and other ingredients of the Christmas cake. I still make the cake, using commercially dried apples, but the flavor is not the same. The difference is subtle, like comparing a recording of a symphony concert with the real thing.

There was, also, mincemeat. For this you butchered a beef, one you had raised from a calf, which had never had a cross word spoken to it in all its life. This slaughter started a ritual known as "trading quarters." Some neighbor who had butchered at an- other time and had let you have a "quarter" was now repaid in kind. If you had received a front "quarter" from him, of course that's what he got in return. The hind "quarter," considered the choice one, was always kept at home at Christmas time. A portion of this we used in making mincemeat.

I remember neither the recipe nor the process except in the vaguest sort of way. The meat was cooked first—this I know. Afterward raisins and currants and spices were added. Also some apple cider which was first boiled down. I think Mama, possessed with the spirit of adventure, might occasionally have tossed in pickled peach juice and maybe some canned cherries and—yes— I think a few fine slithers of apples when baking time came. When she had the mixture to her liking, she packed it into stone jars or crocks and stored them in the cellar, there to wait their ultimate destiny, the Christmas pies.

But of all the preparations, the animal cookies are the most fondly remembered.

Mama made them from a recipe given her by Papa's mother, using the cookie cutters which had also been hers. A sugar cookie dough it was, rolled to paper thinness and cut into the shapes of dogs and horses and camels and rabbits and chickens and reindeer. There were also stars and Christmas trees, but we liked the animal ones best, going back as they did to the legend of that first Christmas when the animals were said to have knelt in worship before the baby, Jesus.

Once the cookies were out of the oven, the work had barely started. They must then be iced with white frosting and deco- orated. I have spent hours setting raisin eyes in the heads of those cookies, and still more time swirling colored icing in loops on trees and stars. Then, red and green sugar must be sprinkled over the entire surface. When they were finally finished, the cookies were almost (but not quite) too beautiful to eat.

Of course, it was necessary to double or sometimes triple the recipe for both cookies and icing on important occasions like Christmas. At such times Mama, finding herself lost in the intricacies of three times one and three-fourths cups, turned to Papa for help. He was a genius in math, but occasionally he would give the wrong answer, just to tease—a deception Mama always caught because it was accompanied by a grin, mischievous yet tender, not devoid of complacency. As if he were saying to himself, "Ah, this dear little woman I married. What would she do without me!"

A very smart woman, my mother.

A cousin once said, "If I woke up in Hong Kong on the Fourth of July and saw one of Aunt Mollie's Christmas cookies, I'd figure the calendar was all wrong and start my Christmas shopping on the spot."

Since we always ate Christmas dinner at Grandma's house, the food we prepared was more of a supplementary nature than the main ingredients for the feast. In this category we classed ham. A sugar-cured ham, considered a great delicacy now, was accepted as commonplace by all Missouri cooks, Mama included. Our smokehouse held any number of them, cured by Papa's own recipe, swathed in layers of paper and cloth, and then hung cheek by jowl with the less glamorous sides of bacon.

Ham, for us, was a staple item of diet, as rice is for the Chinese. No sooner was one finished than Papa cut another, this procedure being considered too difficult for a woman. Fried ham was standard for breakfast; it was always accompanied by "red gravy," a delectable liquid made from the residue of fat and drippings left in the skillet after the ham was fried, diluted with a suitable amount of water, heated to the boiling point and poured over the meat in the platter. Mouth-watering, this ambrosia came to its full peak of perfection when ladled over hot biscuits.

Boiled ham was another thing. After a careful scrubbing it was boiled on top of the stove and then finished off by baking in the oven with a coating of brown sugar and probably sweet peach pickle juice and dotted with cloves. Mama always kept a baked ham on hand "just in case," using the same forethought I employ in stocking up cans of tuna and pork and beans.

When I think of the price we pay now for sugar-cured hams which are, at best, only poor imitations of the ones Papa used to store in our smokehouse, I marvel at the way in which we took them as no more than our due. Sometimes I wonder if the measure of a good life could be the number of lovely things we can take for granted.

At school, preparations were also in full swing as we made gifts for our parents and each other (wobbly works of art achieved with crayons and paper or bits of cloth smuggled from home). By the time we were able to present them, we were almost exhausted from the burden of trying to keep them secret from the intended recipient.

We had a program at school, small and without pretensions. I do not remember that we ever had a Christmas tree there or that the teacher gave us gifts or a treat. I think we usually took up a collection, fancying we were keeping the whole thing a great secret, and bought some sort of a present for him. I am sure it was a dreadfully unsuitable necktie, or something else equally inappropriate. Why our parents did not take a hand in the matter I am not prepared to say.

There was a program at our church on Christmas Eve. Of course we all had a part in it. I remember once Brother almost wrecked it. He was to hang up his stocking. Just that, nothing more. Sister and some of her friends were slated to sing a song about him.

Funny thing, nobody thought about a dress rehearsal, even though Brother was to wear his pajamas, which, for no reason any of us ever knew, he called his "jiggers." I guess we just trusted to luck and a child's natural instinct for acting, if we gave the matter any thought at all.

Usually our programs were simple in nature, but this time we had gone big time and had a curtain, made from white sheets someone had brought from home and pinned across a wire. A few older members thought this innovation rather shocking, but we didn't even listen to them. Progress was not to be stopped by a few old fogies. Everyone settled down in his place, expecting a real production.

The pianist struck the keys, the signal for the number in which

Brother was to appear. Mama leaned forward in her seat, trying not to look smug at having *two* children in one performance. Just then the curtain parted and Brother's head appeared while he held the folds of the curtain tight across his middle.

"Mama," he yelled, "they're trying to make me put on my jiggers and it's not time to go to bed."

Everyone howled. Mama's ears turned pink. Brother disappeared with a speed that could mean only one thing—he had been yanked forcibly from the rear. We heard a round of brief, whispered argument behind the curtain. An agonized stillness, which the audience sat out with as much calmness as it could muster. And then, the curtain opened—a little jerkily, but still it opened—and there was Brother, subdued and amenable, standing by a wobbly make-believe mantel, holding his stocking. Yes, and wearing his pajamas. Someone—maybe the Sunday School teacher, an authority ranking close to the preacher and the superintendent—had evidently persuaded him it was a privilege to wear "jiggers" in a Christmas program. Or maybe they had merely assured him it did not mean he would have to go to bed and miss all the fun; or, what is even more likely, Sister had bribed him by promising him her "treat" when the time came for passing them out.

The song did not fare as well. The singers, so filled with giggles they could barely get the words out, galloped through the number at such a great pace the pianist had difficulty keeping up with them. Brother easily remained the star of the show.

Christmas dinner was, by custom unbroken, eaten with Mama's parents. Aunts and uncles and cousins trooped in, and it was just like a family reunion, with everyone talking at once and food all over the place. There was one difference here, however, for while an ordinary reunion was an end in itself, Christmas Day, for us, was a sort of interlude, set in suspension between what we had and what was yet to be. As a reminder of the first part of Christmas we wore a gift—a new hair ribbon or maybe a locket or bracelet; and to our hearts we hugged the knowledge that tonight there was still the Three Groves Christmas tree.

Papa had belonged to this little rural church before he went over to the Methodists with Mama. Like the school we attended, Papa's father had helped to found it. The smart cousin went there. Certainly we came not as outsiders, nor were we without debt to it. Here was held each Christmas night the annual program. Without this, Christmas would have ended with the dinner at Grandma's and the inevitable letdown which comes of knowing the great adventure is finished.

As it was, we went about all Christmas Day not only enjoying the present but having the added zest which anticipation gives. Once we were home from Grandma's, we dressed in our best, a privilege denied us during the day, and set off once more. We were going to call on our other grandparents, Papa's mother and father, to wish them merry Christmas. This was not the uninhibited experience a visit to Mama's parents offered. Here we were quiet and dignified and certainly less impulsive; here we did not interrupt anybody, not even the smart cousin in whose home our grandparents lived. We visited, we exchanged gifts. The interlude was good for us; in effect it said, "Be quiet, spirit, so that you may be able to endure the joy which is to come."

Recently a cousin said, "I used to feel sorry for all those poor deprived people who didn't have the Three Groves Christmas tree to go to on Christmas night."

For, of course, we brought home assorted cousins with us, to spend a few days of vacation and to attend the program.

"Do you remember that time we went in a sled?" he continued.

If there was snow, we did occasionally go in a sled with a couple of brisk horses pulling it. Papa drove and the rest of us sat on blankets thrown over the straw in the bottom of the sled. I think we sang all the way there and back. All except me, for I was supposed to be quiet so that I would be in good voice when the time came for me to say my piece. At this time I felt the price of stardom came too high.

The tree there was the biggest in the world. Of that we were all convinced. Also, it had real candles on it, a custom continued long after other institutions had deemed them too dangerous for use in community gatherings. Here, the members of the congregation solved the problem very nicely by setting one man—it was always the same one—to watching those candles. Equipped with a bucket of water and a long pole to which a piece of cloth was attached, he sat—immobile, alert, watchful. If a candle so much as gave the slightest indication that it might have burned down low enough to catch the tree on fire, he rose with unhurried and purposeful dignity and touched it with his improvised fire extinguisher. Fire in that small crowded wooden building would have been a disaster too tragic to contemplate. We never gave the matter a thought. Year after year this man sat there guarding us, while we accepted his watchfulness as we accepted sunlight and air and all the rest of heaven's gifts.

Sister says there was a trick to watching those candles. If you peered at them through half-closed eyes, they looked bigger, more numerous, and, also, seemed to twinkle like far-off stars. I think I remember best the smell of it, the pungent aromatic odor of candles so close to cedar; or, perhaps, the voice of the superintendent intoning the numbers on the program until he came, at last, to me. I was never at ease until I was finished—there were so many things I must remember: To push my braids over my shoulder, so that they hung down my back; to walk up to my place, and back, with unhurried ease; to speak clearly and loudly. Not only was I, in a manner of speaking, on unfamiliar ground here, but this program was also inherently more serious than the one in our own church. I can't imagine Brother protesting about wearing his "jiggers" here, if, indeed, such a lightminded number would be allowed in the first place.

But I think the part we all remembered best, looked forward to the most keenly, was the giving of treats.

These came in brown paper sacks of truly heroic proportions. Never have I seen such size or variety of contents. All the while the program was going on you could see them under the tree. When the last speech had been said, the last note of the final song had died down (I have yet to hear any group sing "Joy to the World" with the spirit the congregation at Three Groves put into it), the real business—for us—of the evening began. The superintendent called forward several helpers and then, from a list in his hand, read off the names of the children. As your name was called, you walked up, took your great sack (folded over neatly at the top), said "thank you," and walked back to your place.

The first child ventured only the stealthiest peep; after a few more received theirs, we grew bolder. Presently there was a noise all over the building, like a wind in the forest, growing louder by the moment, as children began to dig into their sacks. You'd think we hadn't eaten a bite in weeks.

In my earlier, more innocent years, I don't believe I ever gave any thought as to how the sacks got under the tree. Maybe I thought they grew there, from seed left the preceding Christmas. Like the program itself, they were a sort of unearned increment, a bonus coming after you had every reason to believe Christmas was over for another year. Even then I suspected dimly that it all went too fast.

Finally I found out the real story back of those sacks. It was worse than learning the true identity of Santa Claus, because I had always had some mental reservations about that old boy, dating back to the time when I opened Mama's closet door and a doll fell out on my head. It was the same one I had seen in Mr. Brunkhorst's store, and begged for, and Mama said maybe Santa would bring it to me. What was it doing in Mama's closet now if Santa was supposed to be looking after the matter?

So I wasn't exactly unprepared for the truth about Santa. But it did sort of hit me below the belt when I found out about the treat.

Our papas paid for them. That's why we got our sacks—every last one of us. The year of discovery was one of disillusionment for me.

"What's the matter?" a kind lady asked, seeing my sack still unopened when all the other children were going through theirs like beavers collecting logs for a dam. "Don't you like what we've put in it?"

"Oh, yes, ma'am," I assured her, with more haste and emphasis than the answer required. How was she to know she had given me a double blow? Not only did the fathers pay for the treats, but human hands arranged them. I handed mine over to a visiting cousin who was, even at that moment, regarding it as a refugee child might look at the first food he has seen in days. I was praised for my generosity, words which did nothing to raise my spirits, knowing they were ill-deserved.

But by and by I grew up, and went no more to the Three Groves program except, of course, in memory. There I still see the brightness of the candles, hear the rustling of the sacks, feel the excitement. And being granted the insight which is the gift of the backward look, I forgive the good people of the church for ruling that the treat must be paid for. I can even appreciate the magnitude of their accomplishment. In their own way, with no apparent effort, they succeeded in implementing the great wish of the world.

They made Christmas last a little longer.

Sister confesses she used to play a game, watching the candles on the tree, giving each a name. Some twinkled brightly, some flickered, some burned out quickly. Others, let us face it, were a bit on the drippy side. Naturally the best and most steadfast always bore the names of kin. These relatives, she felt, were also watching her, winking their approval, assuring her that though absent in body, they were, in spirit, enjoying the occasion with her.

It is a fancy I like to recall now.

A LARGE CHRISTMAS

from *Memory of a Large Christmas*

BY LILLIAN SMITH

Florida-born Lillian Eugenia Smith has led her entire life in activities for the reform of social problems. Although educated in music, after teaching at a mission school in Hutchow, China, she returned to Georgia and has since directed all her energies toward civic improvements, largely through writing and editing. In "A Large Christmas" she revives one holiday celebrated in the warm intimacy of a noble, devoted, and enchanting family, whose Memory of a Large Christmas lives on.

We were not alone in being poor. Times were hard in the South—much harder for most than for us, as our father often reminded us. Our region was deep in a depression long before the rest of the country felt it—indeed, it had never had real prosperity since the Civil War—only spotty surges of easy money. But even the bank did not know—and it knew plenty—how little money we managed on those years. It got worse instead of better as time passed. And there came a winter when my younger sister and I, who were in Baltimore preparing ourselves to be a great pianist (me) and a great actress (her), felt we were needed at home. We had been supporting ourselves in our schools but even so, we felt the parents needed us.

It was our barter year: Dad would take eggs to town, swap them for flour or cornmeal or coffee, and do it so casually that nobody suspected it was necessary. They thought he was so proud of his wife's Leghorns that he wanted to show their achievements to his friends at the stores. Eggs from the hens, three pigs which he had raised, milk and butter from the cow, beans he grew and dried, and apples from a few old trees already on the property—that was about it. It was enough. For Mother could take cornmeal, mix it with flour, add soda and buttermilk and melted butter, a dab of sugar and salt, and present us with the best hot cakes in the world. Her gravy made of drippings from fried side meat, with flour and milk added and crushed black pepper would have pleased Escoffier or any other great cook. And when things got too dull, my sister and I would hitch up the two feisty mules to the wagon and go for as wild a ride as one wanted over rough clay winter roads.

Nevertheless, the two of us had agreed to skip Christmas. You don't always have to have Christmas, we kept saying to each other. Of course not, the other would answer.

We had forgot our father.

In that year of austerity, he invited the chain gang to have Christmas dinner with us. The prisoners were working the state roads, staying in two shabby red railroad cars on a siding. Our father visited them as he visited "all his neighbors." That night, after he returned from a three-hour visit with the men, we heard him tell Mother about it. She knew what was coming. "Bad place to be living," he said. "Terrible! Not fit for animals much less—" He sighed. "Well, there's more misery in the world than even I know; and a lot of it is unnecessary. That's the wrong part of it, it's unnecessary." He looked in his wife's dark eyes. She waited. "Mama," he said softly, "how about having them out here for Christmas. Wouldn't that be good?" A long silence. Then Mother quietly agreed. Dad walked to town—we had no car—to tell the foreman he would like to have the prisoners and guards come to Christmas dinner.

"All of them?" asked the chain-gang foreman.
"We couldn't hardly leave any of the boys out, could we?"

Close to noon on Christmas Day we saw them coming down the road: forty-eight men in stripes, with their guards. They came up the hill and headed for the house, a few laughing, talking, others grim and suspicious. All had come, white and Negro. We had helped Mother make two caramel cakes and twelve sweet potato pies and a wonderful backbone-and-rice dish (which Mother, born on the coast, called pilau); and there were hot rolls and Brunswick stew, and a washtub full of apples which our father had polished in front of the fire on Christmas Eve. It would be a splendid dinner, he told Mother who looked a bit wan, probably wondering what we would eat in January.

While we pulled out Mother's best china—piecing out with the famous heirloom fish plates—our father went from man to man shaking hands, and soon they were talking freely with him, and everybody was laughing at his funny—and sometimes on the rare side—stories. And then, there was a hush, and we in the kitchen heard Dad's voice lifted up: "And it came to pass in those days—"

Mother stayed with the oven. The two of us eased to the porch. Dad was standing there, reading from St. Luke. The day was warm and sunny and the forty-eight men and their guards were sitting on the grass. Two guards with guns in their hands leaned against trees. Eight of the men were lifers; six of them, in pairs, had their inside legs locked together; ten were killers (one had bashed in his grandma's head); two had robbed banks, three had stolen cars, one had burned down his neighbor's house and barn after an argument, one had raped a girl—all were listening to the old old words.

When my father closed the Bible, he gravely said he hoped their families were having a good Christmas, he hoped all was well "back home." Then he smiled and grew hearty. "Now boys," he said, "eat plenty and have a good time. We're proud to have you today. We would have been a little lonely if you hadn't come. Now let's have a Merry Christmas."

The men laughed. It began with the Negroes, who quickly caught the wonderful absurdity, it spread to the whites and finally all were laughing and muttering Merry Christmas, half deriding, half meaning it, and my father laughed with them for he was never unaware of the absurd which he seemed deliberately, sometimes, to whistle into his life.

They were our guests, and our father moved among them with grace and ease. He was soon asking them about their families, telling them a little about his. One young man talked earnestly in a low voice. I heard my father say, "Son, that's mighty bad. We'll see if we can't do something about it." (Later he did.)

When Mother said she was ready, our father asked "Son," who was one of the killers, to go help "my wife, won't you, with the heavy things." And the young man said he'd be mighty glad to. The one in for raping and another for robbing a bank said they'd be pleased to help, too, and they went in. My sister and I followed, not feeling as casual as we hoped we looked. But when two guards moved toward the door my father peremptorily stopped them with, "The boys will be all right." And "the boys" were. They came back in a few minutes bearing great pots and pans to a serving table we had set up on the porch. My sister and I served the plates. The murderer and his two friends passed them to the men. Afterward, the rapist and two bank robbers and the arsonist said they'd be real pleased to wash up the dishes. But we told them nobody should wash dishes on Christmas— just have a good time.

That evening, after our guests had gone back to their quarters on the railroad siding, we sat by the fire. The parents looked tired. Dad went out for another hickory log to "keep us through the night," laid it in the deep fireplace, scratched the coals, sat down in his easy chair by the lamp. Mother said she had a letter from the eldest daughter in China—would Papa read it? It was full of cheer as such letters are likely to be. We sat quietly talking of her family, of their work with a religious organization, of China's persisting troubles after the 1911 revolution.

We were quiet after that. Just rested together. Dad glanced through a book or two that his sons had sent him. Then the old look of having something to say to his children settled on his face. He began slowly:

"We've been through some pretty hard times, lately, and I've been proud of my family. Some folks can take prosperity and can't take poverty; some can take being poor and lose their heads when money comes. I want my children to accept it all; the good and the bad, for that is what life is. It can't be wholly good; it won't be wholly bad." He looked at our mother, sitting there, tired but gently involved. "Those men, today—they've made mistakes. Sure. But I have too. Bigger ones maybe than theirs. And you will. You are not likely to commit a crime but you may become blind and refuse to see what you should look at, and that can be worse than a crime. Don't forget that. Never look down on a man. Never. If you can't look him straight in the eyes, then what's wrong is with you." He glanced at the letter from the eldest sister. "The world is changing fast. Folks get hurt and make terrible mistakes at such times. But the ones I hope you won't make is to cling to my generation's sins. You'll have plenty of your own, remember. Changing things is mighty risky, but not changing things is worse—that is, if you can think of something better to change to. . . . Mama, believe I'll go to bed. You about ready?"

On the stairs he stopped. "But I don't mean, Sister, you got to get radical." He laughed. His voice dropped to the soft tones he used with his younger children. "We had a good Christmas, didn't we?" He followed our mother up the stairs.

My younger sister and I looked in the fire. What our future would be, we did not know. The curve was too sharp, just here; and sometimes, the dreaming about a curve you can't see round is not a thing you want to talk about. After a long staring in the fire, we succumbed to a little do-you-remember. And soon we were laughing about the fifteen-year-old and Town and the thirteen-year-old and their heirloom year, and the hog killing and the Song of Solomon and the tree-shaking and Big Grandma's sausage, the best as our mother used to say that anybody could make, with just enough red pepper and sage. . . .

And now the fire in front of us was blurring.

My sister said softly, "It was a large Christmas."

"Which one?"

"All of them," she whispered.

THE GREATEST CHRISTMAS STORY EVER TOLD

BY JEROME WEIDMAN

Jerome Weidman is perhaps best known for the zest and ultrarealism of his many novels and short stories. One of his several plays, Fiorello, *about New York's former Mayor La Guardia, won a Pulitzer Prize. In "The Greatest Christmas Story Ever Told," however, he writes in a gentle vein with perception, deep feeling, and thoughtful touches of phrase and character. We share with him not one, but two Christmas stories which transform a dismal journey on an almost empty train into something glowing and extraordinary.*

One winter day more than thirty years ago, just before Christmas holiday in a public school on New York's lower East Side, a second-grade teacher named Mrs. Margaret Burke handed to each of her pupils a small paper sack full of hard candies. She then announced that she intended to read them a story.

" 'Marley was dead—' " she began.

I had no way of knowing, of course, that Mrs. Burke had uttered three of the most famous words in the English language. To me—as to all the other boys in that second-grade class who were munching lemon drops and red rocks—it was the beginning of just another story.

Perhaps an hour later, when Mrs. Burke finished, even I— then aged seven—was aware that I had made a grave error in judgment: this was *not* just another story.

I have heard people say that they don't know how many times they have read *A Christmas Carol.* It is a difficulty I do not share with them. I know exactly how many times I've read *A Christmas Carol.* In round figures: zero!

But I couldn't possibly say how often I have *heard* it. For this small masterpiece from the pen of one of the half-dozen greatest novelists the world has ever known is surely one of the most-read-aloud stories of all time.

I have heard it in classrooms, from lecture platforms, on the radio, in theaters, on television, in newsreels.

For years no Christmas seemed to me complete until I saw in my newspaper the photograph of the Roosevelt family gathering at Hyde Park, and the Churchill family assembling at Chartwell, to hear the great men read aloud the greatest—certainly the most popular—story Charles Dickens ever wrote.

Why should this simple tale have assumed in the Anglo-Saxon mind a position almost as indispensable as that of holly and mistletoe in the celebration of Christmas?

I believe that much of the enormous popularity of Dickens' *A Christmas Carol* is due to the simple fact that it reads aloud so well.

When I think that I, who have never read the story, know it so intimately, it occurs to me that there must be thousands, perhaps millions, of others whose knowledge was gleaned in similar fashion—by ear.

And this, I think, is an essential part of the spirit of Christmas: nobody—well, *almost* nobody—reads *A Christmas Carol* to himself. Everybody wants to read it aloud to others. Because nobody likes to celebrate Christmas alone. *Home for Christmas!* That's where everybody, instinctively, wants to be for the great holiday. And that's where everybody who can manage it goes.

Many people spend more time traveling to and from the place where they celebrate Christmas than they devote to the actual celebration itself.

I find it odd that this simple fact has not received more attention from our creative writers. There is a great deal of published material about the holiday itself. There is very little dramatization of the journey toward it.

This may not seem a particularly important gap in a nation's book-shelves. Indeed the existence of the gap was completely unknown to me during the first quarter century of my existence. Until, one day a number of years ago, I found myself by sheer accident in the very midst of it.

I had been in Seattle for about a week, doing nothing in particular, and enjoying it enormously. Then, all at once, it seemed terribly important to be in New York. I can't remember why. But I do remember that the weather had grounded all planes, so I left Seattle by train, in a snowstorm, at 8.00 P.M. Pacific Coast

Time. And I discovered ten minutes later, to my astonishment, that it was Christmas Eve!

I was a little troubled by my own astonishment. During my week in Seattle, the shop windows had been decorated with tinsel and holly. A Santa Claus, clanging his bell, had been posted at every busy street corner. And in order to reach the elevators in the lobby of my hotel, it had been necessary to detour around a handsome tree, gaily hung with colored lights.

I could hardly claim that I had not, so to speak, been put on notice. And yet—as I ate my dinner in the almost empty dining car and stared at the cheerful waiter who had catapulted me into an awareness of the date by wishing me a Merry Christmas when he handed me the menu—that was precisely the claim I felt like making. Christmas Eve? It didn't seem possible. I had the uneasy feeling that, somehow, I had been cheated.

A half hour later I found I was not the only one on that train who had this feeling. There were, to be precise, three others. The first was Mr. Sawyer.

I found him sitting alone in the club car. He was plump, middle-aged, and neat, and he wore a pince-nez. He looked like a Madison Avenue bank official, but he proved to be a Philadelphia lawyer.

"You know something?" he said after we had introduced ourselves. "This is the first time in my life I've ever been on a train on Christmas Eve." He sounded sorry for himself.

"Me too," I said. It occurred to me that I also sounded sorry for myself.

"I've been on trains and planes the *day* before Christmas," Mr. Sawyer said, "lots of times. Rushing to get home in time to decorate the tree. But this—" Mr. Sawyer looked out morosely at the gusts of whirling snow that kept smashing noiselessly against the windows of the club car. "This is the first time I've ever had to spend all of Christmas Eve traveling."

I asked how it had happened. He said he had come to Seattle to close a large deal for an important client. But he had assured his wife and children he would be home for the holiday.

Unfortunately, one of the Seattle lawers on the other side of the deal had proved to be pigheaded. By the time the contract had been signed it was impossible for Mr. Sawyer to get back to Philadelphia in time.

"That's why I'm here," he said glumly. "On an empty train, in the middle of nowhere."

It wasn't quite that, of course. During the next quarter hour, two other passengers came into the club car to join us: a Mrs. Hollister, and a Mrs. Merton. They felt sorry for themselves too.

"You know what I think," Mr. Sawyer said after the introductions were out of the way. "I think we all ought to have a drink."

It seemed a simple enough suggestion. Until we discovered that Mr. Sawyer had meant eggnog! We all watched with a good deal of astonishment while he rang for the steward, then summoned the conductor, and finally went off for a conference with the chef in the dining car.

Mrs. Hollister was on her way to visit her son in New Haven, where he was studying medicine. According to her original plan, she should have been in New Haven two days ago. An attack of flu, however, had caused Mrs. Hollister to cancel her original reservation, and so here she was, still en route.

Mrs. Merton had been the last of the group to come into the club car. She was a motherly-looking woman with almost white hair and a lieutenant colonel's silver leaf pinned at her throat.

Mrs. Merton told us that she had come all the way from Hawaii, where her husband was stationed, to spend Christmas in Chicago with her aged parents.

Unfortunately, the Army transport that had brought her from Honolulu had docked at Seattle instead of in San Diego, as originally planned. So she missed her airplane connection to Chicago.

By eleven-thirty, Mr. Sawyer had managed to assemble the necessary eggs, nutmeg, sugar, milk, cream and flavor. On the small writing desk of that shaking club car, he was actually making an eggnog, using for his mixing bowl a battered aluminum soup tureen provided by the dining-car chef.

Meanwhile, at the other end of the car, Mrs. Merton and Mrs. Hollister were improvising a Christmas tree. They were making it with a feather duster, which the porter had fetched from his locker, and some bits of colored tin foil from a box of chocolates Mrs. Hollister supplied. Mrs. Merton had stuck the feather duster upright in an empty highball glass. She had wadded the handle tight with crumpled newspaper. And both women were distributing the little bits of colored tin foil throughout the duster as though they were fancy glass balls.

As I glanced from Mr. Sawyer and his eggnog at one end of the club car to Mrs. Merton and Mrs. Hollister and their tree at the other end, it seemed to me there was something familiar about the slightly unreal scene. I couldn't imagine what it was.

Mr. Sawyer stopped fussing with the eggnog. He sampled it, smacked his lips thoughtfully and seemed to be satisfied. "Now," he said as he began to fill the glasses, "I'd really like to read you a story, that's what I'd like to do."

I stared in astonishment at the plump, middle-aged man with the pince-nez. All at once I knew what it was about the unreal scene that had seemed familiar. As I took the glass of eggnog Mr. Sawyer held out to me, it was as though the intervening years had vanished and I were taking a paper sack full of lemon drops and red rocks from a second-grade teacher in a public school on New York's lower East Side.

" 'Marley was dead' "—I said.

Mr. Sawyer beamed. Mrs. Hollister nodded and smiled. Mrs. Merton shook her head gently.

" 'Marley was dead, to *begin with*,' " she corrected.

We all nodded.

"That's right," Mr. Sawyer said.

" 'Marley was dead, to begin with.' "

" 'There is no doubt whatever about that,' " Mrs. Hollister said, taking up the quotation. " 'The register of his burial was signed by the clergyman, the clerk, the undertaker, and the chief mourner.' "

" 'Scrooge signed it,' " I said.

" 'And Scrooge's name was good upon 'Change, for anything he chose to put his hand to,' " added Mrs. Merton.

" 'Old Marley was as dead as a door-nail,' " said Mr. Sawyer, and there was a pause while we all sipped our eggnog. "I said I'd *like* to read you a story," Mr. Sawyer said finally. "Unfortunately, I can't. Because my copy is in Philadelphia, where I should be at this moment."

"The copy I would be hearing it from is in Chicago," Mrs. Merton said. "I haven't heard my father read it for nine years."

"I haven't heard it since my husband died," Mrs. Hollister said. "I thought perhaps this year, when at last I got to New Haven, my son might . . ."

Her voice stopped. We all stared at the whirling gusts of snow that kept whipping past the windows.

"There must be other Christmas stories," Mr. Sawyer said abruptly, with a touch of petulance. "Let's try to think."

We did, and soon we were exchanging the results of our thinking.

"But those are all stories about Christmas," Mr. Sawyer said suddenly. "Why doesn't somebody write a story about *getting* to Christmas?"

We all stared at him in puzzlement.

"What do you mean?" said Mrs. Hollister.

"People are always talking and writing about what happens to them at Christmas," Mr. Sawyer said. "But nobody ever seems to write about the things that happen to people on their way to their Christmas celebration."

For the second time that night I stared in surprise at Mr. Sawyer. The point he had raised had never occurred to me before.

"Maybe that's because nothing that happens to people on their way to celebrate Christmas is as interesting as the celebration itself," Mrs. Hollister said.

"I doubt that," Mr. Sawyer said. "People have been traveling to Christmas celebrations almost two thousand years. You can't tell me that in all that time nothing interesting happened to any of them."

I ran swiftly through a list of all the travel books I could bring to mind. Not one dealt with Christmas.

"I'm afraid that must be the answer, though," Mrs. Hollister said. "After all, people who start out for wherever they intend to observe Christmas aren't doing anything unusual. Thousands of people are doing it at the very same time. It's just an ordinary trip. Why should anybody want to write about it?"

"That's not quite true," Mrs. Merton said.

We all looked at the motherly woman with the lieutenant colonel's silver leaf pinned at her throat. She was fishing in her purse.

"I know a very good story that deals with just what we've been talking about," she said. "I'd like to read it to you," she said through her pleasant smile. "It's not very long."

It isn't. But it covers a great deal of ground.

Every year, when the tinsel starts going up in the shop windows, I find myself thinking about that club car speeding through the snowy night, and the extraordinary things that sometimes happen to people who think they are embarking on a perfectly ordinary trip.

From the glowing pages of the Gospel according to Luke, Mrs. Merton has helped me choose for these memories the most extraordinary description that has ever been written about what the participants thought at the time was a perfectly ordinary trip:

And it came to pass in those days, that there went out a decree from Caesar Augustus, that all the world should be taxed. (And this taxing was first made when Cyrenius was governor of Syria.) And all went to be taxed, every one into his own city. And Joseph also went up from Galilee, out of the city of Nazareth, into Judaea, unto the city of David, which is called Bethlehem (because he was of the house and lineage of David), to be taxed with Mary his espoused wife, being great with child. And so it was, that, while they were there, the days were accomplished that she should be delivered. And she brought forth her firstborn son, and wrapped him in swaddling clothes, and laid him in a manger; because there was no room for them in the inn.

And there were in the same country shepherds abiding in the field, keeping watch over their flock by night. And, lo, the angel of the Lord came upon them, and the glory of the Lord shone around about them: and they were sore afraid. And the angel said unto them,

"Fear not: for, behold, I bring you good tidings of great joy, which shall be to all people. For unto you is born this day in the city of David a Saviour, which is Christ the Lord. And this shall be a sign unto you: ye shall find the babe wrapped in swaddling clothes, lying in a manger."

And suddenly there was with the angel a multitude of the heavenly host praising God, and saying,

"Glory to God in the highest, and on earth peace, good will toward men."